MY LIFE ON MARS

Published by the British Interplanetary Society,
27/29 South Lambeth Road, London SW8 1SZ, England
in association with Barnstormpr (www.barnstormpr.co.uk)

Design, Typeset and Production by
Oxford Designers & Illustrators Ltd

Printed in Malta at the Gutenberg Press

ISBN 978-0-9506597-3-2

MY LIFE ON MARS

The *Beagle 2* Diaries

COLIN PILLINGER

The British Interplanetary Society

The British Interplanetary Society is the leading UK organisation for the promotion of the uses and exploration of Space, in particular encouraging new and visionary aspects of Space activities. Tracing its foundation back to 1933, it has as its motto "*...from imagination to reality...*", reflecting its concerns with the past history, current activities and future developments in astronautics and Space. It publishes a monthly, full-colour magazine, *Spaceflight*, providing news and articles for the general reader, a technical journal, *JBIS*, publishing refereed papers on astronautics, a twice-yearly *Space Chronicle* devoted to past spaceflight programmes, and DVDs of interest to members.

It also publishes 'one off' books such as this Autobiographical treatment of the Beagle 2 project by Colin Pillinger which is directly available from BIS via its website at www.bis-spaceflight.com and in high street bookshops.

BIS holds one- and two-day Symposia on specialist spaceflight topics and a regular programme of evening lectures. The Society has a world-wide membership at two levels: Ordinary Membership for anybody with a general interest in Space activities, and Fellowship for professionals involved with any aspect of Space exploration. Membership information can be found on the BIS website or by writing to the British Interplanetary Society, 27/29 South Lambeth Road, London SW8 1SZ, England.

Acknowledgements

A great many people encouraged me to pursue an academic career and helped make it possible. Likewise numerous governmental and philanthropic bodies provided me with the finance to carry out the research without which my life would have been far less exciting. My gratitude goes to them for their foresight.

Various individuals are named in the text according to their role in the Beagle 2 story and special mention is given in the Epilogue to some essential irreplaceable characters. But there were just too many people who put their heart and soul into Beagle 2 to acknowledge everyone properly. If you think you played a part, you probably did, so thank you for your contribution.

Without the groundswell of British public opinion, Beagle 2's mission would never have happened. I'm sorry I don't know all my supporters but I've met many at lectures, on the street, in trains, taxis, pubs, etc., everybody please accept my profound thanks. I also have to acknowledge the members of the media who generated the interest.

There are many others who made major contributions to the book, particularly my sister Doreen whose thirty years of research and photographs I used as a source for Chapter 1, and Sir Patrick Moore who generously provided the Foreword. I'm grateful to Dave Dunford, John Hayes, Everett Gibson, David Leadbeater, Paul Leonard, Mike Malin, Mark Bonnar, Richard Strange, Dave Revell and Andy Lloyd for finding and providing pictures. Max Alexander talked me into posing in the astronaut suit then allowed me to use his efforts, funded by STFC. I have to thank all the secretaries not identified by name elsewhere: Esther, Elizabeth, Julie, Becca (who doubled as fork-lift truck driver) and finally Karen who looks after me like I was her fifth child.

I'm grateful to Bob Parkinson and Suszann Parry for setting up the collaboration with the British Interplanetary Society. Bob also copy-edited the manuscript preventing me from making some foolish mistakes; any left are mine. The use of martian with a lower case m is deliberate; I reserve capital M for Martians should there be any. I'm also pleased to thank Pete, Ralph, Jayne, Tim and Nigel at Oxford Designers & Illustrators and Guy Chamberlain of the Gutenberg Press. All of these professionals I've worked with before and gladly would again.

My biggest fan, Martin, the man who patrols the car parks at the OU, can still be heard telling visitors in 2010 "That's where Beagle 2 was made" – without him keeping everybody else out of my space we wouldn't have got to the launch tower.

Contents

Foreword

Colin Pillinger has had a remarkable career. His family background was certainly not wealthy, and he had many obstacles to face, but he overcame them all, and has become one of our leading space scientists. In this book he tells his story "with no holds barred"; you cannot fail to appreciate his modesty, his sense of humour and the way in which he deals with awkward situations and awkward people!

But there is another theme here: the story of Beagle 2, a robotic spacecraft designed to land on Mars and search for any sign of life. Colin was determined that it should fly, and fly it did, despite serious under-funding and the unhelpful attitude of some of his colleagues. Sadly, no data were received when Beagle 2 reached the Red Planet, but it would be wrong to dismiss the mission as a total failure. It did not send back the expected results, but this was not Colin's fault. Nobody could have done more; the support he received was insufficient. Beagle has unquestionably provided information that will be of immense value to future missions.

This is the most enjoyable autobiography that I have read for many years. Read it for yourself, and I have no doubt that you will agree.

Patrick Moore

For all space dogs

Whoever, whenever and wherever...

Prologue

HOW DID WE END UP LIKE THIS?

On Christmas morning 2003, at 5.30am, I dialled a conference line telephone number in California and, after giving the appropriate password, was connected to the communications centre for NASA's Mars Odyssey mission at the Jet Propulsion Laboratory. At 5.28am this orbiting spacecraft had flown over the place where the British Beagle 2 lander was expected to touch down on the mythical Red Planet, a place of fascination since men first turned their eyes towards the sky.

In the next room there was an expectant crowd of supporters: scientists, engineers, family members, rock musicians, other celebrities, press, TV and radio journalists, government officials – indeed anybody who believed they had become a part of the Beagle 2 project, even a bag lady. They were all anxiously waiting for news. Bill Turnbull was in a BBC studio, anchoring a programme with three hours he expected to have no trouble filling.

The group next door had shared a silent vigil, in a variety of ways, since the moment a gas-filled ball should have rolled to rest and dropped a spare-tyre-sized package of scientific instruments on the surface of a planet millions of miles from Earth. Some had dozed, others completed a jigsaw. A heavy metal guitarist had even proposed to his girl friend, fortunately she accepted. There may have been people secretly praying.

My wife Judith and I had been contemplating this moment for more than six and half years. The rest had been recruited to the big idea as it had built from our sheer bloody-mindedness. What had started as a knee jerk reaction to a suggestion that I couldn't do it had become a crusade that almost everyone in Britain was supporting, just because I believed alien life might have been discovered in a meteorite from Mars found on Antarctica.

1

With the connection made and greetings exchanged, my PA transferred the call to an extension in the main room. At 6.05am I was the centre of attention as I moved to pick it up. With the receiver pressed to one ear and a hand over the other I strained to listen to voices in Los Angeles. At one point I thought I heard somebody say "Congratulations." My mind began to search for something simple but unforgettable to say. I hadn't prepared a statement; I am a strictly off-the-cuff, spontaneous, person; something completely unexpected would come into my head as I opened my mouth.

And then a voice in my ear said "Sorry there is no data for you." I remember distinctly he said "is" not "are". I covered the mouth piece and relayed the message with the words "Unfortunately, we haven't had any Beagle data from this pass; they haven't checked whether the radio signal was working but they have no reason to believe that it wasn't working."

We videoed everything and you can see the anguish in all the faces. The film shows a senior civil servant behind me punching numbers into his mobile phone; he was relaying the bad news to Lord Sainsbury, the Science Minister. I'm told all over Britain kids were getting up and asking "What happened to Beagle 2?" not "Where are my presents?" My daughter Shu, running the Beagle 2 web page, was getting 200,000 hits a minute. Into the phone I was holding, I said "Don't worry, it's not the end of the world."

Indeed I wasn't worried too much at that point. I gave a news conference thirty minutes later to list all the things which might have delayed us getting that first signal from Mars, apart from the obvious one that Beagle 2 had crashed. Amongst them was the fact that the spacecraft's radio antenna was very directional; who hasn't twisted and turned a portable radio in order to receive a programme? Because of this we had a back-up; we were going to listen out for Beagle 2 broadcasting again later in the day using the most powerful aerial in Britain, the Jodrell Bank radio telescope. We had given the radio astronomers a list of times when Beagle 2's transmitter would be on but now I wanted them listening as soon as possible in case there was a computer error and the spacecraft's clock had got the time wrong. I didn't have the home telephone number of my contact, so my son, Joe, was sent to Cambridge to fetch it.

Mars came above the horizon of Earth at 3.00pm. We had been told that there was a version of the Queen's Christmas message recorded containing words of congratulation to the Beagle 2 team. Whilst homes all over Britain were listening to Her Majesty we were straining electronic ears for signs of a missing dog. By this time my family had returned home and were sitting on cold stairs watching strips of fussy noise from a radio telescope on a laptop plugged into our phone line. This marathon went on for nine hours until Mars dropped below the horizon again at around midnight. The only time there was any excitement was when the phone connection was lost and we thought it would be just our luck for the telescope to get a signal when we were off-line. Now I began to worry, but couldn't show it.

Both Odyssey and Jodrell Bank tried again on Boxing Day. The European Space Agency's Director of Science, David Southwood, showed up at the press conference on the morning of 27 December. To the media he said "Beagle 2 was always the icing on the cake." Mars Express, the spacecraft that had carried us to the Red Planet was safely in orbit. He told me in the backroom "I'm going to hold an Inquiry." It wasn't unexpected but I thought it was premature and uncaring, making plans for the funeral already. That afternoon, as we walked around the fields on our farm, I asked Judith if she was willing to go through it all again, if necessary; she answered "Yes, as long as I can have another horse."

It was Lord Sainsbury's turn at the next press conference. He arrived with his own hand-written notes and gave a speech saying "We always recognised Beagle was a high risk project. We must avoid, in future, the temptation to only do low risk projects." It finished "While we're disappointed, we are determined that the search should go on to answer the question whether there was life on Mars." He was asked if the Prime Minister had been kept informed and answered "Yes."

Radio telescopes around the world offered to join in the search. One in California was reputed to be so sensitive that it would be able to hear the electronic noise of Beagle 2's computer, if it was on. But it was raining there and they couldn't get into the dish to make the necessary adjustments to change the radio frequency they could receive.

We calculated where Beagle 2 might be from the parameters we had from Mars Express when the lander was released. Another NASA Mars orbiter, Mars Global Surveyor, provided a picture of the area. Smack in the middle was a one kilometre diameter crater. We couldn't have known it was going to be there nor could we have done anything about it if we had.

On 4 January, Spirit, the first of NASA's Mars Exploration Rovers, which had been 'competing' with us, landed. They had anxious moments whilst they waited for their radio signal but soon they were showing off a picture of their landing site. It looked almost as though they had arrived on a beach. Because they had the luxury of two spacecraft, they could afford to send the first one to a low risk landing site keeping the other back for a place a little more interesting for the scientists.

I couldn't help thinking that the 'competition' with the Beagle 2 team had played no small part in their success. Because we had been trying with minimal resources, NASA, with all their dollars, couldn't afford to fail. I phoned Steve Squyres, the NASA Principal Investigator, to add the Beagle 2 team's congratulations to the plaudits he was receiving. He responded with words of encouragement, "We're rooting for you; spacecraft have been lost and found before."

Everyone believed our best chance of communicating with Beagle 2 would come when the Mars Express communication system, the one we had tested on the ground, reached an orbit which overflew the planned landing site. The date was supposed to be 6 January but ESA felt it had an important manoeuvre to do, and wanted to save fuel, so it was put off. It could have been an opportunity to come riding over the horizon on a white charger to save the day. They clearly weren't convinced they could achieve it, nor wanted to.

During a teleconference I had with ESA somebody suggested trying to send and receive secret signals several days in a row before holding another press conference. I flatly refused, saying "The world is waiting for news of Beagle 2; they should have it as soon as we do, even if it's bad." Then the Agency wanted a meeting to decide what to say if we made another attempt to communicate and failed. "Damage limitation," they called it. Again I refused. They decided to do it anyway; I declined the offer to be a part of it.

On 8 January, I stood up in front of a packed room of British journalists. I had experienced media madness on numerous occasions before, whenever anybody mentioned the possibility of life on Mars. I had never faced so many whirring cameras and flashing bulbs or worn so many microphones. At 3.00pm, a video screen showed pictures from the ESA's Communications Centre at Darmstadt. The cameras homed in on the Director of Science; his colleagues had faces like thunder. I was told later that Southwood had to be psyched up to go on at all. It was obvious what was coming before he opened his mouth to say "There has been a set-back."

I looked out at what had been a sea of expectant faces. I could see hardened journalists almost in tears. I had no choice about what to say – "I don't want anybody to give up" – then I resorted to a dreadful football analogy, "it only takes a fraction of a second to score a goal; we'll play to the final whistle."

I followed up with a troop rallying speech about how we shouldn't think that this was the end "If we didn't make it to Mars this time then we have to try again," I said. We'd achieved so much in terms of creating public interest in Space I believed we would be allowed to. "None of the other spacecraft currently going to, or planned for Mars, is carrying the experiment Beagle 2 had to detect life," I went on, "we could still win the big prize." I finished with "We were going to hold a science conference in March, at the Royal Society, to discuss the results obtained by Beagle 2 in detail with other scientists; instead we'll use that meeting to tell people what we think happened and how we can do it better next time."

Attempts to make contact with Beagle 2 didn't stop immediately. There was an all-encompassing contingency plan programmed into its computer but it took days, in fact weeks, to unfold. If the computer on board Beagle 2 recognised that it hadn't received a message from ground control, after a number of scheduled attempts, or a given time, then it would set itself up to receive a signal of another type or in different way. We had to be patient; if we started making random attempts to send signals then we could confuse the lander, and whilst we could still work out at what point it should be in the software, we were in with a chance of making contact.

It took over two months to run through the entire catalogue of options. ESA were increasingly reluctant to participate. Towards the end of January, when we had six scheduled Communications sessions, they cut it to two. When we wanted to send a command to try rebooting the software, it needed a follow-up session immediately; they said they were too busy! NASA, our supposed arch-enemy, obliged.

We had embarked on Beagle 2, not just to try to discover life on Mars but to share the experience with the British public; to encourage people to take an interest in science and engineering. One of the most satisfying moments we had, during that two month search, was when Judith went into a sandwich shop one lunch time and overheard a group of teenagers, boys and girls, discussing the finer points of the Beagle 2 Communications strategy, and what's more getting it right!

Finally the day came at the end of February when we tried what most people would have done in the first ten minutes. With an apparently errant computer, we sent Beagle 2 the message "If you can hear this, switch yourself off and then switch on again." It didn't work.

So Beagle 2 is history. But, as Napoleon is reputed to have said "History is the version of events agreed upon by the winners." There were no winners in Beagle 2. The Beagle 2 team, I couldn't have had better, who deserved most to win, certainly didn't. You might not want to call them winners but there were some who were jolly relieved when Beagle 2 didn't call home on Christmas morning 2003. They were the people who held a number of Inquiries into what went wrong and predictably came to the conclusion "Told you it wouldn't work," which is to belittle the project's achievements. We had won all the battles along the way but, like two thirds of the attempts to go to Mars, we were defeated by the planet.

Even if you combined all the Inquiries and the enquiries, there is a subtle difference; you would not see the full picture. So it's, perhaps, appropriate that a person who didn't agree with what was said and written, the one who knows most, i.e. me, should, at last tell his version of events to set the record straight.

The story however does not begin in 1997 when the name Beagle 2 was imaginatively coined by Judith. It started a long time before. To understand why and how Beagle 2 came about you need to know who I am, what makes me tick and what my wife and I were trying to do. Therefore this book is a double life story. Colin Pillinger's life story, at least a major part of it, juxtaposed against an attempt to answer some intriguing questions: 'Is there life on Mars?' Which becomes: 'Is life on Earth unique?' And finally, most fundamental of all, it translates to: 'Are we alone in the Universe?' The last question is one that has been asked by virtually everyone who has ever stood outside on a clear night to stare up at the vastness of the heavens. A sixteenth century philosopher, Giordano Bruno, was burnt at the stake when he suggested he knew the answer.

This book is not just about looking for life on Mars. The central theme of the tale will be about how a bunch of anoraks, some of whom wore the most outrageous woolly jumpers, followed their leader to join forces with a rock band and an artist who saws cows in half, designed a tiny spacecraft on the back of a beer mat, built it in a garage and then, against all the odds, sent it two hundred and fifty million miles to Mars. But these were no ordinary anoraks; their leader was a Fellow of the Royal Society, the elite of British science. The 'boys in the band' were the cream of the British space industry; all the companies who could do something for Beagle 2 were in the project. We'd also recruited Damien Hirst, who until very recently was the most expensive living artist, and Blur who had just won the battle of Britpop. As Alex James, their bassist, said to Lord Sainsbury "We've had Britart and Britpop now we're going to have Britspace."

It wasn't an official space mission so we had to invent some novel ways to raise money. When we did get some it didn't, by any stretch of the imagination, match the sums normally spent even in Europe. Dave Rowntree, Blur's drummer, observed "You couldn't buy a screwdriver for that in NASA."

If you tried to publish this story as science fiction you would probably be laughed at and told 'it's too far-fetched'. It is nevertheless true, and as you might expect the great British public took us underdogs to its heart and almost celebrated our lack of success as much as they would have if we had beaten the mighty NASA to the prize.

It's the bit that happened afterwards that is really unbelievable: how did the 'naysayers' come to triumph? And of course there's our reputation for not following through when we have invented something. Instead we step aside to let others reap the benefits. This part has to be told because I don't believe Britain's involvement in Europe's next effort to land on Mars will have anything like the motivational success of Beagle 2, nor inspire the Nation. When the European Space Agency announced it would build its own Mars lander I predicted it wouldn't get off the ground – it still hasn't and it's not likely to get to Mars for another ten years; it may or may not get launched in 2018. Nobody will ever again repeat what the Beagle 2 team accomplished and there are people who sincerely hope they have prevented another attempt.

When you have a unique story then it needs to be written down on paper so posterity will know that at the beginning of the 21st century there were still British adventurers, scientists and engineers with vision, prepared to take a risk, and not afraid of the consequences of failure. Actually you are not allowed to mention failure to anybody who worked on Beagle 2; it has to be deferred success.

I wouldn't have been the obvious candidate to have become a scientist and lead a mission to Mars, but if I can do it anybody can.

Chapter 1

HONOUR AMONG THIEVES

For a family of rather humble origins my ancestors are rather well documented, thanks to my sister Doreen. She takes a rather different view of the question 'where do I come from?'. She is a dedicated genealogist. I'm lucky, if you come from where I come from you're lucky if you have any ancestors to trace.

A couple of hundred years ago Kingswood was a sprawling forest on the outskirts of Bristol until coal was found there; then it became the 'wild west'. To say it was a lawless place would be an understatement. Official 18th century records show that half the crimes committed in the county of Gloucestershire were perpetrated in the Parish of Bitton which included Kingswood. When sentencing yet another hapless thief to death, one Judge was moved to remark "I thought I had already hanged all the men in Bitton." The families that are still there were the smart ones – they had ancestors who didn't all get caught.

Doreen's hobby started seriously when she was wandering aimlessly around a churchyard in suburban Bristol and chanced upon a gravestone bearing the name Pillinger. So began her search for information about past lives, slightly different from the search for ancient life which has preoccupied me. Thanks to her, I know a great deal about how I come to be here and what makes me the person I am.

One of the first things my sister turned up, which encouraged her to believe spending hours with boxes of old papers could be fun, was a document dated 1757. It stated that one Jeremiah Pillinger would be paid the princely sum of thirty-six pounds to act as scavenger for the Parish of Christchurch with St Ewen, in the City of Bristol. As a tiny kid I used to love watching the clock on the tower of Christchurch; two men with pikes would strike the bell every quarter hour.

The family connection between me and Jeremiah was a long time ago but more recently I did have an Uncle who was a dustman, so I know what one looks, and smells, like close up and I know the only things you can scavenge from ashes are cinders, partly burnt coal, because I've picked over ashes to get fuel for the fire. The Pillinger family are undoubtedly working class, and when I say working class I mean working class. My father always believed one day our ship would come in. It did, but not as he expected.

Much later Doreen unearthed another early Pillinger, James, who as a sixteen-year-old was sent on a long sea cruise, courtesy of HM Government, to become 'a founder of the nation' of Australia. Young James was no minor offender, transported for nicking the odd loaf of bread because he was hungry. He was becoming a career criminal committing capital offences, amongst them, at the age of only ten, aiding and abetting one Shuke Milledge, a lady of easy virtue, relieve farmer John Bray of his purse and one hundred and thirty guineas, proceeds from the sale of his cattle. James's share of the take was three and a half guineas. He was caught when another boy in the gang was found in possession of a bent farthing which had been in farmer Bray's pocket.

So James wasn't lucky. He travelled 'down under', at the end of 1791, in a ship called 'The Pitt', hot on the heels of the Second or so-called 'Death Fleet' when 40% of the convicts died on the way to, or soon after landing at, Botany Bay. This was the first time a Pillinger encountered the Royal Society; it was RS President, Sir Joseph Banks, the botanist on Captain Cook's voyage to the South Seas, who suggested founding the penal colony that would become Sydney.

Some of those who, like James, survived the ordeal of the journey, ended up on Norfolk Island, described by one of its Governors, as "a place of extreme punishment, short only of death". When there was a mutiny on the island those sentenced to hang fell on their knees and thanked God; those reprieved wept bitterly.

We're still searching for a close genetic association with James because he demonstrated unequivocally the Pillingers are survivors and moreover his grandson, Alfred Thomas, made good, acquired 15,000 acres of land and an interest in Astronomy. Whilst Bristol used to boast a Pillinger Street and Kingswood still has a Pillinger's Road, go to Tasmania, then known as Van Diemen's Land, and you will find a Mount Pillinger, Pillinger river and a ghost town called Pillinger, named after Alfred Thomas.

Although it hasn't been possible to fold the street urchin James into the bosom of my immediate family it's easier to guess an association between Shuke Milledge and my ancestors. She incidentally also voyaged to Oz but in comparative luxury aboard the notorious floating brothel, 'The Lady Julian', the first ship of the second fleet to arrive and where every man, including the Captain and the Doctor, took a 'wife' from amongst the prisoners as a home comfort during the passage. Don't anybody tell me it should be Juliana: Saint Julian was a nun who wrote the first book by a woman in the English language. Another of Shuke's crimes was to lure a gentleman into an alley where he was robbed by Edward Harris, described as 'a notorious rogue of Kingswood'. This lot sound like the Artful Dodger, Nancy and Bill Sykes from Oliver Twist. Almost everybody who came into contact with James and Shuke was sentenced to be 'transported beyond the seas' and were reunited 10,000 miles from home.

Harris was possibly related to the Pillingers by marriage. He could even have been the brother of Anne Harris, a Kingswood woman who became my great, great, great grandmother when, as widow Stone, she married John Pillinger or John 'the hatter', as my sister calls him. The Harris family were noted locally as bare-knuckle prize fighters. In 1755, Kingswood collier, John Harris, possibly Anne's father, fought Jack Slack, a Norwich butcher, for the English championship in a ring outside the Lamb public house at Lawford's Gate, on the road leading to Kingswood.

Perhaps John 'the hatter' Pillinger's grandfather, Nathaniel, was in the crowd. He had just arrived in the area from the Wiltshire village of Yatton Keynell. We know exactly when he came because he presented his certificate of settlement at Bitton on 2 November, 1754. Some one took it from him and locked it in the Vestry chest of St. Mary's church. Rummaging around in the tower, more than two hundred years later, my sister found this often cursed document and, with freezing hands, unfolded it. But she wasn't the first since 1754 to take it out.

The earliest Kingswood Pillinger was no angel although that's a matter of opinion. He was one of those poor unfortunates who became a thief out of necessity, not from choice. On 7 October 1740 he was delivered to Marlborough Gaol, having stolen a sack from Robert Pearce's barn. Nathaniel, probably employed as an agricultural labourer by farmer Pearce, was either just, or was about to be, married. His wife Sarah was certainly pregnant because a son, John, was born in early 1741. Anyway, winter was coming and in the mid 18th century it would be arctic cold at night. Nathaniel had stolen the sack and converted it into a blanket for the marriage bed where it was found, along with other sacks, "presumed stolen".

The sack episode may have cost Nathaniel close to five years of his life in prison. That's the gap between John and a second child, Betty, in the records; so presumably he wasn't at liberty for a while. Possibly he trudged to Kingswood because someone whose criminal record stated he had misappropriated a few old sacks wasn't going to be noticed or out of place there. It was the new 'Eldorado' – coal – the black gold mines were opening and attracted anybody who could carry a pick and shovel. It was not the sort of place you would bring your family to from choice.

To give an example of what Kingswood was like: it was the home of what history has called the 'Cock Road Gang' led by the Caines family. They ruled there, like mafia godfathers, for more than a hundred years, from before the time Abraham Caines was hanged in 1727. When Benjamin Caines became the latest victim of the hangman at Gloucester in 1817, his body was returned home and his father, also a Benjamin, charged people two old pence a look to see the body of his famous thief son. The proceeds went towards the funeral, an extravagant procession to St Mary's, Bitton, with six women dressed all in white acting as pall bearers. With a party still in full swing, Benjamin lay in his coffin late into the night waiting to be buried; the interment eventually took place by candlelight.

It was said that by 1841 the entire Caines family had been eliminated or transported. Not true, there were two boys with that name in my class at school. Speaking of schools, another of Kingswood's claims to fame is that it was the first place in Britain to boast a Borstal; we called it the Reformatory School.

Kingswood was so bad in the 18th century they had to send missionaries there. I'm not kidding. The best known Evangelists were the Wesleys who were following in the footsteps of George Whitefield, pronounced 'Whitfield'. When George aspired to go to America to convert the natives, his friends asked "Why should you travel so far? Are there not savages enough in Kingswood?" George was a magnificent orator. Not for him preaching to the converted in churches, he took to the fields to address the uncivilised masses. He claimed the congregation at his 25 February 1739 'Sermon on the Mount', this particular mount being Mount Hill, Kingswood, which looked down on Cock Road, was in excess of ten thousand.

Whitefield's detractors always questioned his numbers as exaggerated. There weren't 5, let alone ten thousand, people living in the whole parish of Bitton. To test the veracity of Whitefield's figures, when he was in America, the famous scientist Benjamin Franklin paced out the radius of the semicircular throng listening at Philadelphia. Allowing two square feet for each person he calculated a number in excess of the twenty thousand the preacher guessed. Franklin also noted he couldn't hear Whitefield at the back. Whitefield wasn't against using all types of media to spread his message so Franklin became his publisher but not a believer.

So maybe Nathaniel Pillinger walked to Kingswood in the hope of finding salvation or it could have been for a chance of getting some education for his kids. The bible punchers founded schools for the poor. I spent a year being taught, aged eight, in the schoolroom attached to the Tabernacle built by Whitefield's disciple and schoolmaster, John Cennick. I also passed many happy, and profitable, hours as a student there, doing my bit for goodwill in Kingswood, sorting the Christmas post, when it doubled as a temporary overspill Post Office. I often wonder what vibes I picked up regarding mass communication as a means of getting a crowd on your side.

Nathaniel's tenure as an inhabitant of Kingswood was short-lived. Within two years, aged just forty, he was dead and two weeks later his wife Sarah was buried alongside him, that left son John, aged sixteen, fending for his sister Betty, ten. They soon discovered not all the hard men in Kingswood lived in Cock Road. Some of them made up the Overseers of the Poor. Complaints about one or other of these two sponging off the Parish were received, out came Nathaniel's settlement papers, the sentence "Not on our patch" was passed. On 30 December 1758 Betty was 'transported' back to Yatton, her lawful abode; John followed next day, 1 January 1759. Happy New Year! The papers were put away in case they needed them again.

John returned almost immediately because in 1761 he married Catherine Lear; a son was baptised just eleven weeks later. Catherine bore him several other children but in between times she whiled away the hours in Gloucester Gaol for selling beer without a licence. The last thing Kingswood needed was additional pubs. There was even one called 'The World's End' on the road out of Bristol, probably named as a comment by the people of the city on entering Kingswood. The World's End is still rough; there was a murder outside only recently. On one occasion Catherine was fined £10; her sentence read: "Not to be released until paid" because she didn't "own goods or chattels worth that amount." They might just as well have asked her to finance a mission to Mars! Kingswood is rough, there was a murder outside The World's End in 2010.

John 'the hatter' was fathered by Nathaniel's son John during one of Catherine's absences in prison because his baptism is recorded as 'son of John and Mary'. John, the refugee from Yatton, may have acquired a surrogate wife whilst Catherine was away. An alternative was that Catherine was using a pseudonym or an alias. Interestingly 'the hatter''s immediately younger sibling was called Mary. Make what you like out of that. If John senior was playing away whilst Catherine was in prison, he could have been the father of James, the boy thief, who was a contemporary of John 'the hatter'.

Why John 'the hatter'? Making hats was his profession; it was a Kingswood cottage industry. The process involved the use of mercury nitrate to mat rabbit hair into felt. Mercury is, of course, very poisonous and causes nervous disorders which can be confused with madness. Hence the expression 'mad as a hatter' and the origin of Lewis Carroll's Mad Hatter in 'Alice in Wonderland'.

Making hats was marginally better and less immediately risky compared to the alternative: crawling around two hundred feet down in the Earth with a naked flame candle for light. Nevertheless John 'the hatter' too fell on hard times. In 1801 he presented himself before the Overseers of the Poor and was told the equivalent of "**** off back to Yatton." These so-called benevolent men wouldn't have been so crude, they just paid someone to do the dirty work required to pack the Pillingers' few possessions in a cart and take the whole kit and caboodle out of sight and out of mind. It cost the Parish fifteen shillings plus the cost of the Vicar travelling to Wiltshire to negotiate repatriation.

But the tribe came back to live at 'Made for Ever'. Sounds like a smart new council estate; it wasn't. It was a slum called after the mine which was supposed to provide its owner with a living in perpetuity. In 1803 the Overseers had to do it again. This time it cost them two guineas. Serve them right! Eventually they rid themselves of 'the hatter' for good. My sister searched for a record of his death for years until, by chance, he turned up in a newspaper report of a Coroner's inquest held at the Chippenham Union Workhouse in January, 1848. It read "John Pillinger, an elderly man, found dead in bed by an inmate who had gone to take him his breakfast. Verdict: Visitation by God." He presumably rests in a pauper's grave, a Pillinger whose grandfather arrived in Kingswood with nothing to seek his fortune; when John 'the hatter' departed he still had most of it left!

At least 'the hatter' didn't personally fall foul of the law. His elder brother Jacob did. This particular Pillinger was sentenced to be transported for seven years for stealing sugar. Seven years was a euphemism meaning forever. But Jacob beat the rap; he appears on the manifests of 'the Hulks', the decommissioned warships used to house convicts waiting for their trip, with an 'E' alongside his name standing for 'escaped'. Where he went and what happened afterwards nobody knows. His wife didn't; Jacob never ventured back, and she was left with eight children to bring up as licensee of a pub on Redcliffe Hill in Bristol. A John 'the hatter' son, also named Jacob, after his brother no doubt, escaped in a different way. He stood trial for a robbery but was acquitted; his co-defendant however was not so lucky and was sentenced to hang.

In 1843, the Bitton Overseers of the Poor tried to rid themselves of another 'hatter' son. This time they brought out the settlement papers and targeted Stephen, my great, great grandfather. Stephen claimed not to know where he came from when they threatened to throw him out, an incredible eighty nine years after Nathaniel first arrived. The Pillingers weren't going to be got rid of that easily. The authorities gave up and we have been in Kingswood ever since. We're nothing if not persistent.

The moral of this story is never trust a man who thrusts a piece of paper in front of you and says "Sign [or make your mark] here, it's for your own good"; what he means is "You can't trust me and what ever is written on this piece of paper I'm going to use against you if I need to." Now you know why I prefer Gentlemen's agreements.

Like his father, Stephen was in the hatting trade as a cutter, removing the fur from rabbits. There's a paper in the Royal Society's journal, 'Philosophical Transactions', describing hatting; it was written by no less a scientist than the great Robert Hooke. The handwritten manuscript still exists, so we know Stephen spent hours up to his elbows in urine; it would have been purchased from housewives who sold the contents of their chamber pots at a penny a bucketful. My father could remember ladies standing with their buckets in a street called Pennywell Road.

The brush with the Bitton Church authorities gave Stephen every reason to join the Methodists. He is one of a number of Pillingers buried in the graveyard of the Wesleyian chapel. At his funeral the preacher gave a eulogy which was published in the local paper. He called Stephen "a saint". My sister unearthed a picture of Stephen, the first Pillinger to be photographed, as an old man.

If anybody can be charged with spreading the Kingswood Pillinger genes then it is Stephen, who with his wife Jane Summerill, had twelve children, all but one of whom, unusually for the times, survived into adulthood. Stephen's offspring founded an American branch of the family. They settled in Chicago – where else? It was one of Stephen's sons who gave his name to Pillinger's Road, Kingswood where could be found the Bakery he started.

Stephen's son number four, born in 1841, was Thomas, my great grand-father. He too had a brush with the law, caught with others, by a gamekeeper, in the company of a lurcher, a greyhound cross dog. This was a crime as old as the forest committed by hungry men. It meant only one thing – poaching the Lord of the Manor's wild livestock. In their defence the group said they didn't know who the dog belonged to; it had followed them when they gave it a titbit. "A likely tale," said the Magistrate, "fined a pound." He could have been transported; the last convicts were sent to Australia in 1868 when Thomas was twenty-seven. Despite this we've always been kind to lost dogs.

Thomas married Lavinia Fray. The Frays were a family of Brass Founders (it's as near as I can get to a science background) who anglicised their name from Varoy, when they emigrated from Holland to Keynsham in the early part of the 18th century. Anybody old enough to remember 'Radio Luxembourg' will have heard of Keynsham and Horace Batchelor, the man who told you how to fill out your pools coupon. Anyway Thomas was obviously a bit wild in his youth since he fathered what my own father described as a "love child", his Uncle Fred, who lived next door to the house where my grandfather, Albert, brought up his family of nine children.

Boots and shoes were Albert's calling. As an occupation cobbling was a cottage industry, all the houses had what were called workshops attached. We had one at home. As people got on, the workshops became bathrooms. Ours was always a workshop. As I said, Albert was a shoemaker. This was an amazing skill; men of his persuasion would grab a mouthful of brass tacks, spit them out with machine gun rapidity and hammer them, with the edge of a file, around the sole of a boot in an absolutely regular pattern. Maybe this is the reason I like to 'get down to brass tacks'. To remind me of the man I called Pap, I have his 'lasts', metal feet of different sizes, which were used to hold a boot upside down on a stalk. When Pap was over eighty, and needed cash, he put up a sign outside his house, saying he could repair boots and shoes; the council made him take it down.

Life for Albert's eight children, in Blackhorse Road, Kingswood, was no picnic. They shared a single bedroom with a blanket hung across it to divide the boys from the girls. On Saturday evenings their mother, Hester née Burchill, would walk five miles to Castle Street, Old Market, to shop. She would try to buy a joint of meat just before the shops closed for the weekend, when they couldn't store perishables and sold them cheap. I remember Castle Street, or what was left of it after World War II bombing raids, when one isolated shop remained: J. Sainsbury, Grocers. I trust my Gran contributed as much as she could afford to the Sainsbury billions; a hundred years later I asked for some back, with interest.

Another reason for the walk was to redeem my father's sailor suit from the Pawnbrokers so he could go to Sunday school. My father, Alfred – everybody called him Jack or sometimes John – didn't have a birth certificate

15

until he was fourteen. His mother thought acquiring it would help him get an apprenticeship and a trade. It didn't; he spent his entire working life as another pick and shovel man. People who have written about me have politely said he worked for the Gas Board. They've never asked what he did. To my father a spade was a spade and he described himself as a navvy. He met my mother Florence Honour when he stuck his head up out of a hole he was digging.

There were Pillingers near the Wiltshire/Gloucestershire border earlier than Nathaniel but the records to tie them all together are incomplete. The earliest, Philip, came from Winchcombe, near Stroud, north Gloucestershire to become Rector of the Parish of Ditteridge from 1585 until 1624. This connection is particularly appealing because he owned books; at last a sign of academic ability to pass down through a dozen generations. Maybe we began as really good guys whose luck ran out earlier than Nathaniel and his brood.

Philip owed his preferment to yet another John Pillinger who was 'the Summoner' at the Winchcombe and Stonehouse Prerogative Court. That really would be a turn up for the book, an ancestor with a job mentioned in 'The Canterbury Tales'; John 'the Summoner' got his first mention in the Court's records when, in 1574, he delivered letters asking Thomas Prickett to explain what he was up to with Elizabeth Meane.

My mother, Florence (Flo) Pillinger was an Honour. The Honours were a completely different kettle of fish. You can't trace them through their court appearances. They owned things; they had enough goods and chattels to have to make wills. They had inventories made for Probate and on occasion signed their names. I've always believed you don't get to be called Honour by accident; you have to have done something, sometime, somewhere, to earn it. Whatever it was has never come to light. It must have been a long time ago. It could even have been in Norman times since William the Conqueror divided his newly acquired realm into Honours.

The hole my father was digging when he whistled at my Mum was outside the boot factory where she was working. She found out he would like to walk out with her from Dad's sister Polly, who also worked at the factory. The walking out happened and the wedding took place in 1930. My father, complete with bowler hat, and mother emerged from the ceremony to walk under an arch of picks and shovels provided by his mates. Doreen arrived in 1937 and I came along in 1943.

The Honour with the greatest influence over my life was undoubtedly my grandfather Levi who I have no recollection of. He never knew of my existence since he died six years before I was born. As a kid we made Saturday evening trips to Pap's; they would end with a bottle of lemonade and a packet of crisps for me standing in the Bottle and Jug of the 'Hen and Chicken' public house before catching the bus home.

But of Honour grandparents there was no sign. Instead we had the Honour family bible, a giant leather and brass bound tome that sat on top of what my mother called a 'tallboy' in her bedroom. In the middle of this intriguing volume were names and dates written with pen and ink in ornate copperplate handwriting. Who were these long gone people listed as births, deaths and marriages? Who was the exotically named Esau Whybird? Katherine Hayward? Wasn't she a film star? Who was the man my Mum referred to as "our Dad?" Who was Levi Honour?

Inquiry would gain only tiny fragments of my mother's secret childhood. She had been born into a farming family. Her grandfather Thomas occupied Church Farm next door to the Vicarage where the Reverend Charles Kingsley wrote 'The Water Babies'. Levi and his wife Sarah had been what the Pillingers would have called very rich. This was all before my mother was born. What happened? Why weren't we living in a big house on a farm?

Little by little more information was pieced together by my sister. Levi Honour was a proud man; there's a photograph of him in a characteristic pose, thumbs stuck in his waistcoat, chest thrust out. It says 'I own all you can see in the background'. Levi's problem was he couldn't father a son to give it to. Four daughters in a row, then, wonder of wonders, he did it – a boy. Levi was so pleased he gave him three names, Edward John Thomas; they were names taken from his two grandfathers and the Prince of Wales. Then tragedy, little Johnny died. Levi was a broken man. He blew everything he had on drink, gambling and failed business ventures in a downward spiral of smaller and smaller farms until he was a farm labourer.

My mother didn't help matters. She was his next child, a fifth and youngest daughter. Her birth certificate has a date on it three weeks late. It speaks volumes; Levi almost couldn't be bothered about her. Another son was eventually born but it was too late; everything was gone. My grandmother Sarah died, worn out; my mother and 'our 'Arry', the youngest child, were shunted from place to place, to various relatives who obviously didn't want them either. The horror stories about this time in my mother's life were usually hinted at if someone said they didn't want to eat some particular item of food. Out would come a thinly veiled threat along the lines "When I was living with Aunt or Uncle so-and-so if I left something, the plate would be put on the top shelf in the larder and would come back time after time until I ate it." She never

17

imposed the penalty in practice. Her other favourite threat to restore order between me and Doreen was to say "I'll put my hat and coat on in a minute and go down Hanham river [a favourite spot for suicides]."

My sister prised most of the gory details out of Mum when she was much older; she lived to ninety-six and as people get more ancient they remember what happened years ago better than yesterday. One particularly nasty story was when my mother hurried home clutching a letter saying she could go to the Grammar School. Her newly acquired stepmother, a Mrs Yeomans, threw it on the fire; had she gone who knows what might have happened. Mrs Yeomans got her just desserts. My sister loved it. One night the said stepmother came home drunk. Reaching under the bed for a chamber pot, she pulled out her hat and peed into it; we hope she put it on before she noticed.

Levi blamed himself for not allowing Johnny to have an operation, which might have crippled him but without it almost certainly condemned him to death. My favourite Aunt, more of her later, was under the kitchen table when Levi hammered on it with his clenched fist, shouting at the doctors: "Gentlemen, there will be no operation." Levi's problem was men get very possessive about land and succession. Even now I have a farming neighbour who, if the subject of what will happen to his farm comes up, will say "I only have daughters."

My Honour grandfather didn't leave me tangible wealth but three other things, some of them subliminal, instead. Firstly, to own a bit of land i.e. recover the family fortunes; second to show him that my mother produced the son he never had, and thirdly to live by one of his oft repeated dictums "I go cap in hand to no man!"

My sister also wrung out of my mother's much older sister, the story of what might have been. She got the aged relative to publish it: 'Memories of a Victorian Christmas at Townsend's Farm Hampstead Norreys'. I quote: "It began very properly on Christmas Eve when our Dad [Levi] came in from the fields. He and the men would get busy with ladders, decorating all the picture frames with greenery: holly, ivy, mistletoe…. On Christmas day dinner was the bird and all the trimmings, and a whole roast pig served on an enormous grey and white dish with indented channels leading to a bowl at the end to catch the juices….. Afterwards we had our presents…. We gave our workers pork, ham, coal and blankets. Nobody went without."

It must have been true; my sister still has that grey and white dish. It was all a bit different from when a Pillinger had to steal a sack. Life with the Honours, before the 1900s, is incredibly reminiscent of Scrooge reliving his happier times under Mr Fezziwig. Whereas my mother's memories were more like some of the unpleasant Victorian moments that Dickens described.

The Honour family tree is one created through a line of second, third or even fourth sons. There were however some very considerable Matriarchal figures: Levi's mother-in-law, Susanah, for example. She was also his Aunt: my grandmother, Sarah, was already an Honour when she married my grand-father, her cousin. Susanah, or Susan as she preferred, had an annuity bought when her husband John Honour's property was sold. He was farming more than two hundred and sixty acres, not inconsiderable for the times. Susan's allowance kept Levi and Sarah Honour's family afloat; she must have been heartbroken at her only child's fate.

Susan never expected to have a child; she was not married until she was forty-two to Levi's Uncle John, a recently bereaved widower. She was the original owner of the Family bible. What clever dick gave a forty-two year old spinster a book to record births in is a mystery, I'm just grateful for the faux pas. Maybe it was because she was well educated. You can tell from her handwriting, recording previous generations, she was a cut above. In the census of 1851, she was singled out, possibly as a Lady's companion, in the house of the brother of an Admiral in London's well-to-do Welbeck Street. Susan's daughter Sarah was also 'accomplished'; she played the piano, with long delicate fingers, until Levi flogged it.

Levi's silver spoon had come from his grandmother, another Matriarch, Sarah Honour, widow of Job; he's described in the records as 'of Tackley'. She accumulated a small Empire around Charlton-on-Otmoor, Oxfordshire. Whilst others rioted and broke down the fences when Otmoor was enclosed, this shrewd business woman grabbed their vacated strip allotments. This emancipated lady was the only female listed in the Oxfordshire directories for the 1840–50s as 'Farmer'.

The only time an Honour ancestor crossed swords with the law was when my five times great grandfather inherited two houses. He celebrated his good fortune by forcing entry into the Church at Charlton-on-Otmoor and ring-ing the bells at midnight. He was charged with "Riotously and tumultuously disturbing and terrorising the inhabitants." It was no teenage prank; he was over fifty and a member of the Establishment who had presumably partaken of more drink than he should have.

The whole Honour dynasty in Oxfordshire started several more generations earlier when a Gabriel Honour drifted in, possibly from Bedfordshire about twenty miles away. His ancestors were Lords of the Manor so they could have been the source of the name. Gabriel too was likely a younger son but, in 1610 he married heiress Anne Kerry of Spelsbury, daughter and grand-daughter of a pair of William Kerrys. Bizarrely, William junior left a legacy to his father, William senior, on condition that the old man "didn't interfere" with his son's wife, Grace – the mind boggles! Gabriel and Anne moved into the nearby village of Wendlebury, where he set up as a Maltster. Anne came clutching her mother's 'Great Box', the Tudor equivalent of her dowry. Whatever became of that oak and metal bound chest? My sister would give her right arm for it.

The existence of the box is one of the fun things you find out when you dabble in family history. But there is a down side: you discover tragedy, infant mortality, death in child birth, even suicide, the workhouse and worse still the asylum. Once my sister encountered a vicar, who, when she told him what she was looking for, tried to tap her for something towards repayment of a loan of fifty-five quid his church made to an Honour two hundred and fifty years earlier. Fortunately she knew enough to convince him she wasn't a direct descendant of the defaulter.

Anyway that's Colin Pillinger's family history: an unruly bunch of had-nots mixed up with an ambitious clan of once-had-it-alls. One thing they shared was a moral code. On one side of the family a Gentleman's word was his bond; the other didn't like pieces of paper either. A mix of Honours and Pillingers is a fairly potent collection of genes. Plant breeders would predict F1 hybrid vigour or a recipe for trouble. Either or both would be very helpful for anybody wanting to lead a space mission to Mars.

Chapter 2

JOURNEY INTO SPACE

I made my appearance on the scene on Sunday 9 May 1943. I came into the world at 33 Victoria Park, Kingswood. The mid-wife arrived drunk, not the most auspicious start. My sister, six years older than me, was banished to the park with an even older cousin so, much to her annoyance, she can't tell me any more about what happened.

Victoria Park sounds very grand, leafy suburbia, with spring flowers and manicured lawns right opposite our mansion. It wasn't like that. I can't think why they called the street a Park, it was a cul-de-sac of red brick, working people's houses, with outside toilets; some even had 'thunder boxes' flushed with a bucket of water, no bathrooms, many with gas lighting. I remember the Saturday we got electricity and the day my Dad pulled out the cast iron range my mother 'black-leaded' every morning. Only one man had a car, it always had its bonnet up.

We lived in an off-shoot of the main street, nine houses in two ranks, numbered sequentially, not odds one side, evens the other. Number thirty-three was the last house. My sister parked outside it recently – the new owner proudly told her "The man who launched Beagle 2 lived here." We didn't own number thirty-three; we paid rent to a Miss Gerrish, who came every Saturday. My mother would have loved it if we had got a Council house.

The nearest real park was a mile and a half away, but better than that, right outside the back garden gate, we had a bit of green space we called 'The Patch'. It was a tip, a piece of derelict land, it had once had a couple of ruined cottages but they had long since become buried and overgrown.

The Patch was where my mate Eddie and I played football and cricket. With other boys I dug hidden underground dens we crawled into through tunnels, lit fires to bake the odd potato if we could get it, in between re-enacting World War 2 and the Cowboys and Indians we saw at Saturday morning 'pictures' at the Odeon cinema, entrance 6d (two and a half new pence).

Other people used The Patch to dump their rubbish so our pitches had their fair share of broken half bricks and smashed bottles. Ashes were good for levelling out the pot holes provided you removed the cinders which were hard on the knees but good recycled fuel. Behind the Odeon, there was another piece of wasteland with a disused underground bunker, an air raid shelter, we also played in. We had gas-masks and tin helmets from the war as playthings.

Now here's a good place to start. Not many people can claim to have had a street party for their second birthday. I did, because coincidentally the Second World War in Europe had ended the previous evening. I can't however say I know anything about it but I'm sure the occasion was appropriately celebrated with much decorum. Again I have to rely on my sister to describe the scene. Apparently I was stood on a trestle table in the midst of a crowd, whilst everybody sang Happy Birthday and there were fireworks. You could say I discovered what it was like to be on stage, in front of a large audience, at an early age.

My only other stage appearance was in a school Shakespeare play. I had the part of a king; the only trouble was it was Edward IV in Richard III. My character was dead at the start – it was a non-speaking role requiring little acting ability apart from lying still. Not easy for me, maybe that's why I didn't get another role.

My earliest recollection is of an event which happened before my third birthday. I remember my mother being on her knees to get something out of the cupboard under the dresser, repository of that giant grey and white dish, which only came down to be cleaned. But she wasn't able to get up because of a fearful pain. She had an appendicitis or to be more precise peritonitis; what she said was a burst appendix. Back then appendicitis with complications was serious.

She might have been in pain but she was able to dispatch me across the road to Auntie Elsie. She wasn't a real auntie, just a friend who I called Auntie. My mother was saved because penicillin was available. Until then it had been almost exclusively for the troops. I don't know if this knowledge, subliminally, had anything to do with me ending up as an organic chemist.

My mother's sojourn in Bristol Royal Infirmary brought my real Aunt Emily, my mother's sister, author of the Victorian Christmas story, scampering from London. Just to be confusing nobody ever called her Auntie or Emily, she was universally known as 'Pem', a name invented by me because I couldn't say Emily. She called me her 'Burma boy' because I had a fascination with a picture in a geography book showing rice growing in the paddy fields of Burma. I was reminded of this quite recently when a man came up to me at the end of a lecture. "I've been waiting to meet you for more than fifty years," he began.

Since Beagle 2 I've become quite used to receiving good wishes and words of consolation from complete strangers but what was all this about fifty years? From out of his bag he produced a photocopy of the flyleaf of a book of Bible stories. Written on the page was "To my Burma boy on his 5th birthday, love Pem." He had got the book from his own aunt, a friend of Pem, when I had grown out of it. He generously returned the book to me in exchange for a signed copy of my book 'Beagle – from sailing ship to the British led mission to Mars', more of which later. I hope he treasures his new acquisition for just as long.

A description which fitted Pem would be the caricature Grandma depicted by Giles in his cartoons. Pem was much older than my mother; she was from a by-gone era, the Honour good times. She was more like a Grandma than an Auntie. She was both revered and feared. She didn't take prisoners. She had no children of her own; she didn't even have a husband until very late in life. It was believed her sweetheart had gone off to the trenches of the First World War, never to return. It wasn't true but we knew better than to ask.

She spoiled other people's children rotten. Pem's visitations were eagerly anticipated as the time for treats and expeditions; none more so than the annual post-Christmas excursion to the Panto. Her arrival was complete with a hideous fox fur, knitted twin set and Players cigarettes which she smoked without taking them out of her mouth. Consequently the front of her grey hair was stained with nicotine. She was accompanied by a rubber hot water bottle that went by the name of Pluto. There would follow a pilgrimage to the Bristol Hippodrome. Although Pem only worked for the Post Office, she would pay for a Box! With our supply of sweets, oranges and ice cream we would be in the best seats in the house, right above the stage, ready to shout and sing our heads off. I still remember the popular songs of the day: 'I'll string along with you', 'Slow boat to China' etc. Since these were hits in 1948 and 1949 I must have been five or six; ever since my musical preference, like my desire to spread the science message, has definitely been 'pop'.

During other visits, I would trail Pem around Bristol. She was amazed that, even though I was small, I knew my way. She had left home when my mother and grandfather moved to the city. I showed her the sights: Cabot Tower, built to celebrate that it was a Bristolian, not Columbus, who discovered the American mainland; and the Clifton Suspension Bridge. I was a fan of Isambard Kingdom Brunel, 'builder and dreamer', from an early age. Our expeditions would often end at a shop called Salanson's, on Christmas Steps, almost the only bit of Medieval Bristol remaining. Here we would purchase some of my favourite toy, a building kit called 'Bayko', a sophisticated 'Lego', for making model houses. I toyed with becoming an Architect when I really meant a builder.

I am intensely proud of Bristol and its history. It, like London, was a city and a county, a status achieved for services rendered to the king over six hundred years ago – that is, it lent him some money. The fact was announced on a post at the corner of Blackhorse Road, outside the pub of the same name. The Black Horse was where my father went every night at 9.30pm for a drink with his mates. He wasn't a big drinker; I never saw him with a pint glass of draft beer in his hand, just a bottle of Worthington India Pale Ale. The men in that pub were immensely pleased when I went to University and even more proud when I came home to work on the Apollo programme. Perhaps it was trying to explain science to these, almost uneducated, men that taught me the knack of conveying the excitement of space exploration.

Technically, I wasn't from Bristol but from Gloucestershire; the boundary with Bristol ran across the street, three houses away. Our bit of the street was a forgotten part of the world; neither Bristol nor Kingswood wanted it, only the landlady. At night it was dark, a paradise for astronomers. The nearest streetlight was in Bristol; it was dim, powered by coal gas, lit by a man who came round on a bicycle with a long pole – sometimes! I won't tell you what courting couples occasionally got up to in the pitch black alley that ran beside our home.

You maybe couldn't see my father when he came home from the pub at closing time, but you knew he was coming. You could hear the distinctive click clack, click clack of his heavy working boots until he got to the place where the road ran out. Even the cat recognised it and would wait for him to come in for supper. My father always wore boots; he couldn't get shoes to fit because of a club foot, the result of a botched operation when he was young.

My father worked with his hands and those boots. He was always digging. When he came home in the evening he would dig his garden and then move on to dig other peoples' gardens for a little extra cash. He gardened for two local doctors who had flower beds, lawns, large vegetable patches and apple trees; we never went short of fallen apples for apple pie, still my favourite pudding. I sometimes got to cut their lawns with a petrol driven motor mower.

Another source of extra money was 'standby', being available to make emergency repairs to gas supplies when somebody smelt gas. Often it would be a patrolling 'bobby' in the middle of the night. I loved 'standby' particularly on summer evenings and at weekends. A lorry would arrive and I would have to act as guide to wherever my father was gardening. If I was in the cab, there was no getting me out. I would sit in the middle of the lorry, on the gearbox of 'SouGas Green 6' (that was its radio call sign). I was one of the gang: my Dad, wee Georgie, another Jack, whose surname was Offer, and me. They used to let me sniff out where the gas leak was; they would hammer an iron bar into the road and I would put a meter on it to take a reading.

If it was weekend we would get to do the job. They would put up their cabin: a concoction of bits of old pipe, some sheets of corrugated iron and a tarpaulin thrown over it. They would light a fire in a brazier to make the tea. The same fire would be used to melt lead in a ladle. A treat was a bacon sandwich, with the bacon fried on a shovel which had been scrubbed for the purpose. Even sixty years later, like my Dad, I still polish a shovel every time I've finished using it.

Jack Offer, when he retired, went to work as a doorman at Bristol's Colston Hall, pronounced by Bristolians as 'Colesnaw'. When I became a teenager, he sneaked me in to see some of the pioneers of rock and roll, including Buddy Holly and the Crickets.

I was introduced to proper rock and roll by Harold, a boy of my sister's age, who treated our house like a second home; he came to read my comics. He left a record player and a bunch of Elvis Presley records with me for months. Harold was a rogue with a heart of gold. He ended up in prison, as did another boy from the street making two out of seven. I've since wondered whether the record player was Harold's. He died aged only thirty-two, but he managed to cram a lot of things into his short life including the RAF and Merchant Navy.

After my introduction to pop culture, I sold the 'Bayko', bought a 'Dansette', 'Wake up little Susie' by the Everly Brothers and began combing my hair into a 'cow-lick', stuck in place with Brylcream and soap; I even once owned a powder blue drape coat but alas no bit of imitation fur on the collar.

I'm going too fast; when I was five, I started school at New Cheltenham Infants, and thence to High Street Junior Boys'; where to put that apostrophe was hammered into us. I used to run home at dinner time, posh people called it lunch. My mother would read to me from a comic. Of course I had 'Eagle' and Dan Dare from the first issue. One of the things I loved most about Eagle was the cut away technical drawings: cars, ships, planes etc. that appeared as a centre fold. I cut them out and plastered then all over my bedroom wall.

From there I graduated to 'Hotspur' and 'Wizard', Bernard Briggs the Great Wilson and Roy of the Rovers. After that it was Enid Blyton: the 'Famous Five' and the 'Adventure' series: 'Mountain of Adventure', 'Island of Adventure' and so on. Later, as a teenager, it became James Bond and detective stories. As regards educational books we had two encyclopaedias, one called 'Everything Within', another entitled 'Look and Learn' and a Dictionary. For Christmas there would be an Eagle annual and the traditional jigsaw to do on the front room table. It was about the only time we ever used that room, otherwise it was strictly for important visitors. Holidays weren't exotic; my mother would buy tickets for charabanc outings, a different seaside town every day for a week: Weston, for the Pier and donkey rides; Weymouth, the sand; Bournemouth and so on. The 'chara' would stop at a pub on the way home and a hat would go round for the driver. When Pem got married we went to her house at Shawford, near Winchester, which was described by my mother as "in the country."

When I was nine I came within less than an inch of being blinded. A teenage boy who worked at the factory owned by a company, Douglas's (sic), famous for their motorbikes, brought home some sodium from their laboratories. He was showing off to us younger kids on The Patch. A piece of sodium was put into water in an old boot; it exploded. We ran over to see what had happened with me to the fore. As I bent over to see, it exploded again, full force into my face. From there it was Cossham Hospital, and on to the burns unit at Frenchay for three weeks of skin grafts using a six by six inches flap of skin taken from the inside of my thigh. What worried me most was the fact that I would lose the book I would have got for a 100% attendance record at school. I had a season ticket at Cossham, my mother was always taking me there after some misadventure; I had to have some stitches and a tetanus jab. One of her sisters had had tetanus – what my mother called "lockjaw".

At ten I passed the eleven plus and migrated to Kinswood Grammar School, KGS, known locally as 'the cowsheds' because it was a long low timber building that looked like a cow shed. To make matters worse the uniform was **** brown; it cost a fortune exclusively from an expensive shop in Bristol. To buy us clothes my mother usually got some coupons you could use in shops that participated in the scheme. It was known as 'the Club' and required you to pay back twenty-one shillings at a shilling in the pound every week. Compound interest was something you did in Maths lessons. The school uniform shop didn't participate in 'the Club', it was cash only. But there was no way my mother would let me miss out on the opportunity she never had.

26

I had also been offered a free scholarship to a Bristol private school. They had classes on Saturday mornings. This definitely wasn't on my agenda. I went to 'the cowsheds' a mile and a half away. Unless I walked, the bus fare would have been seven pounds spread over the year. I was bought a bike for passing the eleven plus. It cost twelve pounds, an entire week's wages for my Dad, so again it was paid for by what was known as 'the Never, Never', hire purchase. When sister was at the same school six years earlier she had to walk. She never learnt to ride a bicycle – still can't.

With me at KGS my mother was able to take a part time job, 'charring'. She was able to leave early because I liked school and would go at eight o'clock. Nevertheless she was always home in time to give me dinner. It was an entirely predictable menu: roast beef on Sunday, something derived from it Monday, shepherd's pie Tuesday, Wednesday soup and Thursday egg and chips. We ate on a white, deal-topped, table. My mother scrubbed it with the water left after boiling her whites on washing day. I could cycle home in less than ten minutes and get back by the time my class-mates got out from school dinner for break.

Later on my Mum became a home-help, now called a carer. My mother was really a saint. She had hordes of old ladies she visited. One ancient widow, we called her Mrs Mary, came to watch television (when we got it courtesy of a legacy Pem shared out) on Monday nights, to see 'This is your Life' with Eamon Andrews. It was followed by 'Wagon Train'. I, perhaps not surprisingly, preferred 'Maverick'.

Until we had TV we listened to the Radio. We had 'Rediffusion', what nowadays would be termed 'cable'. It broadcast four stations: Home Service, Light Programme, Radio Luxembourg, and BBC Television (sound only). One programme, which was an absolute must, was 'Journey into Space' by Charles Chilton. I listened to it sat under the kitchen (living room) table. Britain led the first missions to the Moon and Mars. Of course we would, wouldn't we? We'd painted half the countries in the Atlas pink. Before we had our own television I watched the Coronation at a local Sunday school. And much more important, Wolverhampton Wanderers playing football against Honved and Spartak (clubs from Hungary and Russia), gathered with six men round a twelve inch black and white, with a magnifier in front, courtesy of a neighbour called Wilf Mannings.

Football was the reason I liked school, not because of the lessons, but because there were other boys there to play football with. We played before school, whenever there was a break, dinner times and after school on a nearby Common until it got dark. In those days you got pinched for riding without

27

lights so I got a dynamo for a present. Policemen were respected then. My father's only encounter with the Law was fined ten shillings for giving my sister a ride on the crossbar of his bike. He was very honest. He once returned a wallet he found containing £66.00, the money a man had received for selling his motorbike. The grateful owner rewarded my father with a five pound note. It was the only time in my childhood I saw a white fiver. My father never used a wallet; he said he didn't have anything to put in one. He too started with nothing and had all of it left when he died. He didn't make a will; all the money he had was in his pocket. The family fortunes hadn't increased much since John 'the hatter'.

The school's Headmaster was a snob who frowned on football – "A game for gentlemen played by hooligans," he described it; he wanted us to play 'rugger'. We weren't allowed a full-sized ball for soccer, so we made do with a tennis ball. The teachers turned a blind eye but if the Headmaster happened to cross the playground, it would be confiscated. We would then play with a beer bottle top, it requires a quite different technique; your timing has to be good and you have to keep your eye on the 'ball' otherwise you will definitely play the man. I played with one boy who was so good, when he got onto a proper pitch, he scored more than a hundred goals in a season for a local youth team. These days he would have been worth millions. Back then they paid professional footballers twenty pounds a week. On Saturdays I toured local playing fields on my bike with my boots in my saddlebag. I'd play for any team that was short. At fifteen I was playing in men's leagues under more assumed names than I can remember.

I arrived at KGS in 1954 to find I was in the top first form and put into a temporary, pretty dilapidated, asbestos building. My first lessons were taken there. I enjoyed most of them except Latin, I didn't see the point, and French. I can read it a bit but not speak it or understand the French. Why don't they talk to Brits the way we do to them in English, very loudly and slowly, as though addressing somebody who is not quite all there? I couldn't see any reason why a table should be female – only girls and ships are female.

I remember my first Chemistry lesson well. The master, nick-named 'Paunch' came in, tipped a jar of iron filings into a dish of sulphur, mixed them, produced a magnet and separated them again. This was much better, more interesting to know how to do that. Chemistry became my subject.

I must have learnt something else. Oh yes, now I remember, it was a mixed school, so I found out about girls. I did already have inkling about sex. As a nine year old, one Sunday morning I followed a friend into his mother's bedroom to tell her we were going out. We found her smoking with a man

I knew as a local builder. I think it was the fact that they were smoking in bed that surprised me most. When I told my parents my Dad said the man was a 'Spiv'.

Back to girls; a boy who was in my class decided to have a twelfth birthday party. His parents went out, leaving his older sister, she was a sixth-former, and her boy friend, in charge. They decided we should play some grown up games: 'Postman's Knock' and 'Hyde Park Corner'. In the latter everybody would pair off; one couple would be in the centre, with a torch, which they would flash on the other couples. If you weren't kissing, the person who was holding the torch at the time would replace the appropriate sex defaulter, and so on. Everybody who wasn't already twelve wanted a party after that. You tried to catch somebody you fancied.

It was a good game if you were twelve. At several of these parties I somehow managed to be paired with a particular girl. She had a husky sexy voice, with a slight lisp. If you're old enough, think actress Fenella Fielding from the 'Carry-on' films. My 'affair' with husky-voice went nowhere but I did have one long term girl friend at school. Whilst I was going out with this particular girl, she discovered her parents weren't her parents – she was adopted and illegitimate. She was devastated and I realised the folly of what I've always termed "lying by omission."

I went through the school always in the top form until I was fifteen. KGS expected people like me to take 'O' levels early, spend three years in the sixth form, hoping to compete for a place at Oxford or Cambridge. Very few achieved it but as I already said the Headmaster had pretensions. This wasn't for me; I wasn't going into any sixth form. I was getting a job, at what I didn't know, but I was off.

At the beginning of my fourth year in the school something amazing happened. On 4 October 1957, Sputnik was launched. Right outside of the door of our classroom, in front of the library, there was an Honours Board. The second name on that Board was Bernie (now Sir Bernard) Lovell, the man whose telescope was tracking Sputnik and saving the world. It was in all the papers. Everybody at KGS was immensely proud, not least the Headmaster, who taught Physics. Right above Bernard Lovell, was another name: Brian 'Fishy' Sammons, now our Chemistry master. He must have been even cleverer, I thought. All science was the flavour of the month, which suited me better than the other things they tried to teach me. Perhaps I'd have learnt more if I hadn't been prone to interjecting the odd 'witty' comment from the back of the class. I still can't resist doing it in meetings and lectures.

I went into the 5th form and planned to leave the next summer. My form master, Mr Hocking, 'Claude', a Maths teacher, summoned my parents to the school and told them, in no uncertain terms, I was capable of doing more. My mother would have been easier to convince. Like my father's mother, she wanted me to have a better job than him, out in all weathers, all hours. He, however, could never have been cooped up in a factory, let alone an office. The Gas Board offered to make him a foreman after working for them for forty-two years. He didn't like paper work, and couldn't drive, so he carried on with his holes.

I was like him and, reluctantly, went into the sixth-form; I elected for Chemistry (obviously), Physics and a mixture of Pure and Applied Maths. I could easily have done both kinds as separate subjects but it wasn't allowed. That first year in the sixth form I won a Maths prize, beating people nearly two years older. In Chemistry, we began to learn Organic Chemistry, 'chicken wire chemistry'. Lots of people hated it; I found it easy.

To make some money I had a variety of part-time jobs, paper rounds and working in a pub. I began 'sticking-up' in the skittle alley then moved on to cleaning up the party room on Sunday mornings. Scraping confetti off a wooden floor when it's stuck down with beer, and worse, after drunken Saturday weddings, is no fun. I was glad when I moved up to serving in the Bar at 'The Kingswood Hotel'. I was still only seventeen, technically not old enough to drink.

Like others of my age I started to drink before I was eighteen in the back room of 'The King's Arms'. We could also drink at 'The Chequers' by the river my mother threatened to jump in. It was reached via a twisty one track road and therefore a waste of time the Police trying to catch underage drinkers. By the time they reached it all the clientele were outside casually leaning over the balcony looking at the weir. Inside it looked like the Marie Celeste, abandoned drinks everywhere. After a fruitless journey, the unfortunate policeman, they didn't have cars, had to cycle back up a steep hill.

It wasn't the only time the police went to Hanham river and The Chequers because of a Pillinger (not my mother thank goodness). Previously, in the 19th century a nephew of John 'the hatter', son of his brother William, possibly another transportee, returned from Australia and married the Pub's widowed landlady. He was shot by his newly acquired son-in-law who promptly jumped in the river and drowned.

Sometimes I was left in charge of the Kingswood Hotel when the boss went out. If the worst ever came to the very worst, I could always have been a publican. The Licensee and his wife had known my father when they were all young. Their son Bob, his friend John and I became buddies.

At eighteen I threw my school cap over a hedge, literally, and went to University. It wasn't planned. I just drifted into applying because other people in the sixth form seemed to be desperate to go there. I remember sending in three applications to Bristol, Leeds and Swansea. I have no idea why I chose the latter two. Anyway Swansea Chemistry Department offered me a place. So at the end of the summer of 1961 off I went, clutching a little suitcase, borrowed from my sister. She was the traveller not me. She'd been to work in London, hitch-hiked round Europe, came back and got a job in a Travel Agent's. Before her grand tour, she had done more jobs than you could shake a stick at. Sometimes she would start one and quit before the end of the day.

I arrived in Swansea by train via the Lower Swansea Valley, miles of derelict foundries and tips left by the defunct metal smelting industry. Chemistry at school taught all about this. If it was what chemists did after University I think I'd have rather kept a pub. The letter I had been sent from Swansea said "Exit the station and get a number seventy-seven bus." When it came along, it said on the front it was going to Cymrydceceirw – where on Earth was this unpronounceable place? I thought. It didn't get any better, at the end of the ride I had to walk a mile up a steep hill, carrying the suitcase, to a Hall of Residence. It too had a Welsh name beginning with Neuadd, but in English it translated to Clyne Castle.

I don't remember much about the first year I spent there except that it rained all the time. If you looked out across Swansea Bay (the University was across the road from the beach) and could see the other side of the Channel, it was going to rain. If you couldn't, it was raining already. I didn't plan to stay long.

I went to some lectures in Chemistry, Physics and Maths. The students all wore duffle coats and scarves; some smoked pipes. I preferred a donkey jacket like a working man. The end of the year came and we took some exams. They told you which subject they thought you should continue with. To some students they said "None" and sent them home. "Down" was the word used. They told me Physics, but I didn't want to do Physics. They told me Chemistry was full.

Another student, Dave Cadogan, who had become a friend and I decided we would do a general degree, two subjects: Chemistry and Physics. I could just as easily have gone home, I wasn't in love with University that much. The only thing that stopped me was the thought of the sacrifices my parents had made to get me there. Admitting that about twenty people were better than me at Chemistry would not have been something I would have wanted to do to my maternal grandfather Levi, even if he was long since dead. My father would have simply said "Alright, as long as you did your best," but I hadn't. I couldn't have said "I can't do it." If ever I said "can't" he would say "There's no such word as can't."

It was now 1963, what I remember most about it was the big freeze. It started to snow on Boxing Day. Within hours it had filled the gully that ran down the middle of the double pitched roof over our rank of houses. The channel between the two halves sloped down to our end so when it rained all the water had to run away over us. My father was worried the roof wasn't up to the weight of any more snow and, if and when it melted, the lot would come through our bedroom ceilings, not down the drain pipe. All the other houses were occupied by elderly people. We, the only able bodied men, borrowed a ladder and, with a blizzard raging, climbed on the roof to shovel the whole lot out as fast as it fell, throwing great lumps into the street. Everybody else, including Mrs Flue at number thirty-six, who I've been told once attacked somebody with an axe, stayed indoors out of the way whilst we risked our necks.

Shortly after, I returned to Swansea; it wasn't a whole lot better there. It was so cold the spray froze as the waves broke on the beach. My digs, I had moved out of the Castle as too expensive, were frozen solid. There were six of us there, if we wanted the lavatory we had to catch a bus to the College. I don't know what the landlady and her daughter did. Neither did we care. It was the worst place I ever lived. In films about students, the landlady's daughter is always a stunner. Not ours, but she was allowed to practise her cooking skills, or lack of them, on us. Her favourite dish was 'Spam', not seen since the War, and as piece de resistance, cold pilchards and mashed potatoes. I've never entertained eating fish or mash ever since. One day, we decided to have a mutiny. When the dish arrived for our tea, we left six untouched plates on the table and ate toast made on a paraffin stove. The daughter cleared everything away without flinching. The same fare appeared on other occasions. It reminded me of my mother's childhood.

The digs were in the Mumbles; it was like the Kingswood main road in that it had a pub every few yards. It was just as well I enjoyed what the Welsh thought was a good night out – beer, lots of it, and a sing-song. When the summer's exams came I qualified for a general degree. I could have spent a year doing nothing and still left with a qualification but I didn't, I decided to go for Honours in Chemistry. It was sheer bloody-mindedness because the previous year they'd told me I couldn't, not because I enjoyed lectures or practicals. In fact the latter were like cookery classes. You followed the script and hoped you got what was required at the end. Pouring a liquid out of a bottle into a solution in a test tube to see if it gave a precipitate or went a certain colour wasn't very high tech.

I was just going through the motions and went on doing this until a few weeks before I was due to take my final exams. At that point something very significant happened, A lecturer named Betteridge, instead of giving just another recipe, offered a few of us the chance to do a project, a piece of research. I opted to do this as more interesting, even if you didn't know the answer or whether the supervisor would appreciate your efforts. Instead of messing around with test tubes, it involved making measurements with instruments called spectrometers. This was a big improvement; it was like looking for gas leaks.

A short while after, I saw a notice saying that next year the Department was going to purchase a new kind of spectrometer, a mass spectrometer. In preparation for its arrival they had arranged for a very eminent mass spectroscopist to visit and give a course of lectures on how to interpret the new spectra. Although it was supposed to be for researchers and I was only an undergraduate, I slipped in.

It was my first encounter with the great Welsh scientist, John Beynon, a dapper man with a clipped moustache. He showed lots of black and white charts with lines on them and explained that if you hit a molecule with an electron it would break into pieces. The lines represented the masses of the pieces. If you didn't know what the molecule was beforehand, you could work it out by putting the bits back together, like in a jigsaw puzzle. There were hundreds of different ways in which the molecule could break, so it was like having lots of jigsaws, all of which would give the same picture if you put them together correctly. Hey, I thought, this is fun not cookery, a throwback to Christmas Day afternoons in the front room. It certainly had more appeal than the Swansea Valley.

Beynon also told us that molecules didn't break up randomly, there were rules but since the subject was new these hadn't all been worked out. A little bit later, I heard the Department was going to recruit a research student the next autumn, when the spectrometer came. The task was to work out rules for compounds they were interested in. This would allow the people who extracted naturally occurring substances or synthesised things to understand what they had in their flasks and test tubes. I thought about this, maybe I could be a research student and be the first person to know things.

It meant not just passing the final exams but getting a good degree. Usually for exams I just turned up, after reading through whatever notes I had or essays I had written. I only ever started revising the night before. Sometimes I didn't even do it the night before. At school I would rely on my father to wake me at 5.30am, before he set out for work. I would spend three hours mugging something up. To get a good degree I would have to do better, so I got up early every day for six weeks and learnt notes, sometimes borrowed from Dave's girlfriend Marion, to fill in the gaps where I had missed lectures. Practicals weren't going to be easy; I couldn't put the solutions I had spilt back into the flasks or retrieve the reaction products I had put on the ceiling.

The exams came and went. I was annoyed at some papers, things I knew better hadn't been asked. Other students said you could spot questions because lecturers would realise something they had set in the exams was not covered as well as they would have liked, so they would highlight it again at the end of their course. Fortunately I only tried this once; it didn't work. I tried to revise everything equally. At the end of June, along with all the others, I gathered round a notice board to discover our grades; some students, who I knew wanted to stay to do research, turned away disappointed. I had got a II/1, at least I was eligible. Off I went to the bar to celebrate.

What I didn't know was that the other eligible students had hung around waiting to see the Professor to grab one of the research studentships. There weren't enough to go round and to get first choice of the projects you had to be there. I only found this out the next morning. Luckily the position involving the mass spectrometer was still available. Everybody else had clamoured for traditional safe projects, where you simply repeated what had done before with enough variation to make it new. Working with the mass spectrometer was going to be too much of an unknown for them. It didn't deter me, I was sent to see a lecturer named Jim Ballantine. Nobody else had been. He was a quiet, teetotal, Scotsman with a characteristic busy way of walking. The following autumn, I became Swansea's first research student in mass spectrometry. Swansea is now the country's centre for this kind of spectrometry.

The first setback was that the mass spectrometer hadn't arrived. I spent the autumn term working out rules for another kind of spectrometer. It was an enormous success and other people in the department started using my rules to interpret their spectra. Jim said "We'll have to write a paper, I'll show you how." When it appeared, we were deluged with requests for reprints, it was an amazing feeling. I have written a lot of papers since but none has ever proved so instantly popular.

It was only as a research student I had steady girlfriends at University. I seemed always to be clearing up the mess after my mates dumped their latest.

One jilted girl got so drunk, she was literally poured into the battered Mini I had bought from my earnings packing chocolate during my last long vacation and the bar job I returned to whenever I went home. These days, anybody asked to take an incapable girl home would have feared being accused of date rape. I don't do risk analysis. I rely on my wits in a crisis. Worried what might happen if this girl passed out and stayed unconscious, I put my fingers down her throat and made her sick; not in my new, second-hand, prized possession, I hasten to add. Ask any disaster analyst or psychologist and they will tell you "It's the people with confidence in their own ability and react positively who survive, it's the ditherers and freezers who become charred bodies pulled from the wreckage."

The sixties was the decade of free love and experimenting with drugs. The nearest I got to the former was that the top man in mass spectrometry, Carl Djerassi, was responsible for 'the Pill'. In respect of the latter, as a Chemist, I was asked several times if I could make LSD. I didn't need LSD; my brain has always been a kaleidoscope – "Oh, the colours, man."

Jim was an ideal supervisor for me to work for. He saw what I was doing as my research and let me get on with it. He told me "If you ever need to discuss it, my door is always open" and left me to my own devices. Other students' supervisors seemed to turn up to direct their work all the time. If Jim had wanted to do that with me he would have had to get up early or go to bed late. The deal I had for using the instrument was that I got access to it at 6.00pm when the technician went home. Sometimes it took me three hours tinkering to get it working the way I wanted. I would then go to the College bar for a drink with friends, returning to the lab at 'chucking out time'. I would switch on a portable radio and work until Radio Luxembourg closed down. At 2.00am in the morning, when they played 'My prayer at the end of the day', I drove home.

My prayers were answered in 1966 – England won the World Cup. At Swansea this reawakened my interest in playing football and probably helped me stay at University just as it gave me a reason for going to school. The College team joined the Welsh League. It meant a lot of matches because the other teams started in August and had played half a dozen games before the undergraduates returned in October. We would get further and further behind over Christmas and Easter. By the end of the season we would have at least ten games in hand but could achieve something if we won the majority. We would be playing three games a week, tough for some players when the exam season was on the horizon. I wasn't as good as some of the players we had, but I got games and appearances from the 'subs bench'. They only allowed one 'sub' in those days; we only had one – me. In my football career I was lucky. Whenever I played for good teams, it was as left back behind a skilful left winger who couldn't tackle for toffee. We would come to an amicable arrangement – I would get the ball and give it to him; he didn't come into my half of the pitch and I wasn't going into his.

A lot of the teams we played football against were from mining villages, "Up the valleys" as it was known. They had ex-professionals and players who would go on to be professional. I once marked a Welsh amateur international out of the game. I don't think he'd ever met an opponent who could dispossess a winger of a beer bottle top. It was the pinnacle of my career.

Valley teams seemed to think, as students, we had nothing to do all day but train whilst they had full time jobs down the pits like Kingswood once had. They tried to kick us off the park. I remember one team that had a player, Hughie, who they must have kept chained up during the week. We inevitably became battle-hardened and when it came to matches with other Universities, unstoppable. Swansea won the Universities Athletic Union Championship on top of gaining two successive promotions to get into the Premier division of the Welsh League.

But it was time for me to leave. I had been accumulating results from the mass spectrometer and, like many others doing research at that time, believed that to get a job I would have to go to the United States. Even though I had no particular desire to go, an American mid-west University had offered to take me.

I had tried for a couple of jobs back in England, one with British Petroleum. I told them they needed to have a mass spectrometer and me to run it. They obviously didn't agree. I also harboured a desire to get into forensic science. I was asked to go for interview with the Police, but didn't make it because something else was happening; it must have been a football match. They didn't ask me to help them with their enquiries again. I'm glad now I didn't go, I might have got the job.

Because I was getting on well with my research, I was allowed to go to a Meeting of the Chemical Society. It wasn't an exotic location, just two days in Manchester. On the morning of the second day, I received a message to phone Jim in Swansea, urgently! Such a call was totally out of character, I assumed something had happened to the mass spectrometer or its technician. In the past, when the technician had gone sick, I had run an unpaid 'stand-by' service for the Department. Without any enthusiasm I rang Jim from a phone box at coffee break. He had been reading job adverts and found one saying that the University of Bristol needed somebody skilled in mass spectrometry. "They're setting up a new laboratory to analyse lunar samples to look for evidence of life on the Moon. They want somebody to get a mass spectrometer going," he said. "You've installed a mass spectrometer before," he continued, it was clearly an instruction to say I had, even if I'd only helped a bit.

Everybody knew about the Apollo programme and John F. Kennedy's brash speech committing America to landing a man on the Moon and bringing him home safely before the end of the decade. He'd said "Not because it's easy, but because it's going to be hard." This, I liked the sound of.

Apollo was going to return bits of the Moon. I had no idea the British were involved. If the project had made much progress it hadn't been obvious to me. I knew that three Astronauts had been killed in a disastrous fire. That was about all. It was now nearly summer 1968. Time for NASA was running out or they were nearly there. Anyway Jim had a telephone number and thought I should try for it. I couldn't get some more change for the phone fast enough. I spoke to a secretary in Bristol who asked me how soon I could come for an interview. We agreed on Tuesday the following week. She asked "Do you need directions?" "No thanks," I said, "I know where the University is" – opposite that shop where they sold the ****brown uniforms.

On the way back to Swansea, I was telling Dave and another research student, who had been allowed to go to Manchester, about what had happened. It was a Friday night, the train was full and we were joined at our table by an attractive lady, about forty, who sat in the spare seat opposite me, alongside my flat mate Dave. You wouldn't call him Brad Pitt – he's the only person I have ever met who played football in glasses, which he took off, with one hand, when heading the ball. Our new table companion listened to the conversation and even joined in. Dave, whose wedding to Marion was imminent (I was going to be best man) was strangely quiet but kept fidgeting. When she left the train, he told us the whole time she had been rubbing her hand up the inside of his thigh. The third student was upset; he was the only one who hadn't scored that week.

I duly presented myself at an office on the fifth floor of a concrete building, just off Park Row, Bristol. I met a man with glasses and unruly hair, which he put his finger in and twiddled during the interview, whilst I sat in an armchair in the corner of his room. It wasn't so much an interview – more him telling me what he needed. He had recently moved to Bristol from Glasgow. They had had a gas chromatograph-mass spectrometer (gc-ms) there; gc-ms used a flowing gas to separate a mixture of compounds, then produced the spectra for each one. He had money to buy the gc-ms they would need for their involvement in the Apollo programme. It was due to arrive in Bristol in the autumn and he needed somebody to get it working. He had expected somebody already working in his lab to do it but the guy had come to him and said words to the effect "I don't see working on the Moon as a long term career." I often wonder if he kicks his cat every time he sees me on television.

Geoff Eglinton, that was the interviewer's name, must have asked "Do you think you can do it?" But all I remember was him saying was "How soon can you get here?" I knew I still had quite a lot of samples to run on the mass spectrometer in Swansea to confirm all the pieces in my jigsaw puzzles fitted, but I didn't hesitate. I made a wild prediction to match Kennedy's, which I hoped would satisfy him. I said "I can be in Bristol by 15th September." It gave me six weeks work and six weeks' to write my thesis. He said immediately "If you can make it by then, the job is yours." I found out later that he received a reference from the Professor in Swansea warning that I was a 'barrack room lawyer', so I don't know who took the greater risk. I went back to Swansea not even contemplating that I might not succeed. I was too busy embarking on my own journey into space.

Chapter 3

A SMALL STEP FOR SOME, A BIG STEP FOR OTHERS

I made the deadline of 15 September by five days. As I had estimated it took me six weeks to finish the experiments; then I started writing. I also typed the final copy on what were called 'skins'. These fitted onto a drum in a machine known as a 'Roneo'. When the handle was turned multiple copies could be produced. The diagrams and molecular structures were drawn in individually by hand afterwards on each copy. Jim returned everything I gave him within twenty-four hours and found me an examiner who was prepared to read the thesis over the weekend before the oral exam.

After twelve weeks' incessant effort, crunch time came. The examiner walked into the room, casually tossed my pride and joy onto the table and said "Let's talk about electron spin resonance." This was a completely different kind of spectroscopy, not the sort of thing I had been doing. I didn't think I knew anything about ESR. All I could think was "This has blown it."

I don't remember anything about what happened after that, only that he didn't open the thesis or refer to it. He and Jim left together at the end. I waited around for a while but they didn't return. Next morning I was outside Jim's office the moment he showed up. I always knew when he was in because he parked his Ford Consul in a space, right outside the building, which I could see from the library window. When I asked what the result was, all he said was "I thought you realised you passed. I didn't think I needed to tell you." So I packed my stuff and went. Of course I thanked him and a few others who had encouraged me to stick with Chemistry.

The following Monday I arrived at Geoff Eglinton's office. He wasn't there. "He's gone to a conference abroad," his secretary said, "so too have all the other members of the group." James Maxwell, who had worked for Geoff in

Glasgow, then gone to California for a year, arrived back that day. The film 'The Good, the Bad and the Ugly' had made Mexican moustaches popular around that time; James had a bushy 'Viva Zapata' and smoked a lot.

There was no sign of a new mass spectrometer – déjà vu. I didn't mind because Geoff had told me that the grant which was paying me to carry out the lunar sample analysis had been given to him jointly with Jim Lovelock (of Gaia fame) on the strength of an idea Lovelock had to increase the sensitivity of detection of gas chromatography by replacing all the hydrogen in organic molecules by fluorine. I hadn't had time to learn anything about fluorine chemistry, so that first week at Bristol, I indulged myself in the Library.

I was to find that Geoff was a great man for delegating power. He would disappear to the USA leaving James to run the group and me to organise the lunar project. I was happy with this arrangement, just as I had been in the local pub and as a research student. I started with experiments with 'kerogen', the organic macro-molecule common in sedimentary rocks on Earth. This complicated and very stable molecule was evidence for life; if the lunar Mare were dried up seas, the only organic matter that was going to survive on the Moon would be kerogen.

A month after I arrived in Bristol, NASA launched Apollo 7. It was a confidence booster showing that the US could put three, rather than two, astronauts at a time into orbit. But so what, it didn't bring the Moon any closer. The rocket used for the launch wasn't the Saturn V needed to go to the Moon. Still, the mass spectrometer had arrived. It was the first of its type to be delivered so there were the inevitable teething troubles. I had a company engineer camped at Bristol.

Over the Christmas holidays 1968, the World looked on in awe as Frank Borman flew Apollo 8 to the Moon, around it and back to Earth. For the first time human eyes were feasting where only robots had seen. One of the most iconic pictures ever produced by the Apollo missions, or any other space project for that matter, was that of 'Earthrise' photographed as the spacecraft which carried the astronauts emerged from its self-imposed hiding place.

Back in the lab after Christmas, we held a 'realism at last' meeting. Geoff had gone to the United States, to the Johnson Space Center (JSC), where they were going to keep the lunar samples, because he was part of the Lunar Sample Analysis Planning Team (LSAPT). It was clear now that NASA was going to get lunar samples and, with Geoff on LSAPT, some would be coming our way. I now had some more firepower. James, with his experience of analysing ancient terrestrial rocks for evidence of life, was going to play a part. Another post-doc named Harry Draffin, also a Scot, skilled in converting involatile molecules to volatile ones for gc-ms was recruited.

Two Americans joined: firstly John Hayes, who looked like Paul Newman. He had been drafted for service in Vietnam but had opted to work for NASA on the space programme instead. He had decided to come to Geoff's lab to avoid working on Apollo but now found he was helping me. I learned a lot about isotopes (nature's accidents, elements that contain one or more extra neutrons changing the mass but not the chemical properties, except some become radioactive rather than stable) from John. Our other American was Paul Abell, from Rhode Island, on sabbatical leave. How do you describe Paul? The 'oldest swinger in town' would fit the bill. The first time I met sixty-odd-year-old Paul, he was wearing a floral neckerchief and a pair of white bell-bottomed trousers with a banana tree design sewn up one leg. He made all his own clothes! The skill he taught me, however, was how to glass blow.

At the 'realism at last' meeting we divided up the tasks we needed to complete to be ready for a lunar sample. James and John, with Paul's help, were going to design and build a closed glass system to allow us to use very pure solvents to dissolve any soluble organic molecules hidden in the lunar soil. Once we had a solution Harry could carry out his chemistry. Thus the system would do all the jobs that were normally used to investigate the compounds that are evidence of life in ancient rocks, but in a way that would preclude contamination by terrestrial material. We didn't want to discover life on the Moon, only to find out later that it was something we had picked up on Earth. I had to concentrate on getting the mass spectrometer going. Ideas of fluorinating things were shelved. It wasn't possible now to develop a completely new technique; nor did we have enough hands to work on it. We called ourselves the 'Just Four Men'. We knew American groups working on the Moon were far bigger.

I had to go to tell Jim Lovelock 'perfluorination' had fallen by the wayside, but first I was given the opportunity to feel that I was a genuine part of the Apollo programme. After piloting Apollo 8 on its epic journey, in February 1969 Frank Borman came to London as part of his world tour. Geoff was, again, out of town so I was allowed to take his place when Bormann spoke at the Royal Society, a magnificent Regency building at the bottom of Lower Regent Street, overlooking the Mall on Carlton House Terrace.

When I got there the lecture room was packed, standing room only. The vast majority of the audience were far more advanced in their scientific careers than I. It was quite amazing seeing some of these rather elderly men jostling to get a better view of a rather diminutive astronaut, who had been on a unique voyage. Astronauts are supposed to inspire kids; these senior academics were just as enthusiastic about space travel. I was right at the back – I knew my place in this company. As I walked back to Piccadilly underground station, I remember thinking that it would be fantastic to be invited to events like this all the time.

Lovelock lived somewhere in the middle of Salisbury Plain. It was not the sort of place that you could reach without a car. The weather wasn't good when I set out. Still, I got there and had my eyes opened by meeting the inventor in his private lab. He wasn't at all perturbed by developments in the lunar activities, his mind was elsewhere. What he was keen to show me was what he was working on for Mars.

There was going to be a gc-ms on NASA's Mars-exploring Viking spacecraft which meant there had to be a way of removing the gas. On Earth a big pump is used. With a bit of lateral thinking Jim had come up with the idea of using hydrogen as the carrier gas for the chromatography because he knew a way to get rid of hydrogen. The precious metal palladium becomes porous to hydrogen when heated, so Jim invented something he named the palladium separator. It was delightfully simple. To demonstrate he connected a hydrogen cylinder to a length of palladium tube; to show hydrogen was flowing, he lit a flame at the end. He then attached a couple of wires to the tube and turned on an electric current to heat the metal. As the tube warmed up the hydrogen diffused away before it reached the end of the tube. As if by magic the flame went out. The effect on me was like the chemistry teacher with the magnet. In a matter of a few seconds Jim had saved an awful lot of mass (weight) for the spacecraft. It was my first insight into space technology and the message was: to get to fly a mission or an instrument to Mars you had to be clever and simple.

The return trip to Bristol was by no means as simple. By the time I left in the late afternoon, it was beginning to get dark and fog was descending. The first few miles, whilst it was light, weren't so bad but afterwards it was a nightmare. I drove on, hoping I was staying on the right road. Whenever there were street lights I got out of the car to find a signpost to check. In the suburban streets of Bristol it was next to impossible. I just couldn't see the side turnings, so I got home by trial and error. Still, I had rid myself of a lunar problem but I'd been seduced by the next destination in the solar system – Mars.

In March and May the Apollo programme moved on relentlessly with Apollos 9 and 10. Apollo 9 was the first flight of the Lunar Module, LM, in Earth orbit. It tested the crew's ability to dock and undock from their command module. Apollo 10 must have been incredibly frustraing of for the crew. To go to the Moon, undock the LM and swoop to the lunar surface and not be allowed to take the ultimate step. I'm sure the crew often think the history of the world could have been entirely different. I doubt if I could have resisted the temptation, orders or no orders.

To be absolutely honest Apollo 9 and 10 didn't mean too much to us at Bristol. All the action was going on elsewhere, in Mexico to be precise, at a little place called Pueblito de Allende. Right on NASA's doorstep a couple of tons of meteorite crashed to Earth. The scientists in Houston preparing the Lunar Receiving Laboratory hot-footed it to the site. Soon car boots (trunks for Americans) were being filled with a special kind of meteorite called a carbonaceous chondrite. I got a kilogram from a friend who made the trip. Now we had some extraterrestrial material to practise with.

In Bristol, the Just Four Men were busy getting ready for our big test. I had the mass spectrometer working at a specification better than promised by the manufacturers. John and James had got the Chemistry Department's glass blowers to construct a glass apparatus which would deliver all the solvents and reagents needed to process a lunar sample and pass a tiny drop of solution to me. Everything would be done in a clean room, a restricted access room where all the air was carefully filtered.

Harry was preparing the service laboratory next door to the clean room. One of his jobs was to provide glassware which had been cleaned to remove all trace of organic carbon compounds. This was being done by oxidising the various components in chromic acid, a liquid made with concentrated sulphuric acid. Some of the items were quite big and had awkward shapes, so Harry made five litre (more than a gallon) vats of the cleaning fluid in enormous glass beakers, in a sink.

It was whilst doing this one day that Harry had his most embarrassing moment. He was lifting a heavy beaker out of the sink, only he didn't lift it quite high enough so when he began to bring it towards himself he caught the bottom on the edge of the porcelain. Crack! Five litres of concentrated acid down the front of his trousers. If the 'Guinness Book of Records' is interested, I can assure them that Harry Draffin holds the world record for removing a pair of trousers. The girl technician who was helping ran screaming from the lab, saving him, and her, further embarrassment.

I did manage to get a few hours a week off during the run up to Apollo 11. BBC television was showing 'Civilisation', an art series presented by Kenneth (Lord) Clark. My education in terms of the art world, up to this time, had been sadly lacking. I had been banned from Art at school for using a paint brush to flick paint at other people. They were flicking it at me; I just happened to be the one caught in the act. Lord Clark's tour of the Gothic cathedrals of Europe held me spellbound. How on Earth did puny humans, with primitive hammers

43

and chisels, without massive cranes, do it? I hope, a thousand years from now, our involvement in the space programme, particularly Apollo, will be seen as the 20th Century equivalent of those creations.

July came at last. The giant Saturn V that was going to do our field work was standing on the launch pad. Geoff flew to Florida to watch it take off on its adventure. When he came back he was going to be one of the pundits who explain what was going on for BBC coverage of the lunar landing. A couple of days before the appointed day came the news that the Soviet Union had a rocket on its way to the Moon. The world wondered if they were they going to stage a massive pre-emptive strike to win this lap of the space race. Thankfully it was nothing more sinister than a stunt to annoy NASA, it was a false alarm. Forty years later Bernard Lovell told me it crashed.

On 16 July, Apollo 11 was on its way. It was going to make its attempt to land in the middle of the British night, prime time for American, west coast TV. I watched the activities on the lunar surface with a girl I had been going out with at her flat in Clifton, the part of Bristol built on the proceeds of the city's own programme of exploration and trade. Although I have seen those pictures many times since, it is the first time I witnessed them that sticks in my memory. Everybody who was living then knows where they were and what they were doing when Neil Armstrong took his 'one small step'. I certainly do. But I was one of the few watching in anticipation of handling what he and Buzz Aldrin scooped up and put in the bag to bring home. I didn't know then, years later, Armstrong would put his arm round me and say "You analysed some of my samples."

Apollo 11's time on the Moon was all over too quickly for some. For me, and I suspect a few hundred others, it couldn't come back soon enough. It was like having to wait for the best Christmas present of all time. The astronauts and the samples were quarantined, in case they were returning with some uncontrollable lunar nasty bug. NASA had to protect the planet. The suspense was almost unbearable. One lunar sample PI (Principal Investigator) offered to eat some material to demonstrate it wasn't harmful to humans to speed things up "As long as I get my samples to analyse before anyone else" he said. His offer was politely turned down. I thought he was smart.

Everybody couldn't be given their share simultaneously so there was an undertaking with NASA that all the groups studying the specimens would remain silent about their results until they were revealed at a Conference in Houston the following January. As soon as I knew Apollo 11 was safely down in the Pacific Ocean, I took a holiday to distract me whilst I waited. I went to see some of the places mentioned during Civilisation. The girl who watched

Neil Armstrong with me acted as my guide; she knew about these things. I wanted to make sure I was inspired to take my turn for Apollo 11.

Our destination was Rome by way of some of the best architectural sites in Europe, starting at Chartres. The list of things we visited included St. Peters, the Vatican and Michelangelo's Sistine chapel ceiling. Whilst walking around the streets of the Italian capital, our reverie was shattered by a newspaper hoarding. I couldn't read Italian but it was obvious from the screaming headline that somebody had broken the Apollo results embargo; they had data that pointed to life on the Moon. It was the first of many times since I've experienced the power of the 'life discovered in space' news story.

I had to get back and in a hurry. We had planned to stop at many places on the way home to Britain. As a compromise we went straight to Florence, and spent a full day there. The plan was to leave as early as possible the next morning. It was a good idea up to a point. We were up very early, packed up our gear and drove out of the campsite where we were staying. There was a double barrier at the gate; the left hand side was open, presumably left that way for late-comers the previous night, when it would have been the way in side on the right. I drove through and automatically turned left onto the left hand side of the road. At that time of the morning there was nothing around. Not until the first bend that is, when coming straight at me, at speed, Italians don't do slow, was another car. His reaction was to swerve right; mine was to go left, to our respective near sides. We collided head on.

Thankfully, despite the severity of the crash, both cars were totally written off, nobody was hurt. Well not quite, when I got back to England I found I had broken my kneecap. The other guy's biggest problem was explaining to his brother, whose eight day old car he had borrowed to go on a fishing trip. A nice Italian policeman kindly told me that they drove on the right and sent me packing. Maybe it happens all the time in Italy. Ever since I've loved Italians, I could have spent Apollo languishing in an Italian prison.

We returned to Bristol by train. The cause of all the trouble, the story in the Italian papers, was a leak from one of the scientists working for the so-called Preliminary Examination Team (LSPET) at Houston. They were doing some measurements in house at the Lunar Receiving Laboratory to help allocate samples to the PIs world wide. The guilty party had found that lunar dust contained a few hundred parts per million of carbon. He had broken the embargo and told journalists the lunar regolith was "like a lean Earth soil".

Geoff was at Houston at the time as part of the LSAPT. Indeed throughout Apollo he spent far more time there than in Bristol, leaving me to my own

45

devices. Other members of the LSPET had also suggested the lunar samples were rich in carbon. One mineralogist, who worked on carbonaceous chondrites, told Geoff "It's all black, it must be loaded with carbon."

If there's that much carbon, I thought, a lot of it might be in the macromolecular form, like the kerogen I was working on. My attempts to break it up had been making slow progress because of difficulties with access to a high pressure hydrogenation apparatus. In those days, despite going to the Moon, you couldn't just pick up a phone and make a transatlantic phone call. To contact Geoff, I sent a telegram explaining the situation and asking "Can I spend some money on a pressure vessel exclusively for my use?" Geoff is a man of few words when it comes to messages. He invented mobile phone text speak years ago. His reply came straight back, in another telegram, via the Post Office of course: "Buy hydrogen bomb, funds available." With it came two policemen wanting to know what was going on.

When I got back from Italy, we had the rest of August and September to get ready. There were no more leaks of information to grab the headlines. The official line from Houston was that there wasn't much carbon in the lunar soil. The rocks were basalts erupted as lavas, not sediments formed under water. The clean room I was equipping would be vital but it wasn't ready – a workman had fallen through the ceiling. I had found him, rather distressed, swinging on the fluorescent light fitting, one leg either side.

Geoff had been talking to other members of LSAPT, who speculated the soil might be full of solar wind. "What's the solar wind?" he asked, and was told "It's a stream of atoms coming out of the sun.". "You find evidence of it trapped in some meteorites called gas-rich meteorites," somebody helpfully added. That only prompted another question from Geoff "Is there any carbon in it?" The answer was "Yes, it's the fourth most abundant element." As a back-up to looking for evidence of life Geoff suggested to me that we try to measure solar wind carbon since nobody else had thought of doing it.

Paul and I began building a vacuum line to extract gas from lunar soil. We thought about the problem and made an educated guess. The solar wind was mostly hydrogen. This might react with carbon to make methane. We could measure methane with the mass spectrometer. Geoff had told us that most work on gas-rich meteorites involved extracting noble or rare gases, such as argon, by heating. Such a process might manufacture methane from organic matter if there was any there. We didn't consider doing a heating experiment for long. Instead we got the workshops to manufacture a steel cylinder with two steel balls inside to grind soil to a very fine powder. We tried it but even empty it produced methane, presumably from the steel, so we made a spherical crusher from toughened glass. This worked and didn't produce any extraneous methane when vibrated empty. John christened it "the scrotum."

We needed a gas-rich meteorite to try it on. That's how I came to meet Robert Hutchison, yet another Scot this time with an almost pure white goatee beard. He was the Curator of meteorites at the Natural History Museum (NHM), at that time still called the British Museum. Our first contact was not very productive. I wrote asking for a sample. He replied saying words to the effect "I don't deal with minions. Get your Professor to ask me." That got him the 'no cap in hand' response: "I'm doing the work, I want the sample. Geoff trusts me, so can you." I got the specimen and a friend for life.

It was not until October we got any lunar sample. It was decided by NASA that all the material coming to Britain (there were fifteen labs getting a bit, the most anywhere in the world outside the US) would be sent in one package to the Science Research Council (SRC), who were funding our research. The BBC wanted to cover the samples being distributed on their weekly technology news programme 'Tomorrow's World'. They staged a scene with a box of samples ringed by a host of security men in visors, crash helmets and carrying truncheons. Next day I fetched our share from London. No security men to protect me, I popped my 4 × 4 × 6 inch box into a briefcase and headed for Paddington station for a train to Bristol.

Before leaving SRC's offices in High Holborn, I rang the lab to say "I have the sample and am on my way." I was told by way of an answer, "Somehow journalists are aware you're bringing a piece of the Moon today and have staked out Temple Meads station with a welcoming committee." In 1969, I was a shrinking violet and had never spoken to a reporter, so I got off the train at Bath and caught the bus. One journalist eventually caught up with me by phone. His questions taught me about how some hacks try to put words in your mouth. He was determined to write that my 'battered' briefcase had carried both the precious lunar samples and my sandwiches!

We had our sample. It was one hundred and five grams, the biggest in Britain, but first we had to get at it. Inside the box I had carried we could see a canister wrapped by several layers of Teflon bags to keep it clean. We had been informed that inside the outer canister there would be an inner one. We decided we would take it out of the various layers in the rebuilt clean room and load weighed subsamples straight to the various pieces of apparatus that were being used to carry out experiments. Paul would seal them with a glass torch, pending the experiments being done. James was to do the opening, I would be handing clean implements so he could avoid touching anything that might introduce contamination. John would be photographer and poor

Harry got the Michael Collins (the Apollo 11 Astronaut who didn't land on the Moon) role. Harry would be outside the clean room to find and clean any equipment we needed but hadn't already taken in.

At the very last minute, James said "I have to go out for a fag to steady my nerves." Then Geoff turned up. We had decided we didn't want him fussing around so to keep him out of the clean room I had hidden all the spare garments. Somehow he found a set, except for a hat. Not deterred, he put a very fetching polythene bag on his head. John took a picture, I still have it. Geoff's contribution to the rest of the proceedings was to use a piece of glass tube up one nostril trying to find a smell of solvent he swore he could detect. When we gave news interviews later, John, straight-faced, made a statement that "Professor Eglinton monitored contamination with a differential sniffo-meter." The journalist, who had tried to trap me with the sandwich questions, dutifully wrote it down and published it.

One of the sample vessels we filled was a capsule to display this special material to the public. The following weekend I had arranged for the people of Bristol to see a piece of the Moon. It was exhibited in a burglar-alarmed glass cabinet at the top of the magnificent double staircase in the vaulted entry to Bristol University's Wills Memorial Building. The public filed up one side, paused for their turn in front of the sample, then away down the other side. The queue stretched the complete length of the staircase, across the entrance hall, out on to Park Street and up to the Bristol Museum. It must have been well over a hundred yards long. Amongst the crowd was a fourteen-year-old boy from Keynsham, brought by his father. After his day out, the boy, Mark Sims, decided to become a scientist. He of course didn't anticipate he would be Beagle 2's Mission Manager.

Now it was down to work. A sample was extracted with various solvents, the solutions concentrated, treated with various reagents to make any compounds present volatile and finally tiny drops of solution were injected into the gc-ms. Only they weren't solutions, just minute amounts of solvent that we recognised in the analysis. At least the instrument was working. In the way of extractable compounds 'zilch'. At least we could say we hadn't contaminated the sample and measured a false positive. There was no evidence that there was ever any life on the Moon. Maybe the guy who had turned the job down had been right. Maybe there was no long term future in it.

Geoff's back-up idea however was going rather well. Paul and I shook a gram of soil in the scrotum overnight and the next day measured small amounts of methane gas along with the argon isotope mass 36 in the bottle. Argon-36 was tell-tale of the solar wind, it occurs in only infinitesimally small amounts on Earth. We were definitely on to something. The way of extracting gas however was very inefficient. It took hours of grinding to get anything, clearly we weren't seeing all there was to see. Then somebody, I forget who, had a brain wave. They said "Why not dissolve the sample up in acid to release trapped gas?"

Geochemists dissolve rocks all the time. They use an acid containing fluorine, called hydrofluoric acid. It also dissolves glass (and bones) so they do it in plastic, preferably Teflon beakers. We wanted to do it in glass so that we could glass-blow the vessel on to our system to transfer any released gas into the vacuum of the mass spectrometer. I decided we would chance it, put the acid into a glass tube, add the sample separately, seal the tube, tip the two together and stand well back. After the mixing, there was an enormous fizz. I certainly hadn't anticipated it would be so violent. Now we were really worried the pressure of gas inside would turn the apparatus into a glass bomb, a Molotov cocktail that would spray lethal acid everywhere.

Whoever had this bloody stupid idea certainly wasn't anywhere to be seen. But the experiment had had the desired effect. The soil had gone; there was only liquid in the tube. There was no point in stopping now, although it was still risky. Quickly we attached the vessel to the mass spectrometer, opened some valves and let the gas into a bigger volume. Safe, but not that safe, so Paul took his glass torch, cut the part still containing acid off, and put what was left in a metal bin. It was time to analyse the gas released. Sure enough it contained methane and this time some carbon-containing gases with two, three or even four carbon atoms. Also present were large amounts of argon-36, plus lots and lots of hydrogen. It was only then we realised we could have had a firebomb containing lethal acid as well.

We had some data but we wanted more to refine the experiment to get quantitative numbers, and we needed blanks. And we needed to do all these things before going to the first Lunar Science Conference in Houston starting 3 January. The only thing we felt confident of was that nobody else would be daft enough to dissolve lunar sample in a glass bottle with hydrofluoric acid; it had been nerve-racking enough for us. There had to be a better way, if not we would have to go through the nightmare at least five or six times.

After a good deal of soul-searching, we decided we would try a weaker acid, hydrochloric acid, that did not attack glass. Maybe it would etch the surface of the lunar grains, which was all we wanted since the solar wind was not supposed to penetrate far. Paul and I set it all up and did it again. It was still violent but not quite so nerve-racking; the results were essentially the same and obtained with a smaller sample.

49

Time was running out for us, and to make matters worse NASA had launched their second mission to land on the Moon, Apollo 12. Geoff was again going to be a talking head on BBC television with Stuart Agrell, another goatee-sporting geologist who smoked a foul pipe. This time they decided they wanted their own research assistant; somebody who would constantly monitor the science activities of the astronauts to feed them, the pundits, information whilst they were on screen. I got the job for the duration of Apollo and the chance to meet the BBC anchor man, Patrick Moore, who I've been friends with ever since.

Another young scientist also worked on the programmes, a research student from Imperial College called David Southwood. He wasn't analysing lunar samples and so got the boring management job of listening to the astronauts' more mundane conversations, including "We're going to eat now. We're going to the toilet now." Our different roles matched our personalities: him, a theoretician, handling the scripted no-risk activities, practical me responding to the unknown and unexpected. I was supposed to react to anything scientific. For example, when Apollo 14 Astronaut Alan Shepherd dropped the hammer and the feather to show that they would hit the ground at the same time in a vacuum; I had to search the BBC to find the props necessary to repeat it live. I found the feather before the hammer.

With Apollo 12 another resounding success, it was now the last week before Christmas 1969. Together Paul and I carefully prepared a complete suite of experiments. He was going home to Rhode Island, but would fly on to Houston at New Year for the Conference. I was happy to leave the samples reacting for days without fear of them blowing up. There was just one small snag: Paul did all the glass blowing. He had to give me a crash course. I learnt to glass blow with no regrets; it had been my hands that were holding the bomb and that got burned when Paul misdirected the torch.

My last action before Christmas, about 2.30am on Christmas morning, was going home via the lab to set up for a rapid start the day after Boxing Day. Over the next week, I ran all the experiments but had no time to work out the quantitative numbers. So I left for Houston, for my first trip to America and my first flight, clutching rolls of photosensitive chart paper. I was meeting James at JFK airport; he had gone home to Scotland for Hogmanay. I had a long wait on the airport concourse with charts spread over my lap. Every time one fell on the floor it rolled away to be recovered by some friendly passer-by who, of course, had no idea they were now a part of the Apollo programme.

All the flights were delayed and we didn't get to Houston until after midnight, US time. There was still a twenty mile ride in a stretched limo, again my first, along with a crowd of other scientists, all attending the Conference and excited about the prospects. We were the only passengers who got to the Texas State Hotel to find they had lost our reservations when every room in town was taken. I learned that in America you stand your ground, complain and somebody will sort it out.

After just a couple of hours sleep, we convened in Geoff's room; we still had to produce our two thousand word paper without which we would not be allowed entry. We had not only to write it but find a typist willing to bring her typewriter to a hotel room, occupied by a bunch of arguing scientists, on a Sunday afternoon in January. But we did it, except for making six copies. Finding a shop with a Xerox open at 8.00am on a Monday morning was a challenge even in America, nevertheless, just before 9 o'clock, we were in a line, each with a handful of individual pages, going round in a circle to sort the copies. Our next problem occurred when a Japanese scientist, who needless to say didn't speak English, infiltrated our line and began gathering up the pages which he thought were a handout. A Monty Python-like scene followed as we tried to get sheets of paper back from him intact and into the correct order.

We made it in time. Geoff gave our paper on the first day along with other keynote speakers discussing the age, mineralogy and chemistry of the Moon and addressing questions we all wanted to know the answer to, like what were the latest theories for the origin of the Moon?

We had to wait until nearly the end of the week to hear what others had found out about carbon. We were the only group to report methane. However whether it was trapped as a gas was queried. Other scientists thought we might be dissolving iron carbide that existed as bits of meteorite debris in the lunar soil. Another group claimed to have found trapped carbon monoxide but it was from a heating experiment. Geoff wanted to know why we didn't see it in the dissolution experiments and got the answer "Because it wasn't there." Nobody had found any significant amounts of organics, just a hint of porphyrins, a degradation product of chlorophyll, which was highly unlikely.

The strangest presentation was given by the man who had announced the lunar regolith was "like a lean Earth soil." He gave his talk with his briefcase and mackintosh hanging from the lectern on the podium. As soon as he finished he bolted for the door with cries of "Wait a minute, I have a question..." ringing in his ears.

I returned home determined to resolve the question: was methane there as a result of the solar wind or had we made it? The solution to the problem lay with a technique I first used to unravel the mechanisms by which molecules break down in a mass spectrometer – we would put an isotope label into the experiment. To do this the sample would be dissolved with the heavy hydrogen version of hydrochloric acid, i.e. containing deuterium (abbreviated as DCl). Within a week I had shown that the methane was a mixture, but a sample of genuine iron carbide extracted from a meteorite proved very difficult to dissolve and I felt this couldn't be the source of deuterated methane. The DCl method however worked really well and became the cornerstone of my efforts to understand lunar/solar wind carbon chemistry.

In September 1970 I had to go to another conference in America to report our latest results. The week before I was due to leave a new technician arrived in the group. Nobody seemed to know what she was supposed to be doing so I commandeered her to help me prepare. My first impression of her was Corr!! When she turned up in thigh length boots and hot pants it was amplified to CORR!!! And what's more she was good at making slides. It was too good to be true there had to be a snag: I noticed almost at once she was wearing an engagement ring. She had come to Bristol to marry her fiancé. She had already started another job but decided to quit and come to the University. She was a microbiologist. Her name, by the way, was Judith Hay.

By now the Just Four Men had broken up. John and Paul had gone back to the US, Harry had joined a drug company, James returned to terrestrial sediments. I now had Peter Cadogan, a blond, curly haired, PhD student from Birmingham helping me. We were trying to separate metal grains from the lunar soil in search of iron carbide. Geoff had met a man (Geoff was always meeting people) who told him that there was a guy in the University Physics Department who was expert in mineral separations.

I phoned up and was told "Bring over some sample and I'll show you how to do it." Clutching a bottle containing a gram of lunar soil, I hared off to the Royal Fort, Bristol's turreted Physics building which stands on the crest of a mound surrounded by immaculate gardens. I was greeted by somebody I can best describe as an 'old timer'. After a bit of social chit chat, with me explaining what I wanted to do and why, the old timer went to a cupboard, took out a round copper pan, filled it with water from the sink, and began to swirl it gently. "Pour the sample in here," he said, "I think I can help." I was going to get lessons in panning for gold. I made some excuse about not having time right then and left; we started developing our own methods.

By the 3rd Lunar Conference, I had found collaborators who helped me simulate the solar wind, implanting ions, deuterium and carbon-13 isotopes, using a giant particle accelerator. After giving the paper about this at Houston, on the way into the Gents I was intercepted by Nobel Prize winner, Harold

Urey, who had discovered deuterium. He shook my hand and thanked me profusely, saying "I now understand much better what is going on on the Moon." It was apparently not the first time he started a research colloquium in the toilet and was affectionately known as 'Harold Urinal' because of it. I once spent a delightful weekend showing this legend around Bristol. He worked on the Manhattan Project making the atomic bomb, but decided to study the Moon because he thought there couldn't be any politics involved. I learned a great deal about the philosophy of a research career that weekend.

When the USSR landed on the Moon, and returned samples by a robot spacecraft, the Royal Society made me Curator of the small amounts of material they gave to Britain and I was visited at the lab by a very senior Russian scientist. He came complete with a taciturn man, who never spoke, but walked a discrete distance behind, in a belted trench-coat, as we discussed isotopes whilst crossing Brunel's Suspension Bridge. Isotopes probably meant 'bomb' to our escort. It was still the time of the Cold War and Urey was wrong about politics and the Moon.

For Apollo 16, I went with the BBC to the Cape. I saw the giant Saturn V take off. The noise was so incredible. Stuart Agrell, his wife Jean, and I had to be six miles back; the rocket was clear of the tower before the sound reached us. Even at that distance the shock wave shook our car violently. I know, I was standing on its roof. In addition to being closely associated with the TV coverage I was doing my field work. By listening to every word the astronauts said, I knew which samples were the most interesting for me and what to request from NASA.

By 1972, NASA had completed the Apollo programme. For Apollo 17 there was no TV coverage; going to the Moon was now passé, but as far as I was concerned the best part of Apollo was yet to come. By 1973 the annual Lunar Conference had moved to March. I met with Geoff the week before to discuss our results and to distil them into the presentation which I would give. I had to prepare the necessary slides. I was having my regular row over what to include with Geoff. He always wanted to put too much information on the screen whereas I believe that a good slide should be simple. This time it was worse than usual. I stormed off to prepare what I wanted on my own.

I have my most incisive scientific moments when I'm cross; it's an 'I'll show 'em' attitude. I was still pondering on what was this component in the lunar soil that dissolved in DCl to give deuteromethane? Suddenly it all clicked now that I had samples from six different parts of the moon. I could see that the amounts of gas were going up, not just according to how much the samples had been exposed to the solar wind, but rose faster in places where there were lots of iron-containing minerals. It was obvious to me, the solar wind was making iron metal and incorporating carbon from the sun; the product was reactive. It was a good idea but I now had to plot all the data numerically to turn my hypothesis into a form that would convince an audience of sceptical lunar scientists in a week's time.

That evening I was planning to work late, so approaching six o'clock, I stood by the lab's kettle to make a cup of coffee. I was joined by Judith Hay, whose name was now Hunter. Technicians, particularly newly married ones, don't normally work after hours. I had noticed Judith had been spending more time in the labs lately and came to social events on her own. One or two of the other red blooded post-docs who worked on other projects for Geoff and James had also noticed and were paying her more than academic attention. What I said I don't remember but I know why I said it. The gist was "If it looks like you're available, after all, I'm interested."

It was really throwing caution to the wind, but that's the way it is with risk-takers. They do it for a variety of reasons but it's ultimately to win big prizes. Before I could get my face slapped I grabbed my coffee and headed back to my office in the basement, five floors below. No sooner had I got there and shut the door, it burst open again to reveal Judith. She obviously wasn't about to hit me but asked "What did you mean?" I started to explain but then suggested we got out of the Department. A few minutes later we were sharing a drink in a public house next to the bus station where she could get her bus home. I know now, if I hadn't said what I said, none of the events described in this book would ever have happened.

The rest of the week I spent knocking my theory into shape. In the evenings Judith helped me to make the slides. Really make the slides; we worked together with a camera in the Chemistry Department's darkroom. Sometimes we had to wait quite a few minutes for the film to develop. Late one night I drove her home. We pulled off the road at a local beauty spot called Burrington Coombe and would you believe it, my car got stuck in mud. A kind man towed us out. I still wonder what he was doing there himself. He probably has no idea just what he did for the British space programme.

Judith and I had taken a step at least as big as Neil Armstrong. Next day I flew off to Houston and would be away for three weeks. I went expecting to return and be told she had seen sense.

Chapter 4

WHERE DO WE GO FROM HERE?

I arrived back on a Saturday afternoon, three weeks later. The next day I received the expected "I have to see you" telephone call. As the Lloyd Webber song sung by Marti Webb says 'Let me down easy, in a park that's filled with trees. Tell me on a Sunday please.' We went to a local clump of trees, probably all that's left of Kingswood forest and just talked; no goodbye anyway.

The next night the crunch came. I was at my parent's home, it was 11.20pm. I was watching the movie 'Casablanca' with my father when the phone rang. "It'll be Geoff looking for me," I said. Geoff starts work just about the time everybody else is going to bed. "Tell him I'm not here," I finished. My father came back from the phone saying "It's not Geoff. It's a girl." I rushed to the phone; it was Judith. All I heard was "I've left, come and fetch me, please." I also left immediately. I've still never watched Casablanca to the end, even though we have the video and the DVD.

We went to Liverpool to see Judith's best friend from her school days, Cal. It was a seaside honeymoon – I remember seeing a bus with 'Wigan Pier' on the front. By the end of the week, back in Bristol, Judith decided we had better go to Redditch to tell her parents what had happened. On Saturday, driving up the A38 somewhere near Tewkesbury, we were overtaken by a red Mini which skidded to a halt. It was Judith's husband. But it wasn't the fisticuffs you might be imagining. He was going to Judith's mother to rid himself of the burden of a black cat called Trampuss. The victim of the broken home climbed gratefully into my car, to hide under my seat from the ensuing shouting match. I now had an adopted family.

The next week Judith went looking for a flat suitable for all three of us.

We wanted something especially nice so that we could feel 'normal', not like runaways. She found a basement apartment in a four storey Georgian property in Clifton. It was newly modernised, nobody had lived there since its renovation, and we had a small enclosed garden. The drawback was the landlords lived next door. Not that that was a problem, it was the fact that they had a ginger tomcat. He and Trampy hated each other like poison, there would be blood curdling screams whenever they met. Trampy would retire to the top of a tree and from the high ground swat his disadvantaged adversary.

After a short while we voluntarily moved to a miner's cottage in Winterbourne Down. Judith's mother lent us the thousand pounds for the deposit. The cottage had tiny rooms, two foot thick walls and a large garden; none of the neighbours had a cat. I could get on with working on my idea to explain what was happening with the solar wind on the Moon. Judith was now doing the project Geoff had recruited her for, trying to understand what happens to DDT in the environment, wading around in the deep mud of the Severn Estuary. My attempts to use the noble gas argon as an independent measure of how long samples were exposed to the solar wind was having problems; the trouble was I was using data obtained by different labs on different instruments, by a variety of techniques.

That summer we went to the Meteoritical Society meeting at the ski resort of Davos in Switzerland; it torrented with rain the whole time. For my talk I had some slides made by Judith. They were black and white negatives with the symbols from different missions coloured in with felt-tip pens. They showed how the iron content of the minerals from various locations had to be taken into account to explain what I now called hydrolysable carbon. I had different graphs for the argon data from various labs. Some of my plots had straight lines drawn through single points; they weren't even two point graphs! I expected to be given a hard time because I had too few data. Instead of attacking me the noble gas community started fighting amongst themselves. I slipped out quietly with comments like "I always thought your numbers were too low," which was answered by "No, it's yours that are too high!" echoing behind me.

We left Davos, hopefully for drier climes. Judith also had a conference to go to in Jerusalem. We had bought an ex-army Land Rover and intended to drive through the Balkans, across Turkey to enter Israel from Jordan. We had two passports each so that we didn't reveal where we had been. The rain continued unabated, so much so that roads had been washed away in what was then Yugoslavia. It was just as well we had four-wheel drive. It was taking longer and longer. By the time we got half way across Turkey it was obvious we wouldn't make it in time for Judith's paper so we gave up. A few days later another Israel-Arab war started, we would have been in the middle of it in a Land Rover still fitted with gun racks! Judith had already 'survived' the Russian invasion of Czechoslovakia (she was in a Land Rover then too) and was somewhat relieved, I had been all for going on. In Czechoslovakia she had 'flown' her knickers on the radio aerial as a white flag.

My ideas for the production of iron on the Moon caught on. The abundance of finely-divided metal normalised to mineral iron content became the recognised way of quantifying solar wind exposure. I persuaded what was then called the British Steel Corporation to give me my first ever grant (i.e. pay my salary) to investigate 'Making iron out of this world'. Soon, I was invited to lunch with a senior manager in a Directors' Dining room. He began the meal by looking down at his knife and fork, commenting "I see we have some new cutlery." He turned the knife over to reveal written on the blade 'Made in Japan'. The look on his face could have done a 'Yuri Geller' on the spoons. He leapt up and left the room. The offending objects were removed.

Because I had divided and distributed the Soviet lunar samples amongst nearly a dozen UK scientists I had to go to a Lunar Conference in Moscow. Despite having an invitation, getting a visa was fraught with difficulties. "Don't worry," said the Royal Society, who were arranging my travel, "it's just gamesmanship. Go to the airport and check in for the flight." I did as I was told for once, the flight was called. All the passengers except me and another UK scientist, from Newcastle, boarded and it left the terminal. As it departed, a breathless lady arrived waving our paperwork. We were driven out to the plane stopped on the runway and climbed aboard the antiquated Aeroflot jet via a ladder. It's little wonder I don't like flying.

The thing I remember most about that trip to Moscow was that we were escorted everywhere and told which way to go when we got off the bus. One time I and another guy agreed next time they say "Right" we 'misunderstand' and go left. A few hundred yards away from the coach we found ourselves in a street which looked much as Kingswood might have done at the end of the 18th century. We even saw a woman filling a bucket with water from a communal pump on the corner. Another time I escaped I came across the Russian version of 'happy hour'. I never found a pub but a man with a barrel of beer on a wheelbarrow and two glasses. As fast as he filled one someone would drink it with the man next in the queue impatiently tapping him on the shoulder indicating that he should hurry. I didn't partake; I don't like to rush my beer.

Judith and I were married in January 1975, I always have to ask my daughter the date. The event took place as soon as she obtained the required divorce papers. The marriage was far from conventional. We booked a slot at the Registry Office on Bristol's Quaker's Friars, went to the lab, gathered up Geoff's secretary, Sue Trott and my technician, Ann Gowar and that was that. We went back to the lab and told people what we had done.

The scheduled lunchtime seminar was cancelled. Everybody trooped to the Cellar Bar of the Hawthorns Hotel. On the back of the envelope containing her marriage certificate, Judith has a list of the drinks we bought as the first round. The much engaged MP, Lembit Opik, he of Sian (my favourite weather lady) Lloyd and Cheeky Girls fame, once asked Judith why she married me. It wasn't clear if he meant why did she choose me or why didn't we just live together. Anyway she answered "To get a visa so I could go with him to Russia next time." We – me, Judith and the children – eventually went in 1990, the summer after the Berlin Wall came down; in fact we helped demolish it.

Almost a year to the day after our marriage, our daughter Shusanah was born, we got the spelling for her name from one of those old Parish registers although my mother's grandmother, the Matriarch Susan, also contributed. Shusy's (she prefers Shu) birth took all day and I was banished from the event after the doctor in charge asked me how big my shoes were, I guess it was another good reason for calling her Shu. I was overjoyed when I left the hospital, but it was too late to find anybody to celebrate with. Instead I drove home through gently falling snowflakes. Shusy was a good baby; Judith had to wake her up in the night to feed her. After the third night she didn't bother, even if it meant missing out on the pint of the Guinness she enjoyed whilst breastfeeding.

Now I had more responsibilities it was time to think about a proper job. I had been employed as a post-doctoral fellow on a series of grants. The Chemistry Department at Bristol was made up of four sub-departments. Organic Geochemistry, Geoff's group, was a sub-sub-Department. Every time Geoff asked the four department heads about me he got the same answer from each individual "I just have to get so and so into post, after that I'll support Colin." My turn never came. Angry with the 'Robber Barons', I resolved to seek my fortune elsewhere.

My first application was for a job to catalogue the standing stones of Scotland. I never got a reply so I turned my attention to a more realistic target, a lectureship to run a Geochemistry course in Oxford. By this time I had exchanged Chemistry for Geology and because of the solar wind interests could even be counted as a Physicist. I gave Stuart Agrell as a reference, not only had I been supporting him as a pundit on TV but I was collaborating with him, working on lunar rocks. I was offered an interview at Oxford and arrived to find the other four candidates were all internal. I immediately smelled a rat. I had been asked to come so that the Department could claim: "Well, we interviewed an outsider but our own men were better." And sure enough one of the people already at Oxford got the job.

When I told Stuart, I think the noise he made would be described as a snort, followed by the pronouncement "If Oxford doesn't want you, you shall come to Cambridge." Mineralogy and Petrology (Min and Pet), the place where Stuart worked, was one of two Geology Departments in Cambridge. This bizarre circumstance arose from an argument in the 1850s; one of the participants walked out of Geology and started his own department across the road. Now the Professor of Min and Pet was about to retire, there would be a new man and Stuart thought he knew who was coming; he should have, he was on the Selection Committee. Stuart believed the new Professor would want to keep extraterrestrial work going. Stuart himself was also due to retire, so there were going to be opportunities. "What's more, Oxford can't offer teaching in extraterrestrial subjects," he said, "they were turned down when they applied to NASA for lunar material."

I paid a visit to Cambridge and stayed at Stuart's home, a period-piece, oak-beamed house at Milton. The ceilings were a foot lower than he was. Next day I visited the Department and talked to numerous people. Everything went according to plan. A reciprocal visit was arranged. Stuart and two other lecturers from Min and Pet came to Bristol. It was a powerful triumvirate; they were all about six feet four tall. Some wheeling and dealing was done. Geoff was very accommodating; he told them he would let me move the lunar project to Cambridge. He would even let me take some of his equipment, including a high sensitivity mass spectrometer, which I had just built.

To make the move, I had to ghost-write a proposal to carry on lunar research. It was submitted on my behalf to the Science and Engineering Research Council (SERC), SRC had added an 'E'. I couldn't submit it myself because they didn't allow you to ask for your own salary in a grant application. To apply you were supposed to have a permanent position at a University already. On top of this I had to persuade NASA to let me be a Principal Investigator in the Apollo programme and take the Bristol allocation of lunar samples with me to Cambridge. I could never have worked with Stuart's specimens; that was unless I wanted to discover that the lunar soil contained a component of pipe tobacco. We went ahead, NASA agreed and the grant was awarded.

Thanks to Geoff's generosity, I was getting a good start, but I wanted to do something different. It would be suicidal to try to compete with Bristol for money for projects. If I was going to become a permanent member of staff at

Cambridge I had to be able to offer something more mainstream in Geology. The magic moment of inspiration came to me, again when I was angry with someone. Judith and I were going to Switzerland to discuss with some people, who had been collaborators with Geoff, whether they would still work with me after the transfer. We were travelling by car and had agreed to take a passenger as far as Strasbourg to spread the cost. He turned up for his lift nearly two hours late; the whole schedule was thrown into disarray, we missed our ferry. I was fuming and sat silent in the back of the car trying to think about something else to avoid there being a fearful row with someone who was going to be in the car for the next twelve hours. I was contemplating what new things I could do with the mass spectrometer I had inherited.

One of the enormous deficiencies in measuring carbon in lunar samples was our inability to obtain carbon isotope data, the proportion of carbon-13 to carbon-12 (ratios) from small samples. I suddenly thought I knew how to do it using the same principles used for measuring noble gases. I couldn't wait to get to Switzerland where the people I was visiting were expert with noble gases. During the visit, I was told "Nobody ever tries to measure carbon that way; we go to a lot of trouble to get rid of carbon compounds." That did it – I was going to try to study carbon; I like a challenge. The Swiss wished me good luck. It was clear they didn't believe I had a cat in hell's chance, but were humouring me. They were wrong; I knew all about cats.

My next priority was to get to Cambridge with a lab full of equipment, a wife, a small baby, Trampy, a second cat (Burmese) and two research students. Summer 1976 was one of the hottest on record. After a couple of car trips, with all the paraphernalia that goes with a six months old daughter, Judith flatly refused to travel again. One Saturday morning, I was despatched with a pile of Estate Agents' particulars and an unambiguous message "Don't come back until you've found somewhere for us to live." That evening I agreed to buy a bungalow with a big enclosed garden in Toft. It wasn't what we wanted but I believed we could resell it when we found our dream property.

The other thing of significance for me that summer was NASA landed two Viking spacecraft on Mars. Viking 1 was supposed to make it on 4 July 1976, the 200th anniversary of American Independence, but didn't, it was delayed whilst they searched for a safe place to land. Viking 2 followed its compatriot down to the surface of the Red Planet in September.

Driving up and down to Cambridge, catching snippets about the exploration of Mars and the search for life there, on the radio and in newspapers, I felt I had a vested interest. After all, I had seen the prototype of the gc-ms gas separator at Jim Lovelock's the day of the fog. Geoff Eglinton and I had written a proposal to NASA suggesting we could supply a device, derived from our system to recover organic compounds from lunar samples, that would be appropriate for coupling to Viking's gc-ms. We got a polite 'thanks but no thanks' letter back. I still have the drawings I made at the time.

Geoff, with some help from me, had already told the world how it should go about bringing martian samples back to Earth by 1985. I provided the bit describing how the sample should be divided and shared out amongst interested scientists. The input necessary to explain how an appropriate spacecraft could be built came from an engineer who worked for the British Aircraft Corporation (BAC) based at Filton in Bristol. I well remember the lunch we had with him at a local pub. I would go to the same pub to discuss with Matra Marconi Space (they were BAC taken over, renamed and rebranded) a possible involvement in Beagle 2 going to Mars twenty-five years later.

But back to Viking, as the various experiments designed to detect living microorganisms played out; it seemed highly likely that Viking had discovered bugs on Mars. Then the gc-ms quashed the euphoria. There was no organic matter to measure. The scientists were in a dilemma; they had results that indicated a working biology but couldn't find evidence of the body, either living or dead. As one of them, the famous Carl Sagan, said "If you want to make an extraordinary claim, the evidence has to be extraordinary." They didn't have that unambiguous proof, so the consensus was the chemical conditions on the surface of the Red Planet might be mimicking microbiology. Some of the Viking team however believed, secretly at first, then vociferously, that martian life had been discovered.

The Viking mission didn't have the outcome everybody wanted. The money men decided no life, no money, no more missions. The dreams that Geoff and I had about understanding the Red Planet from returned samples, weren't fulfilled. By the time Viking closed the book on the search for life on Mars, I was in Cambridge. Stuart Agrell, as well as being a lecturer, was Curator of the University's collection of rocks. To find room for me, he gave up part of his rock store. One of my research students was clearing it out when he came across a box labelled C. Darwin. "Do you think it's the C...?" he exclaimed. Before he could finish the question, I said "Laurie, this is Cambridge!"

Making the space was easy; getting the instruments to run was more difficult. In those days the vacuum systems we needed to analyse gases were still made of glass. They didn't take kindly to being bumped around for the best part of two hundred miles in the back of a lorry. In a Geology Department we had no professional glassblowers, so whilst I could join bits of glass together more complicated structures needed a greater degree of skill which had to be acquired painfully. We did it, but it was functional rather than pretty.

Next we set to work trying to find the carbon-containing gases which were most stable in a noble gas-type mass spectrometer, usually referred to as a static mass spectrometer because during the analysis the instrument was closed off from the pumps. It meant that most of the sample didn't disappear down the pumps to be wasted. But I knew from my first involvement with mass spectrometers that carbon-containing compounds are smashed to fragments and destroyed by the hot ionising filament. Noble gases don't break to pieces. We had to find a carbon compound that didn't.

Judith and I now had a bigger family. Our son Nicolas Joseph was born at Mill Road Hospital. He was a much easier birth, he announced his impending arrival at about half past seven in the morning, and I had just enough time to call into the lab to switch off the experiment I had planned for that day and still get his mother to the delivery room in time. I was at the birth; Joe literally shot into the world and was caught by the attending nurse, in front of a clapping crowd of medical students. Judith was home the next day, sitting up in bed feeding her new offspring, when she heard that Elvis Presley had died. I had promised to take her to Memphis to see him perform; it's a promise that I haven't been able to keep.

Whilst I tried to demonstrate that we could measure isotope ratios precisely, I accumulated a huge amount of data from scores of samples carefully separated from lots of individual lunar soils using the methods developed in Bristol. By now I felt I had the definitive explanation of what was going on when the solar wind irradiated the lunar surface. The stream of charged particles, containing a mixture of many elements, including carbon, penetrated different minerals to a different depth and destroyed them by a process called 'sputtering', a kind of mineralogical snooker with the various atoms as the different coloured balls, where colour was representative of an element's mass. I played a lot of snooker at the local YMCA when I was about seventeen. It has been said that ability with a snooker cue is a sign of a misspent youth. It proved very valuable to me for understanding a complicated scientific problem.

A most important facet of the process was that mass of the elements wasn't the only thing that had to be taken into account; the strength of the bonds between them was critical. I'd learnt that much from the John Beynon lectures I had attended in Swansea. Bond strength accounted for the fact that iron metal, and only iron metal, trapped carbon atoms giving hydrolysable carbon. I called the process 'preferential sputtering'.

If you put all these ideas together then the amounts of carbon present at the various lunar sites could be matched with what my theory predicted. Likewise it accounted for the fact that carbon isotopes on the Moon were fractionated (changed) so that they became more and more enriched in the heavier isotope carbon-13; carbon-13 was more difficult to knock around, a bit like a bigger snooker ball. This was another example of 'preferential sputtering'. I wrote it up as a giant paper mostly whilst sitting in our large new garden watching Shusy explore and Joe, who Shusy called JoJo, sleep in his carry-cot.

For two years, Judith and I had been looking for an even bigger garden. We scanned the Estate Agents' adverts looking for somewhere with a piece of land. Sometimes I would take a day off and we would cruise Cambridgeshire just looking so that we would know, as soon as we saw an ad, whether we would like the village concerned. If a property came up, we would know instantly whether it was worth visiting. One particularly dismal day, we drove through a village called Wendy. It was a nice sounding name but it was dull and damp; we didn't think much of it.

Most of the available land was north of Cambridge in the Fens. We didn't fancy living there; it was too flat. We were becoming despondent when a small-holding in Wendy was advertised for sale by auction. We almost dismissed it out-of-hand but eventually decided just to take a quick look. Wendy was entirely different in early summer. It was tiny, pretty and well away from the main road. The property, although it was a small bungalow, had potential. Better still the plot was four acres, two of which had been market garden. There was a one acre paddock, three sheds, home of six hundred chickens, and fifty apple trees of various varieties, eating and cooking. But since it was going to be sold by auction, we had no idea what it was going to cost. Nevertheless we decided we would go along anyway.

The event was in a nearby village called Croydon at the local pub. Very soon the bidding reached what we thought our property in Toft was worth but we had realised by now that finding anywhere with land, which wasn't north of Cambridge, was next to impossible. Wendy was south west and not featureless. We decided we would chance a bid so we entered the competition at just below £30,000, the maximum we thought we could afford. Our maximum was soon past but the bidding had slowed considerably. When it reached £32,000 I went five hundred more. A man in a suit, near the front, immediately countered with £33,000. The room fell silent, sensing the end was near. The auctioneer looked around and asked for more bids. He wanted another five hundred but it was not forthcoming so he said. "I'm going to sell." Judith nudged me and said "Go another hundred." I didn't think there was much chance of succeeding, the man with the suit had responded to my last try too quickly. I thought he must have more money than us, but I put my hand up and said "£33,100." The suit shook his head; the small-holding was ours; we were landowners at last. A field of trees for Trampy to climb; it was time we got a dog. My first ever dog, a Dalmatian, was christened Sputnik; we called her 'Sputter' for short.

We later found out the man with the suit was bidding on behalf of a client who had given him an absolute limit. Judith always says "We bought Sunavon," for that was what the house was called, "for a hundred pounds." Our immediate minor discrepancy was that, whilst we had told the Bank we were going to an auction, we hadn't arranged an overdraft or a mortgage. We would have to get there before the Estate Agent presented our cheque. It was just a little risk; I hoped it said somewhere on the file that, under a previous manager, I had acted as a local celebrity, someone working on Apollo, at the Bank's social events entertaining important customers. Unfortunately that particular Manager had disappeared because he did a wife-swap, literally; he and his next door neighbour exchanged partners and went their separate ways. We got away with it; the cheque didn't bounce but our house in Toft didn't sell as quickly as we hoped and soon we were paying two mortgages.

Many of the groups who had worked on the Apollo programme were now studying stones that had accidentally fallen from the sky – meteorites. The new in topic involved 'isotopic anomalies', isotopic compositions distinct from values encountered on Earth. There seemed to be some connection to carbon, but nobody had measured an anomaly for carbon. All the samples available for study had been stored in Museum collections for years. Like the specimens Stuart pulled out of his pockets, they were contaminated.

Then luckily I found a very old paper that provided a solution; I named it 'stepped combustion'. It seemed that if we took a meteorite sample and heated it through a series of temperature steps, adding oxygen at each step, different kinds of carbon would burn at different temperatures. I thought maybe we could remove not just the unwanted contamination but other forms of carbon as well to find an anomaly.

We tried it on my old friend the Allende meteorite. The experiment was done during the Christmas holiday; I was at home at the time. With Trampuss deceased in a traffic accident, we now had several Burmese cats. As the results were being measured one of the cats started to have kittens. The telephone calls relaying the results got more and more excited because as the temperature was increasing, the small amounts of carbon were showing isotopic compositions very different from the norm. The kids were even more pleased because the number of kittens was going up in parallel.

The Allende 'stepped combustion' experiment had an enormous number of repercussions. There were exciting results to be had from very small samples. As a result my group, working with the man who offered to eat lunar samples, discovered that tiny, tiny diamonds existed as interstellar grains, probably made in supernovae, stars that lived and died before our solar system was formed. We now had a route to understanding what happened before our sun began to shine. Later, using the same method we found diamonds as evidence of the asteroid that wiped out the dinosaurs.

Although my group was doing so well in the laboratory, I still didn't have a permanent job. Within a year of my arrival in Cambridge, as Stuart had predicted, the Head of Min and Pet retired and the search for his successor was on. The first choice candidate came to Cambridge from the USA to negotiate his dowry. He was someone with more than a passing interest in rocks from above the atmosphere. I had a meeting with him strolling along 'The Backs', the manicured green strip behind the Colleges, leading down to the river Cam with tourists messing around in boats and punts. It was the way I had always imagined deals were done in Cambridge; it was like that in films anyway. He explained his plans and how I was going to be a part of them. Cambridge made him a good offer. He used it to persuade his American University to give him a sweetheart deal to stay put.

The writing was on the wall for me. As far as the new Head of Department was concerned Geology stopped a foot above the top of Mount Everest; it didn't seem as though I was going to get an academic position at Cambridge. I thought I might become a farmer. We had already bought a house cow, called Geraldine, for our four acres. She came from an auction at a farm closing down sale. It was pretty clear if I didn't buy her she was destined for the 'knackers'. So, a bit like Jack in Jack and the Beanstalk, I came home with something Judith wasn't expecting. We decided to use Geraldine's milk to create a Jersey herd. We notified the Ministry of Agriculture, now DEFRA, of our intentions, which were to buy heifer calves a few days old, and rear them for two years until they could have calves of their own to produce milk. In the meantime we had to find a farm.

In 1981, something happened to change all that. When I arrived at Cambridge I applied for, and got, an allocation of one research student per year from SERC. In 1977, I gave this post to Ian Wright, a tall blonde guy who idiosyncratically wore his jumpers inside out. The next year, the studentship was allocated to Monica Grady, a 'Yorkshire lass'. Monica's research career was almost very short. On her first day she was shown a brand new mass spectrometer that she would be running and told "It cost £35,000, don't break it." She almost turned tail and was on the verge of leaving for good. Anybody who knows her won't recognise this timid girl from my description. I sent this pair to the 1981 Houston Conference; it resulted in a phone call from a senior academic at another University accusing me of not adequately funding my students at International meetings. When I enquired what he meant, back came the answer: "They had to share a hotel room." Incidentally they're now married.

Ian Wright came back from Houston with the news that the big talking point of the Conference was the suggestion that a group of meteorites, called the SNC meteorites, came from Mars. My first reaction to this was that some-body must be off their trolley. The evidence at the time was as follows: these meteorites were geologically much younger than lunar rocks and it was known that volcanoes stopped erupting on the Moon 3.2 billion years ago – QED the SNCs must have come from a bigger object than the Moon, i.e. a planet. The idea that Mars was that planet arose because a scientist at JSC had measured noble gases in some of the SNCs and noticed the isotope ratios of these were similar to the values found when the same gases had been studied in the atmos-phere of the Red Planet by the Viking landers.

It all seemed pretty tenuous to me but Ian and I were still talking about it when we went to lunch at the 'White Rose' pub on Trumpington Street. It used to be a proper pub with a nice little garden at the back; unfortunately it's now a trendy wine bar and fish restaurant. It gives me the creeps and reminds me of pilchards. Anyway, running over the argument about these meteorites containing traces of the martian atmosphere, I said "If we were talking about the major component of the atmosphere [it's 96% carbon dioxide] then I'd be more convinced."

Over the next few months we gathered together samples of the three meteorites which gave the SNC their collective name: Nahkla, a stone that fell in Egypt in 1911 (it supposedly killed a dog); Shergotty, collected by a District Commissioner of the British Raj in 1865; and oldest of the lot, Chassigny, from a village in central France. The latter was certified as a meteorite by the local Doctor, just at the end of the Napoleonic Wars, in 1815. We measured the isotope ratios of carbon, nitrogen and hydrogen, from water extracted by heating the samples, and found nothing unusual. In fact we found nothing at all, the amounts of gas released were too small to be analysed by conventional techniques and the new high sensitivity instrument we were trying to build was still not working. We put the experiment to one side pending solving the instrument's problems. I had more important things on my mind.

Our ambitions to be dairy farmers looked to be on dodgy ground. The European Union had introduced milk quotas. Judith and I went to the Ministry of Agriculture who told us "Don't worry, we have your plans on record. You'll get a quota." We couldn't rely on it so I began to look elsewhere for a living.

SERC had had enough of me and other long term researchers on their books being funded on research grants. They called it 'soft money'. They were supporting the work we were all doing but couldn't go on giving us grants to pay our salaries for ever. They had decided to force the issue with the various Universities involved by holding a one-off competition for our various projects. The prize would be a five year grant for the salary of the winner but, and it was a big but, the University submitting the proposal had to make a promise that at the end of the five years, a permanent job would be created. The new opportunity to get funds was called the 'Special Replacement Scheme'. I enquired whether the University of Cambridge would make such a commitment and was told "Statutes", this was a thick book that lived in the library which told you what you could or couldn't do in Cambridge, "won't let the University make such a commitment." So I was casting around for an alternative but the deadline for submissions was approaching fast.

One possibility I'd found was in Scotland. The Universities of Glasgow and Edinburgh would offer me a post shared between them at their joint Research Institute at East Kilbride. Judith took one look at the trees growing horizontally there and declared she wouldn't come. Negotiations were not proceeding very rapidly anyway when I saw a lectureship advertised at the Open University, only just over thirty miles west of where we lived in Wendy. The post was for someone experienced in an aspect of Geology I knew nothing about. Likewise I knew little of the Open University, but if they were recruiting maybe they would be interested in backing me with SERC. I wrote a letter to a Professor Gass and in response got a phone call from a geophysicist called Geoff Brown. He was later tragically killed when a volcano he was studying suddenly erupted. Geoff said "I've just taken over as Head of Department, I'd be interested in chatting about you joining it."

A couple of days later I went to the new town of Milton Keynes, the place famous only for its concrete cows. At least we had a liking for cows in common. I went to see Geoff Brown, my zillionth grey bearded geologist, who explained to me Ian Gass's vision for the Department of Earth Sciences at the OU. Although its students were unconventional, part time and living at home, in respect of research it was the same as any traditional University. Indeed it aspired to be top rank in Earth Sciences. It had earmarked stable isotopes as an area worth getting into. They would be interested in creating a position for me if the Special Replacement application came off but only if their Vice-Chancellor would give them an additional post. "Do you mind if it is for a research job only?" Geoff asked, going on "we don't want to jeopardise the lectureship we already have and be told to use it to recruit you."

I went home thinking that's that, this was going to be like the Robber Barons in Bristol. Getting additional posts is like flying to the Moon; ones just for research are fairy stories. There would be a straight "No" or another few months of thinking about it, by which time it would be too late. Geoff Brown must have been very persuasive because, within days, I had a telephone call saying the OU's VC, John Horlock, would take the risk and authorised us to go for it. I made my application and a few days before Christmas 1983 learned it had been successful. I could start at the OU from 1 January.

Once again the group was moving laboratories. This time there were advantages, the OU were buying a new conventional stable mass spectrometer and giving me a full time technician to run it for the Department. The downside was that we had found that carbon dioxide didn't break down much in the static mass spectrometer very much and the instrument was obtaining good carbon isotope measurements using a thousand times smaller samples than anybody else. Now it had to move just when we were all set to have another go at the SNC meteorites.

Remembering how long it took to get instruments operating last time we went walkabout we decided to do a moonlight flit. We hired a van, closed all the valves on the machine, took the pumps off, and with it still under vacuum (we hoped) carried it down the stairs for the ride to MK. At the other end we reversed the process, reattached the pumps and opened the valves. To everybody's amazement the instrument hadn't leaked. It was working exactly as it was twenty-four hours earlier.

A sample of the meteorite Nahkla was loaded immediately and a stepped combustion begun. By Friday, we had the results for this and another meteorite, EETA79001, collected on Antarctica in 1979. The latter released a small amount of carbon dioxide at high temperature. It was there in exactly the correct abundance, compared to the noble gases, for it to be the main constituent of a trapped sample of the martian atmosphere. After we saw this nobody talked about SNCs anymore; they were martian meteorites. Now we knew where we were going from here; not just to Milton Keynes, next stop Mars.

Chapter 5

A MARTIAN CAN OF WORMS

A s soon as I saw the high temperature carbon from EETA79001 I was convinced. But there were more data we hadn't anticipated. It's the reason why I like scientific research, it's full of surprises. 90% of the results you get are usually things you didn't realise you would find out by doing the experiment – new knowledge. For a few days or weeks maybe you know something that no one else in the whole world is aware of. The stepped combustion of the martian meteorites using our new high sensitivity instrument proved this rule. Both meteorites contained something that was released at low temperature. From previous experience, we believed this might be organic matter. They also showed that some carbon was released at intermediate temperatures. Again, results from other samples made us think this might be the mineral deposited from water – carbonate. But we couldn't believe it, this type of meteorite was an igneous rock, it shouldn't have any carbonate minerals.

We thought hard, if it was carbonate it should dissolve away in dilute acid. We didn't have enough EETA79001 to try, but there was plenty of Nahkla, Robert Hutchison had fifty kilograms. I got material from him, washed a sample with acid and took the residue for another stepped combustion. The intermediate temperature carbon had gone – it had to be carbonate. When the results were published in the journal *Nature*, we had trouble persuading other scientists to believe them. Mineralogists and petrologists had been looking at thin sections of martian meteorites, with ever-increasingly sophisticated microscopes, for much more than a century. What they couldn't see with their own eyes, they didn't accept; they didn't like minerals being discovered by geochemists.

Things were going even better with our aspirations to be farmers. Judith and I had found out about a farm which was for sale in Croydon, the village with the pub where we had bought Sunavon. The farm was huge; it was really two farms, 600 acres and had belonged to an old couple. The husband had just died at ninety-three. It was quite out of our league but what interested us were the house and the immediately surrounding grass fields. Judith had discovered from a friend of hers that a group of farmers who owned adjacent properties wanted to form a consortium to buy the whole farm then split it between them, each taking the bits nearest to their own borders. They had a problem; none of them wanted the house. They needed to off-load this to make their plan financially viable. We had to get into this consortium. I left it to Judith to find out more; I had to go to Sheffield to be the external member of an interview panel.

There were five candidates for the job; the interviews were in the morning. At lunch, the panel was discussing the merits of the candidates, when Judith managed to track me down and persuaded a secretary that she needed me urgently, so urgently I had to be fetched to speak to her on the telephone, immediately! She now knew where the consortium was meeting, at four o'clock that afternoon, and we had an invite to be there. I quickly stated my preferred candidate, said "Have to go," and hit the road. I had less than two hours to get home. I broke every traffic law existing to do it in a Triumph Herald.

The meeting went well. Judith and I had already seen the Farm. To appear to the Agent as prosperous potential purchasers of 600 acres, we borrowed the OU's V8 long wheel base station-wagon Land Rover. The consortium took us on board and we all signed an agreement drawn up by a solicitor, who would bid up to a maximum authorised limit at the forthcoming auction. Judith and I were committed £150,000, despite having spent only fifteen minutes looking around, probably less than five in the house. It only took us ten seconds to realise that the couple hadn't been upstairs for years; in one of the bedrooms there were three iron bedsteads that had been used when the farm had billeted Italian prisoners of war forty years earlier.

During our visit we pretended to be more interested in the land. We never went back; now we were in the consortium we didn't want to alert other potential buyers to our existence. We wanted everybody to believe nobody was interested. It worked; just as well, another big land owner wanted the whole farm for his son. He and his whole family occupied the front row at the auction and he opened the bidding. He was definitely unaware of us.

When our solicitor put in a bid he was acknowledged by the auctioneer staring into the distance towards the back of the crowded room at the Farmer's

Club, with a "Thank you, John." Our opponent thought the auctioneer was attempting to wind the price up. This particular auctioneer was notorious for taking bids off the wall and all the local farmers, even I knew it. The consortium's only adversary immediately stopped bidding and the property was knocked down to the mysterious John.

Now everything was done and dusted, the whole front row stood up smiling and gathered round the auctioneer, believing they had spotted his little game and they were about to complete a private deal. Instead they were told John wasn't a figment of the auctioneer's imagination. He was real; he was the consortium's solicitor and just happened to be called John. Judith and I were farmers with thirty acres. The sale was completed; we moved into our Farm on Lady Day, 30 September, 1984, this time with two children, two dogs, a host of cats and forty cows and calves. Again we were the owners of two houses, one with no facilities. No inside toilet; there was a khasi suspended over a ditch and flushed by rain water from a pond. The pressure of the water wasn't enough to supply a tap upstairs so no bathroom although thoughtfully the widow had left the galvanised tin bath. The electricity looked like it had been put in by Michael Faraday. Judith might not have been used to such houses, but I was.

The risk we had taken was bigger than we imagined. We found out later that the piece of paper we had signed made us liable for a much bigger share of the purchase price. If any of the others had dropped out we would have had to help make up the missing share. It was designed to keep the group together. We were the only members of the consortium without sufficient assets or 'goods and chattels' to cover the extra commitment. It was just as well we hadn't read the small print.

To move on with the analysis of martian meteorites the group needed some new samples. They duly arrived when the mineralogist who was NASA's Curator of lunar samples at last found pockets of carbonate in Antarctic meteorite EETA79001 with his microscope. I applied for and got specimens for analysis. We studied them and Monica measured isotopic compositions for both the carbonate and the organic matter they contained. Ian Wright included the results in a talk presented at the Lunar and Planetary Science Conference, as the annual jamboree in Houston was now called. Nobody took much notice of the paper we wrote afterwards. I believed it was more important than that, so we decided we would write the study up separately again for the prestigious journal *Nature*. At the time I was applying for what was called a Rolling Grant from the SERC. If the application was successful it would give the group stability, with two years current funding and an optional additional two years, renewable.

Nature accepted our latest paper; the only dispute was with a referee who didn't like what we were hinting in our last few sentences. We titled the paper: 'Indigenous carbon in a martian meteorite', implying that we thought the carbon came from the planet. We discussed possible origins for the organic matter and suggested it could be geological or added to the martian surface by impacts of carbon-containing meteorites. Then we added that there's another possibility: "it's truly organic" meaning biological. To stake a claim on the third possibility being correct, I added some words to say that if the indigenous carbon was truly organic "the implications are obvious." We stopped short of saying it was evidence for microorganisms – life on Mars – because I believed the journal would refuse to publish such an amazing claim. The referee smelled a rat. He spotted the intent – if life was ever found on Mars, I was going to say we had a hand in its discovery and what's more claim "We saw it first." He was absolutely correct. The data were certainly a significant step in the right direction. The journal agreed and the sentence was allowed to stand.

The time for consideration of the Rolling Grant application was drawing close when we found out that our paper would appear on the morning of the day the bid would come up before the funding Committee. Honestly, I didn't engineer it but I was going to exploit it. I invited the Chairman of the Committee to visit our labs on his way to the meeting, to see how well we were set up and be brought up to speed with all the work we had in progress. After touring the labs we were sitting in a meeting room with him going over our plans when I was called to the phone to be reminded Friday, the day when our paper would be public knowledge was the 20th anniversary of the landing of Apollo 11. My informant in the *Nature* press office told me "We're making your paper 'Paper of the Week'; it will be released to the press for news coverage tomorrow in advance of publication."

The next day was pandemonium. The implications of what we had written were obvious to the gentlemen and ladies of the media. The interviews I gave generated forty-two newspaper reports that we identified and numerous TV appearances. I did one on BBC's Breakfast News; I took a big chunk of the Nahkla meteorite and had to run down Scrubb's Lane to the White City because the traffic was so bad. I was still pretty breathless when the interviewer asked me "How do you know this rock is from Mars?" I started to tell her about the trace of atmospheric gas we'd found. "It's the fingerprint of Mars" I said. She immediately leaned forward, peered at the meteorite, expecting to see finger marks, and asked "Where?"

During an interview Monica Grady gave, unbeknown to her, there was a little green man prancing around in the background. Live that night I did a chat show with Derek Jameson; he was a former Editor of the *Daily Mirror*, the John Humphries/Jeremy Paxman of his day and renowned for giving his guests a hard time. At the end of my piece about the possibility of life on Mars, he turned to the audience and said "Remember folks, it was discovered first here in Britain." It paraphrased Edmund Halley's prediction of the comet that bears his name when he said "If it turns out to be true remember it was an Englishman [who said it first]." We got our Rolling Grant and learnt another lesson: the public couldn't get enough of the subject of extraterrestrial life, and we could use it to our advantage.

We had no more samples of the appropriate martian meteorite so Mars was put on the back burner again for a while. Anyway, I had a new interest. In 1986 Halley's Comet made its periodic appearance in the inner solar system, an event which happens only every seventy-six years. The European Space Agency, ESA, had flown a space mission they'd named Giotto through the coma, obtaining the first ever picture of a comet's nucleus. It was a scientific success even if the public firework display wasn't as spectacular as Halley sometimes puts on. Mrs Thatcher wasn't impressed; she is reputed to have said of the picture "Is this what I pay forty million pounds a year for?" Her words created the impression Britain wasn't interested in space.

I played a minor role in Britain being involved with ESA's Giotto spacecraft by calling a parish-pump meeting at the Royal Society when it looked like our contributions to the mission wouldn't be funded. Maybe it was this that got me an invitation to the discussions when ESA decided to think about how to follow up Giotto. It was my first visit to ESA's Technical Centre, ESTEC, at Noordwijk in Holland. It was only 1985 and Giotto hadn't even reached Halley, nevertheless everybody was in a bullish mood. The planetary scientists gathered there wanted a mission to return a sample of a comet nucleus for lab studies. Now this was the group's forte; it, and our work on presolar grains, was probably another reason why I had been included. There was only one realist in the room, Jerry Wasserburg, a very brash American. I was in awe of him, at the first Lunar Conference, everyone was. He waved and shouted and said "isotopes" a lot, his nick-name was 'Wassertope'. Now he treated me as an equal; he liked my kids and delighted in buying them as much ice-cream as they could eat. In the pub that evening, he said "If this mission goes ahead they should make the PI-ships hereditary."

After several more meetings, the Americans pulled out. ESA decided they couldn't afford to continue with such a grandiose plan alone. They descoped the mission to a less ambitious but still adventurous orbiter carrying a soft lander. I had been regularly attending the meetings run by Marcello Coradini, a bald-headed, moustachioed Italian. You'd know he was Italian anywhere, especially if he stuck his head out of an ice cream van with a white hat on. He was dedicated to ESA being a world-class player on the space stage and very short tempered with anybody who might get in the way of that aim. He could be very disparaging about the Brits, who he thought weren't pulling their weight. I immediately liked him and I think he saw me as someone who might change the British attitude to space.

When the decision was taken to abandon a comet sample return, Marcello took me to one side, thanked me for my contribution, then said "I don't see any point in you coming anymore, now we're talking about making instruments to fly on a spacecraft." Disappointed, I said "Marcello, I build novel laboratory instruments to measure stable isotopes. We need isotope data from comets; maybe I could make a space instrument." He looked doubtful but said "You'll still be most welcome at the meetings."

I had no intention of missing out. At the next ESTEC meeting, I presented ideas for building an isotope mass spectrometer to fly on the mission, now called Rosetta because it was believed a close up study of a comet might answer questions about the origin of the solar system. Comets are supposed to be a sample of the dust and gas that condensed to form the sun and planets. The name Rosetta was chosen because the text on the Rosetta stone was the key to deciphering hieroglyphics and learning about ancient civilisations. During the discussions about returning samples it had been recognised that isotopic measurements might be the equivalent of hieroglyphics so the other scientists there were enthusiastic about my ideas. Some of them so enthusiastic, that they decided to adopt my principles to build instruments which would compete with our group if I decided to make a bid to supply a mass spectrometer for Rosetta. They had what the business calls 'heritage' and probably thought I, or more likely the Brits, would fall by the wayside.

The planning for Rosetta lumbered on through the all the hoops space missions have to go through to get selected until there was an Announcement of Opportunity (AO) to provide the payload. I bid on behalf of my group and we won the competition to provide two instruments, one for the lander and another on the orbiter. The SERC, now called the Particle Physics and Astronomy Research Council (PPARC), agreed to pay for them. Because I had no previous experience of building space instruments I would have to work with the Rutherford Appleton Laboratory (RAL) part of PPARC's Establishment. Throughout the selection process the French and the Germans bickered continuously over who would be responsible for the lander. The Germans eventually won, but as a compromise the role of lander PI would alternate between the two countries on a six monthly basis. It was a silly arrangement. It reminded me of the days when Governments changed at every election; the new one immediately proceeded to undo everything the previous lot had done. You can't run anything like that, someone who knows what they're doing has to be in charge and responsible.

Rosetta was a big eye-opener into the way Europe worked. ESA is a microcosm of it, fraught with national self-interest. It seems like more than two people trying to make a baby, too many people involved; they get in each other's way. Within ESA, the Germans and French have much bigger space budgets and expect to call the shots. The Italians always seem to have plenty of money; if someone says they can't afford something, the Italians jump in with "We'll provide that." Sometimes even Marcello doesn't believe them but for Rosetta, he was in his element, negotiating deals and compromises in the corridor – pulling the strings.

Whilst Rosetta was untangling or more realistically tying itself in knots, there had been a development on the martian meteorites front. Unbeknown to us while we were writing the paper on EETA79001, there was already another new martian meteorite in captivity. A lady meteorite curator from the JSC called Robbie Score, a member of the US field team looking for new meteorites on the Antarctica ice during the 1984 field season, had spotted something of interest whilst driving a skidoo, an ice motorbike, around the Allan Hills ice sheet.

She pulled over and, being savvy about Antarctic meteorites, popped the stone in a bag. It wasn't the first sample collected that year but it became ALH84001; its low number guaranteed it would be processed early as potentially important. ALH signified it had been collected in the Allan Hills. Back at Houston, someone unpacked the bag, looked at the specimen and said "It's a diogenite," a useful igneous rock but not that rare. ALH84001 was put away in a drawer. Nearly ten years later a man called David Mittelfehldt asked for a diogenite and was given a sample of the rock collected in 1984. He was a skilled meteorite petrologist so, when he looked at ALH84001 under the microscope, he must have exclaimed something like "Holy ****, it's martian!" and that's how the ugly duckling became a swan, a very fine swan indeed. Coincidentally Mittelfehldt's nick-name is 'Duck'.

What was most interesting was that ALH84001 contained carbonates, masses of carbonate, running through the rock in orange veins. As soon as we heard about it we asked for some. I was waiting for it to arrive when one Friday afternoon my phone rang. It was Everett Gibson, a long time 'all-American boy' friend from Texas, who spoke with a drawl and called all ladies 'Mam'. Everett claims he met me when I burst into his office at JSC, to tell him the talk he had just given at the Lunar Conference was "crap." I think it was earlier. But, no matter, Everett and I had been friends for a long time; he had spent a year working in my lab to pick up isotope techniques. "Have you analysed the carbonate in 84001 yet?" he opened up. I said "No." He said "I have." Working right next to where they processed the Antarctic meteorites it was inevitable his sample would reach him before we got ours.

"Come on, what did you get?" I asked. "The carbonate was heavy, in fact plus 43, just like you said for the tiny samples you measured of Nahkla." Plus 43 is isotopers' jargon; it means enriched in 13-carbon by 43 parts per thousand relative to a standard which we all know the answer for, even though it no longer exists and we all use our own standards. This way of working allows us to compare and discuss results.

This phone call was a bit of a blow, it would have been nice to confirm our own earlier data. Taking a new tack, I now asked "What's the oxygen? What have you done with it?" Oxygen isotopes from carbonate samples are used to calculate the temperature of the water in lakes, oceans, lagoons etc. where the mineral deposits are formed. So Everett's reply came as a bit of a surprise: "Nothing," he said. "Give me the numbers then, we'll work it up," I responded. "OK," he answered. I could sense a chance to recover from my earlier disappointment.

With the phone call over, I hot-footed it up the stairs to Ian Wright to break the bad news. "But he's going to send us the oxygen data," I finished. As soon as it arrived, Ian did the calculations and found that the water containing dissolved carbon dioxide, from which the carbonate precipitated, must have been at a temperature somewhere between ten and ninety degrees centigrade. It meant there once must have been liquid water on Mars. We wrote another paper putting Everett's post-doc as first author, after all he did the measurements. Again we published it in *Nature*. It caused another media storm: 'Warm fizzy water on Mars' was how these results were described in one newspaper. The data signified the conditions on Mars could have been wet and warm – appropriate for life.

By this time it was 1994, the Pillingers' plans for being dairy farmers had fallen by the wayside. Despite having registered them with the Ministry of Agriculture on another worthless piece of paper, we were given a milk quota for only three cows when we had forty. In other words the Milk Marketing Board wouldn't pay us for the milk that thirty-seven produced. We could tip it down the drain or Judith, like Cleopatra, could bathe in it. We were employing a young guy to help look after our cows; we told him he no longer had a job and went into beef.

Fast forward to July 1996; now there was no longer a Soviet Union or Eastern European block, the Meteoritical Society had decided to hold its annual conference in Berlin at the Humboldt Museum on the famous street Unter den Linden, just beyond the Brandenburg Gate. The Museum, and its wonderful meteorite collection, put together over the previous two hundred years, had been out of bounds for a half a century and although the Wall had been down since 1989, many scientists had never been to Berlin and were itching to see what it was like. There was bound to be a big contingent of Americans.

A conference like this always begins with a social event. In Germany beer and pretzels are guaranteed. Sure enough, on a Sunday night in July in Berlin everyone was milling around looking for old friends and making new acquaintances whose names they might know but had not met. Such events are a time for saying "I see you've got an abstract on such and such." You make arrangements to discuss mutual interests after you have presented your formal papers. You notice immediately when someone you expect to be there, isn't. Everett Gibson wasn't there. Although he's been described as having a beer belly, he's teetotal. Still he wouldn't miss the conference opening get-together. It's where the deals are done, collaborations arranged, Curators to be cornered for sample requests etc. Whilst I was looking around, I was button-holed by a guy who wanted to press on me his new theory, based on our isotope data. He wanted to tell me the carbonaceous chondrite meteorites were martian sediments. Since he was using my group's data to back up his arguments, he expected a sympathetic hearing. I was interested, but it was perhaps a leap too far.

I excused myself to join a small group containing some of the people who worked with me and Americans with common interests. They were discussing the absence not only of Everett but everybody else who worked at JSC. It seemed very odd that nobody from there had taken the opportunity to come to Berlin. One of the Americans volunteered some information: "They're adopting a low profile. The grape-vine has it they're making a big announcement to do with life on Mars." Another American added "A paper is going to be published soon but Everett and his buddies don't want to talk about it or be asked questions at a conference." I was intrigued but could do nothing in the absence of someone from JSC to ask.

I had brought my daughter Shusy and a boyfriend to Berlin to do some sight-seeing, so I didn't plan to spend the whole week there; the family had been to the German capital in 1990 and we had done our bit to help dismantle 'the Wall'. I felt I needed to. I had been in West Germany on an exchange visit when it started going up. As a group of eighteen year olds we had expected to see Russian tanks in the street any second.

Instead of hanging around to the bitter end of the Conference, we drove back, taking a day to get home. The next night I rang Everett to find out what this big thing was. "I can't tell you; I'm sworn to secrecy," was all I could get out of him despite all the "come on you can trust me, I won't blab it around" promises.

I eventually decided I would be provocative. It couldn't be anything to do with organic matter or water, we had been there, done that; it had to be going a bit further. I took a stab in the dark with "I hope you aren't going to do anything as stupid as saying you've found a fossil." It was supposed to prompt the answer "Of course not!" but it was also a word of warning. Periodically, since the 19th century, usually looking in carbonaceous chondrites, somebody would claim to have found small fossils in meteorites. A few people have even announced the discovery of living microorganisms. One pseudo-scientist who claimed success wrote a letter to Charles Darwin saying he would bring the samples to show the great man. All these nutters were rapidly shunned and their names only mentioned in sentences advising how not to do science. The one and only Louis Pasteur was an exception. He was encouraged by the President the Royal Society to have a go at cultivating microorganisms from several extraterrestrial stones; he found nothing and didn't even trouble himself to write up his negative results.

I was surprised and bothered when Everett didn't deny he might be working on meteorite fossils. I didn't ask him any more; it was his funeral! About a week later, a tiny paragraph in a trade newspaper for the Space Industry, *Space News*, mentioned that the journal *Science*, the US equivalent of *Nature*, was about to publish a paper about a fossil in a martian meteorite. I didn't see it; *Space News* only gets to Britain some time after publication. Not many other people noticed it either; it's not a regular read for meteoriticists. But there was a journalist on the track of the story, James Wilkinson, science correspondent for the BBC, had been sleuthing. On the afternoon of 5 August he took a camera team to see Monica Grady at the Natural History Museum. Robert Hutchison had retired; Monica had left the OU and was now in charge of the NHM's meteorite collection. James reckoned he had enough information to take a punt at a 'Life on Mars – Found!' story for the BBC's 9 o'clock News. It was run and for ever after he will claim a scoop. Even though *Space News* was actually first it had been ignored.

At 2.20am 6 August, my life changed for ever. The phone rang. I staggered down the stairs and picked it up. Before I could say anything a hoarse voice at the other end demanded "Is it true this rock is full of worms?" It was talking about ALH84001 and the possibility the carbonate veins contained fossils. All

I could say was "I don't know." I must have said some other things but this journalist, from the *Daily Mail*, didn't print any of them and frankly I'm not surprised. What would you say to someone with a question like that at that time of the morning?

Anticipating that where one journalist went there would be others following, I drove the thirty-five miles to the lab early the next morning. Media mayhem had already broken out. I had lived through Apollo, Viking, indigenous organics and fizzy water in martian meteorites, but this was, for me, bigger than all of those press clamours combined. America was asleep; I found out later anybody belonging to NASA, who was up, was under strict instructions not to answer their phone. That left me and the OU.

We were overwhelmed. There were camera teams running around filming anything that had OU on it whilst they waited to get a spokesperson in front of their camera talking to an interviewer. Ian Wright, Monica and I, who had worked on the meteorite ALH84001 with the supposed fossil, were under a continuous barrage. Monica had obtained a pirate copy of the unpublished *Science* manuscript that was the cause of the furore. She got it courtesy of *Nature*, who wanted to commission us to write a review of the work. It was entirely unethical but we knew a bit more about what was going on. Nevertheless I steadfastly refused to disclose full details of colleagues' work before they had announced it themselves; I stuck rigidly to what I thought was our contribution. Monica also had a picture of the carbonates in the meteorite which she had photographed. Every newspaper picture editor wanted a copy for his front page. These days the OU would have copyrighted it and demanded money but we allowed free access to anybody and everybody.

Numerous secretaries handled the phones and told me who was next: this journalist, that radio programme. The journalist I remember best was Roger Highfield of the *Telegraph*. He asked a lot of questions about our meteorite organics work from 1989. I thought he was going to write an article giving us a lot of credit for precipitating this media three-ringed circus.

One of the few non-journalists who got through was Paul Murdin, a well known astronomer, who walked with two sticks. I had encountered him previously because he was a member of various PPARC committees I was also on. Now he was seconded to the British National Space Centre, BNSC for short, part of the Department of Trade and Industry. They were the people who handled space affairs for the Minister of Science. Paul's question to me was "Can I bring the Minister on a visit to the OU?" The Minister was nominally on holiday during the summer recess of Parliament but wanted to be informed. I don't know what Paul had said to get the Minister out of his deck chair in such a hurry but he had answered a question from a journalist inquiring "How important is this [the fossil]?" with the comment "It's about the same level as Copernicus saying that the Earth goes round the Sun, not vice versa." A visit for the Minister was agreed.

Meanwhile back in Washington, NASA had woken up and got their ducks in a row, literally. They flew Everett, Dave McKay, someone else I knew from my lunar sample days, and a cohort of co-workers to Washington, for a hastily convened 1 o'clock press conference. They also intended to field an expert who studied tiny fossils found in Earth's oldest rocks to give an outsider's opinion. This was one press conference I wanted to hear even though I had already read the very fuzzy draft of the *Science* manuscript faxed by *Nature*. All day the BBC and others badgered me to disclose what I knew rather than talk in general terms and reiterate what we had done towards the discovery. Finally I agreed to stand in front of the cameras and comment as soon as the news was officially public.

At the OU we set up a screen so we could tune into NASA TV. Before the press conference began Bill Clinton said his piece from the White House lawn: "If this discovery is confirmed, it will surely be one of the most stunning insights into our Universe that science has ever uncovered. Its implications are as far reaching and inspiring as can be imagined."

Before I could take in the magnitude of being involved in an event which needed a comment from the most powerful man on Earth, the BBC hauled me out to follow the American President, live. It's the only time I've ever had a President as the warm up act. I watched a recording of the presentations and the question and answer session afterwards.

Knackered, I struggled back to my office just after 7.00pm. I had been talking non-stop for more than twelve hours and I had been rudely awakened at 2.20am. I saw immediately my answerphone was flashing. More journalists, I thought. Nevertheless I picked it up. I was gobsmacked that there were two recorded messages, from senior astronomers, berating me for damaging the British research programme in Astronomy. Neither left their name, but I recognised both voices.

The critique of the *Science* article that Mon, Ian and I wrote entitled 'A martian can of worms' appeared in the very next edition of *Nature*. It was published before the article it was discussing. *Nature* didn't worry it had opened another can of worms as well.

Chapter 6

NOT WANTED ON VOYAGE

A rather more enjoyable telephone call followed a few days later. It was Marcello Coradini. Marcello wanted to know if I would be a member of a panel being set up to evaluate the possibilities of life existing on other planets in the solar system. This wasn't under the auspices of the Science Programme that he was in charge of but was being commissioned by the Human Spaceflight Directorate of ESA. The person who was organising it was Irishman Paul Clancy, and the Chairman was to be Andre Brack, a bald, grey-bearded French scientist renowned for his work on the origin of life on Earth. I would be bringing to the party my expertise on the subject of extraterrestrial life gleaned from the study of meteorites, particularly martian meteorites. I immediately said "Yes," and was told Paul would be in touch about arrangements. In due course I received an invitation to a first meeting, on 4 November, in Paris.

I avidly read all the newspapers the day after the fossil story broke. Most gave us a good write up and lots of cartoons depicting Martians appeared. Several cartoonists had linked the story of life on Mars to the sports headlines; Alan Shearer was being sold to Newcastle United by Blackburn Rovers for a record fee of £15 million. Science doesn't often get equal billing with football even in the close season.

Comment on the significance of discovering life on Mars had been sought from all the obvious sources, not least of all religious leaders. The *Sun* newspaper was running a competition with a prize consisting of a trip to Mars, a holiday village in the south of France, not the planet. Bookmakers were debating whether to pay out on bets concerning the possibility of life elsewhere being found; I was asked if I would go to the White City Greyhound Track to hand over winnings to one successful punter.

Amongst all the good news stories and light-hearted banter, was one piece which depressed me. It was Roger Highfield's, published under the by-line: 'The man who missed it'. It implied that I had not realised the significance of the results in the 1989 *Nature* paper. Of course I hadn't missed it; the implications of our earlier work had been obvious as we had said, and the press coverage we got conclusively showed that the media had got the message.

The one place where our contribution had not been fully acknowledged was the place which matters most to scientists, the references to previous work in the *Science* paper. Our paper 'Indigenous organic carbon in a martian meteorite' wasn't amongst those listed by Everett and his colleagues. I asked Everett "Why not?" He told me "The editors at *Science* wanted the martian fossil paper reduced in size. They removed the references to earlier work."

There was going to be an opportunity to rectify the situation. During the second week of August the Minister for Science, Ian Taylor, visited the OU. I had met Ministers before but he was different. Politicians like to visit the OU because it has two hundred thousand undergraduates and has awarded two million degrees to potential voters. Politicians tend to spend their time with us looking around to make sure the cameramen catch them looking interested.

Ian Taylor was genuinely interested. To prove it he brought his son, who was about to go to University, with him. We fielded my daughter Shusy, now an undergraduate at Cambridge, to take Taylor junior in tow. During a tour of our labs, I mentioned the fact that some of the British contributions to the discovery of life on Mars had perhaps not been given as much credit as they deserved. To redress the balance, I was thinking of organising a scientific meeting soon to get people in Britain together to discuss the subject of extra-terrestrial life. The next thing I knew, the Minister was announcing to the Press that he was sponsoring the meeting I had told him about a few minutes earlier. I never asked him to lend his name to it but this was a big boost.

I was soon going to have a new way of regularly communicating science to the public. I had applied for an honorary position in the City of London with the title Gresham Professor of Astronomy. When Sir Thomas Gresham, the man who founded the Stock Exchange, died in 1579, he left some of his fortune to endow a college which was to bear his name. He may have intended it to become London University but he was particularly keen for it to be a sort of fledging OU; its six Professors, one in Astronomy, were to give lectures in Latin, the language of philosophers, but again in English, with free entry for the public. Previous Gresham Professors include Edmond Halley and Robert Hooke, just to name-drop two of the most famous.

During the interview for the post I had to give a five minute presentation to demonstrate I was a good communicator. Sitting across a table from a panel, made up of members drawn from the Mercers' Company and the City of London, I asked for a clean saucer from the tray of coffee cups. Carefully I tipped onto it a piece of the Nakhla meteorite and passed it round, as I made my pitch about life on Mars. Not an eye left the saucer whilst I was talking. A few days later I received a letter telling me I was in. With it came an invitation to lunch at the Reform Club with the College's new Provost, Andreas Prindl, who was Chairman of the Nomura Bank. At the lunch I suggested bringing Everett Gibson to London to give a joint public lecture. Incidentally, it was the best steak I've ever had.

To prepare for the 'Minister's Meeting' Ian Wright and I decided to revisit our 1989 paper to see if we really had missed something significant during the first look. We also went through the analyses of EETA79001 conducted since. Four specimens of carbonate-rich inclusions had been picked out of the part of the rock called 'lithology C'. Each released several thousand parts per million (ppm) of carbon during stepped combustion and always showed an enrichment in 13-carbon. All the other specimens of EETA79001, from other parts of the rock, had very low carbon abundance, a few ppm, and a nondescript, distinctly terrestrial, carbon isotope composition.

What we hadn't noticed before was that the results from lithology C defined a straight line on a graph of carbon abundance versus isotope composition. This observation meant the samples were a mixture of two components. If one was carbonate rich in 13-C as a result of being produced from the martian atmosphere, then the other had to be the organics. The overall carbon isotope composition was the result of mixing the two forms of carbon together. To obtain the numbers we had measured, the organics would need to be present in amounts too great to be contamination. With other samples of EETA79001 showing very low carbon abundance, we asked ourselves "How could 'lithology C' get contaminated without the same happening to the rest of the meteorite?" There of course wasn't an answer.

We decided that it was high time we carefully examined some carbonate selected from ALH84001. A piece was chipped out and our technician doing the experiment, Jenny Gibson, noticed that it contained a small amount of what she called 'black stuff'. The analysis gave results that we could interpret as the presence of carbonate, because it had the very high 13-C we now associated with this, but there was something else burning at a lower temperature. It had to be organic but it had low 13-C abundance, lower than anything we had previously seen in a martian meteorite. The only organic matter we knew about with such low 13-C is the organic matter produced on Earth by microbes using methane gas as a carbon/energy source.

The ALH84001 carbonate experiment had to be repeated, and it duly was with much the same result. If anything the signals were stronger. Unbeknown to me at the time, in order to get enough material the sample taken for analysis had included all that remained of the black stuff, so unfortunately black stuff was never looked at with a microscope. Nevertheless we had duplicated the experiment and the data were consistent with the carbonate-containing organic matter which could have come from a fairly primitive organism.

Ian and I discussed these results over and over again. Perhaps we had the missing piece of the jigsaw, in which case we were sitting on a bomb. Eventually Ian and I decided we would submit the results to *Nature*, but simultaneously we would release the information to the scientific community, and everybody else interested, by talking about it at the Minister's meeting now with the title 'Life in the Solar System and beyond'. Alan Penny, an astronomer who wore a rumpled white suit and was promoting a space mission designed to look for planets that might support life around other stars, had muscled in. He didn't just want to be part of the meeting; he tried to take it over.

We realised our plan to reveal new data might cause grief because in the wake of the fossil story, both the journals *Science* and *Nature* were declaring it was their policy not to publish work that had been previously announced elsewhere. We had been publishing lots of the data in *Nature*, so to clear the ground I phoned the Editor, Philip Campbell, and explained what we were about to do: a week before standing up to talk about it at the Royal Society, we would submit a paper to him describing what we had found during the analysis of EETA79001. "This will give you a chance to send it out for review," I said. "It's not getting to the press via a leak. Only me, Ian and our wives, Judith and Monica know about it."

I didn't elaborate on my reason for saying that, but I had heard from Everett the reason why a leak of his *Science* paper had reached *Space News*. Because he works for NASA, news of JSC's discoveries concerning ALH84001 was passed up the chain to HQ. He and his crew were summoned to Washington to brief the NASA Administrator, who in turn, through a variety of civil servants, informed Vice-President Dan Quail. Too many people got to know NASA might have discovered life on Mars. As a result there's an article in an American tabloid newspaper claiming it heard the story from a prostitute who was told by a White House official during pillow talk. She had offered the story for sale, only she got it wrong saying her 'client' had said it was life on Pluto. The idea of life on Pluto was too much even for a tabloid so they didn't buy her original story and publish it sooner. *Space News* had picked it up.

If there was going to be a life on Mars media bonanza we weren't going to miss out on taking full credit first. *Nature* agreed to go along with the plan; the incentive, presumably, being the opportunity to upstage *Science* who had had something of a coup with the fossil. I was taking a calculated risk but, as it turned out, the risk I took wasn't the one I imagined. I assumed I was secure in believing that *Nature* would not leak our information since it would have no motivation to upstage itself. What happened however was entirely unanticipated.

For a few days only four people and the journal knew what we intended to say. It was pretty certain there would be no extracurricular activity so nothing leaked. The day of the meeting arrived. We had heard nothing from *Nature* about the paper being reviewed, nevertheless we went ahead with our intention and talked about our data anyway. Ian Wright presented it; as soon as he finished answering questions, I gave copies of our manuscript to James Wilkinson of the BBC and Roger Highfield, of the *Telegraph*. It was a deliberate attempt to reverse 'the man who missed' it headline. Both of them bolted for the door, James to get a story on BBC's 1 o'clock News. His coverage led to yet another media scrum throughout the afternoon as other journalists descended on the Royal Society.

Ian Taylor, as good as his word, had opened 'his' Meeting in the morning and that evening hosted a reception; his office paid for the drinks. I saw Philip Campbell amongst the guests but he didn't speak. A few days later *Nature* published a scathing attack on me for releasing data which hadn't been peer reviewed. As far as I'm concerned talking about a subject in front of an audience of fellow scientists constitutes peer review and this we had done; we had not talked to the press about our experiments until Ian Wright had taken questions at the end of his talk. Thousands of scientists do similarly every time they go to International conferences; indeed *Nature* and other journals send reporters to such meetings to cover the scientific 'news'.

Something I feel pretty strongly about when it comes to communicating science is the rationale that, if you want the public to take an interest, then you have to let them join in the excitement. It's no good showing edited (sanitised) highlights, I believe you should let the media come to real events and get the message real-time. I reject the argument often put forward by the 'they have to trust us, they wouldn't understand' scientists who say "The media sensationalise and the public isn't qualified to judge." If that's the case scientists had better start explaining in a way that the public can understand, otherwise the public will never be capable of judging. And what's more they won't give us funding to do our experiments. Scientific journals, even ones that appear on news-stands, shouldn't be in the business of scooping each other. The only thing that I know of that increases in value, if you share it, is knowledge. Somebody must have said that before but, if nobody claims it, I will. Anyway, this wasn't the last time sharing what we were doing with the public caused upset.

I wrote to the Editor of *Nature* to refute his criticism, asking him to admit publically he was party to what we were doing all along. I wanted my letter to be published in the journal explaining the circumstances surrounding what had happened. Whereas his editorial criticising me, like our review of the *Science* paper, had managed to get into press immediately, my letter appeared three weeks later. The sentences that explained the Editor had prior knowledge of what was going to happen, and already had a copy of our manuscript for review, had been edited out of my letter – NO COMMENT!

Not surprisingly, *Nature* rejected our paper. I wish I could say we found more black stuff and characterised it, but we didn't. We did find that a sample of Teflon used in the valves employed in the analysis system decomposed to produce something which burned at a temperature similar to organics. We had checked Teflon as a potential contaminant in our experiment before and had never had any problems during hundreds, if not thousands, of experiments.

I don't think we could have been so unlucky as to have a flake of Teflon to fall into two separate experiments, especially when it never had before, nor has it since. Also Teflon is white, not black, and the black stuff was seen before the sample was loaded into the apparatus. Like lots of Professors, I accept what the people who work for me tell me. If we didn't, science would soon fall apart. I have no doubt that Jenny's results came from the samples she measured.

During the weekend I spent with Nobel Prize winner Harold Urey he told me "If you think you have discovered something significant then stick with it and try to prove you are right. If you prove yourself wrong, or somebody else does, drop it." I still think the black stuff was something significant in the story of life on Mars. I haven't proved it but then nobody has proved us wrong. Beagle 2 was all about proving it; like many other things to do with science, absolute proof proves elusive.

'Life in the Solar System and beyond' certainly caused lots of excitement. Roger Highfield's coverage in the *Telegraph* was accompanied by a Matt cartoon, on the front page; it showed a scientist poking a martian meteorite causing a voice from within to cry out "Ouch!" Next day was to be the first session of ESA's panel to consider the possibilities of life on other planets. It was held in Paris. I arrived there to be greeted by the German member of the Committee, Heinrich Wänke, probably best described as a portly figure, brandishing a newspaper with a screaming headline about life on Mars. He had picked it up at the airport on his way to the meeting. It set the tone for a day discussing a subject which couldn't have been more topical.

The Committee spent a lot of time deciding what we needed to cover. Questions like: what is the definition of life? Our answer would be something that can reproduce and evolve. We would have to suggest ways of recognising extraterrestrial life if it existed or if it had perhaps existed in the past. We undertook to write a report covering all the angles. We agreed to visit each other's laboratories, in turn, and address a particular subject at each meeting. We decided to start early in the New Year in Germany and on that occasion consider what martian meteorites might be trying to tell us.

On 17 January 1997, we reconvened in Mainz. For the benefit of those who didn't work with meteorites, Wänke had prepared a list of all the martian meteorites we knew about (at the time, twelve) giving their crystallisation ages, i.e. the time they solidified from molten rock. Quite a number had been formed 1.3 billion years (byr) ago, some were younger but ALH84001 was the oldest, formed as long as 3.6 to 4.0 byr ago. "Thus," he said, "if the fossil is evidence of life on Mars, then it could be very ancient life." Sitting there looking at his slide, I noticed that the youngest rock in the list was EETA79001. It had solidified only 180 million years ago, but I knew from other evidence that it had only set out for Earth 600,000 years before it landed on Antarctica, where it waited 17,000 years to be collected.

It suddenly dawned on me that I could reach the opposite conclusion to Wänke: in geological terms, there was only a very short time for EETA79001 to have acquired its organic matter. Material that could be the evidence of life could only have got into the rock after it solidified, and before 600,000 years ago; 600,000 years is a human timescale not a fossil one. Hominids, early men, were walking around on Earth that recently. Suddenly the penny dropped; if what we had discovered in EETA79001 was the evidence of life then, there could be life on Mars now, just waiting for somebody to find it!

That little Committee had a couple more meetings, moving around to the country of each of the participants as guests. By April, it was down to me to organise a session in Britain. Rather than have the group come to Milton Keynes, I decided to hold my meeting in London at the Royal Society to make the travelling easier for those coming from abroad. Everybody had already accepted that Mars was a strong candidate for finding life and we planned to discuss what instruments would be needed to detect life if a space-craft could be landed there. I was going to nominate a mass spectrometer, a version of the instrument we had used to analyse martian meteorites in the lab. I was going to say we needed to repeat the experiments we had done on Earth, in situ, in a way that could be relied on to eliminate contamination.

We assembled in the Royal Society's Council Room on 14 April but, before we could get down to business, Paul Clancy dropped a bombshell. He said "There's going to be a meeting at ESA in Paris, next Friday, to discuss a European mission to Mars." The decision had been thrust on ESA; the previous November, the Russians had launched a mission called Mars 96, destined for the Red Planet. The engine, supposed to boost the spacecraft's speed to over 25,000 mph so that it could leave Earth's orbit and begin its journey, had misbehaved. As a result Mars 96 had ended up in Chile and the South Pacific. This created a problem for Europe; although the mission was Russian, a lot of instruments on board had been made in the west as a result of collabora-tions born out of glasnost. Incidentally glasnost is Russian for openness and maximum publicity.

Mars 96 had been Europe's second calamity in a few months. Just prior to the Russian failure ESA had launched a mission called Cluster (four satellites to observe the Sun) on board a new version of the Ariane rocket: Ariane V. Unfortunately, its computer had been programmed with Ariane IV software. Ariane V was getting close to its budget limit, and saving effort by re-using 'well-tested' software looked like a good idea. It would have been if, also to save money, they hadn't eliminated the end-to-end system test as well, or had remembered the software expected the rocket's fuel to run out after thirty-four seconds. As a result the expensive package had set off like a demented firework and the mission had been aborted, that is blown up. ESA don't like people to know that things like this happen. To save their embarrassment, the Agency announced immediately it would have a recovery mission; it would pay for a new set of instruments and launch them on a second rocket to make sure no science was lost.

Now the investigators who had instruments on Mars 96 knew all about Cluster; they expected similar treatment. They wanted ESA to step in and recover the science planned for Mars 96. The meeting in Paris was going to consider an ESA recovery mission to Mars in 2003. "It's the best opportunity for many years," Clancy said to us, adding, "Marcello is telling everybody, Mars is as close as it gets to Earth, ideal for sending the biggest payload possi-ble; we mustn't miss it."

All of a sudden our meeting had a real purpose; we could be putting together a 'straw man' payload for an actual mission to Mars, which we duly did. We then began to debate how we could get our ideas considered as part of Friday's deliberations. The problem for our committee was that the meeting would be under the auspices of the ESA Science Directorate and we were a study team commissioned by its Human Spaceflight Division. These two arms of ESA operate independently and jealously guard their territories. Getting them to collaborate is far more difficult than working with another country's space agency. Paul Clancy said "As an ESA official, I expect I can get in." Asked if anyone else could go, he said "I might be able to swing an invite for Andre as our chairman." I pressed him: "What about me? I have a vested interest; I'm the only one here who could build an instrument capable of detecting life on Mars, if we can get it there." By this time we had agreed that a mass spectrometer was an essential part of any lander sent, but Paul replied "I don't think my influence will stretch that far." To which I responded "I'll get in some other way then."

The following day, I began phoning people I knew who had been involved in Mars 96. There had been only a marginal British participation, because it was a serendipitous opportunity that arose as result of the Russians being strapped for cash. Britain didn't do optional space programmes; it was as much as the space community could do to get the Government to cough up for the mandatory programme that being a member of ESA required. My phone calls therefore were mostly to French scientists. They were greeted with variations on a theme from Fawlty Towers "I know nothing!" to "it's strictly by invitation only." It was patently obvious that I was dealing with a closed shop.

Frustrated, I decided to call Giacomo Cavallo, an Italian ESA Headquarters Administrator, who I had sat next to and got on well with, at a dinner a few months previously. After all the prevarication I had met with so far, it was blissfully simple; he said "Come if you want to, it's not a secret." So everything that happened from here on is Giacomo's fault. It would turn out to be somewhat ironic that the dinner where I first met Giacomo was in the National Maritime Museum and took place against a backdrop of famous British ships. On Thursday evening Judith and I drove to Paris. Early the next morning I presented myself at the door of ESA's HQ in the Rue Mario Nikis, saying "I have come for the Mars meeting." Giacomo had thoughtfully added my name to the attendance list.

Having gained access, I wasn't surprised at the attempts that had been made to block me coming. The majority of the people assembled in the room were French; all except one had had instruments on the Mars 96 orbiter. They were intent on carving up the proposed new mission in the very early stages. The exception was Philippe Lognonné, but he too was French, and was the spokesman for a project that wanted to see ESA distribute a network of small geophysical stations on Mars, primarily to find out if the planet was seismically active and still had molten rocks. This idea, currently called MarsNet, had been put to ESA several times already, but had never quite made it to a final selection.

I sensed that Lognonné might be an ally. At least he wanted a lander or, to be more precise, several landers. During the discussion I tried the tack: "Since Mars 96 was conceived in the mid-1980s, Mars science has moved on," I said. "We didn't know that martian meteorites were going to give us such a strong hint about life on the Red Planet. Any mission now has to have a lander on board and it will have to be capable of looking for life." To get Lognonné on my side, I threw in "A lander could also include geophysics experiments." There didn't seem to be any enthusiasm for this idea, even from Lognonné. Clutching at straws, I decided an appeal to French patriotism might be in order so I said "We could call the lander Pasteur." I was guessing they'd like to honour the French scientist whose experiments had shown that life was not generated spontaneously on Earth. This went down like a lead brick. They were clearly not in the mood for anybody encroaching on their orbiter cartel.

I guess Marcello Coradini thought now was the moment to kill off landers completely; he'd probably had enough of the arguments about the Rosetta lander. He looked at me and said "Who's going to build a lander? Not you! And who's going to pay for it? Not the Brits." My response to that was "Finding life on Mars is so important, somebody will pay for it." I had done as much as I could and that wasn't much. They were a pretty impenetrable clique.

Afterwards in our car, heading out of Paris back towards Calais and the coast, I related the events and the dialogue to Judith. She said "Are you serious? Do you believe somebody would pay for a lander to look for life on Mars?" Without any idea who, I said "Yes." "OK, then we're going to have to have a name for the project that everybody will recognise as synonymous with what we're trying to do," were her next words.

She thought about it for a while and said "If it's going to be British then it ought to be Darwin, not Pasteur." But we knew from the Minister's meeting that Alan Penny had already claimed the name Darwin for the Astronomy mission trying to launch a telescope to look for planets around other stars and analyse their atmospheres as a means of searching for life. "I know," she said, "we'll call it Beagle, in honour of the ship that took Darwin around

90

the world and led to him writing *On the Origin of Species*. She then added "Besides, it will annoy Alan Penny." She had had lots of arguments with him about whose logo should appear first on the press release announcing the meeting. After some more thought, she said "It can't be Beagle, it'll have to be Beagle 2."

I've told this story thousands of times, including on live radio, when the presenter looked me straight in the eye and asked "Were you on that mission too?" I answered "I'm old but not that old." HMS Beagle's voyage was in the 1830s. I've never before, however, revealed that it would have been Darwin, but for Alan Penny. Would everything have been different if it had been Darwin? Of course we'll never know. Anyway, the name Beagle 2 stuck; everybody would come to agree it was an inspired choice.

Our first action the following week was to post out a letter to all the people we could think of in the space community who might be interested in having a role if the British tried to build a lander for a mission to Mars. We invited them all to attend a meeting at the Royal Society on 20 May. In preparation, I phoned Alan Wells, Director of the Space Research Centre at the University of Leicester. I didn't want to get on the wrong side of Alan, an over-six-foot rugby fan, so I asked "Are you interested? If you are, I'll be looking to recruit Mark Sims." Mark worked for Alan as a Project Manager. It was the same Mark Sims who had been inspired by my lunar sample display in 1969. He had prematurely grown through his hair but still dressed in Mum's Christmas jumpers. Whilst we were discussing his future, unbeknown to him, Mark was writing his response to our invite asking if he could come. The letter said "I'm pessimistic that anything will come of the idea." He didn't know he was already recruited and would be one of the people who worked hardest to get Beagle 2 to Mars.

My next move was to arrange a meeting with Sir John Daniel, the OU's Vice-Chancellor, in his Walton Hall office at 9.30am Friday 25 April. I explained the idea of a British mission to Mars to confirm what we believed we had discovered from martian meteorites. I told him "There's no money, we would have to raise it." Maybe I should have told him "But I can count about ten generations of ancestors who found a way of getting by without any cash." Instead I put it to him "If I try to do this, is it going to be a 'Pillinger Enterprises' effort or can I expect the OU's backing?" The answer I got was "I think <u>we</u> should go for it."

You would never get a response like that now, but it was typical of how Beagle 2 progressed. People didn't think twice about it, they didn't say "I'll have to consult," "Has everybody signed a non-disclosure agreement?" or

"A legal contract will have to be drawn up." People just wanted to be involved and everything was done the old fashioned way on the basis of Gentlemen's Agreements, sealed with a handshake.

The next port of call was the Minister's man Paul Murdin. He was also PPARC's and BNSC's representative at ESA. I knew before I embarked on this course of action the response I was going to get, and duly Paul didn't disappoint me with his answer to my proposition "PPARC has no money for an involvement in a Mars mission." What I hadn't bargained for however was his next comment, sitting in the Fellows' room of the Royal Astronomical Society. After I made my pitch, he said philosophically "I can't tell you to go ahead, but then I can't tell you not to." I wonder if he ever regretted that sentence. In truth, he was probably as game for it as the rest of us.

It was all the encouragement I needed. "A wink is as good as a nod to a blind horse," my father would have said. Nobody had told me to stop, so things moved on to the first meeting of Beagle 2's prospective crew. Strictly speaking it was to be a gathering of academics, all of whom wanted to go to Mars for the purpose of doing some scientific research. A few days before it was due to take place, I was called by Rodney Buckland. Rodney is somebody who has done the rounds of the British space scene, worked at ESA and had even tried to raise money to launch the only 100% British astronaut to have flown so far: Helen Sharman. He once told Judith "I only raised a packet of pansy seeds." She wasn't sure whether he meant he'd grown the pansies or if he was being metaphorical. Nevertheless he has a wealth of contacts. "Can I bring a colleague from industry, John Hobbs from MMS (Matra Marconi Space)?" Rodney enquired. I had no objections "The more the merrier as far as I'm concerned," I told him. Having industry along in the form of MMS was a development I hadn't thought of but, if I hadn't agreed to John Hobbs joining in, Beagle 2 wouldn't have got very far.

So our first Beagle 2 meeting went ahead with everybody who was there in favour and gung ho. The first concept of how the lander might look was put up on a screen courtesy of the late Ray Turner. All the people there knew jolly Ray; he'd shared his favourite lunch, a pint, with most of us at some time. He was a life-long space enthusiast engineer from the RAL. He had been seconded to me to kick-off our involvement in the Rosetta comet mission. When I asked him if he was up for a mission to Mars his answer was "I'd give my right arm to land a nut and bolt there." His idea for how we might land involved building a spacecraft with a base made from crushable material that collapsed on contact with the surface. We didn't use it, but later I found a job for Ray; he had to be on board.

Now I had a mandate from the British space science community, which was just as well because ESA had decided that a follow-up to the Paris session would be held at ESTEC. It would specifically consider the possibility of including a lander or landers on board Mars Express, MEx, as the orbiter was now being called. It had this name because it was going to be built very rapidly from spares and with designs acquired from the comet mission. Judith thought it was a stupid choice. "Why?" I asked her. "Because a lot of web search engines will bounce it; it's got SEX in the middle," she answered. Judith should have been a PR agent.

I had to go from the Royal Society straight to Noordwijk, where the meeting was next day. That was the immediate problem. Whilst we were upstairs discussing going to Mars, somebody stole my passport and foreign currency from my bag in the normally secure basement cloakroom. Not for the last time during Beagle 2, I wondered whether there were Martians who were determined to stop the project before it discovered them. Anyway I foiled the attempt by carrying on with my journey regardless. At Dover, I acquired a piece of paper from Immigration to serve as a temporary passport.

The ESTEC session was chaired by a Spaniard, Agustin Chicarro, who was now the MEx Project Scientist. Agustin is immediately distinguishable. He has a penchant for navy blue Marks and Spencer's cardigans; I've never seen him wear anything else. At Noordwijk, I again encountered Philippe Lognonné. He had gathered reinforcements in the shape of a group from the Finnish Meteorological Institute. They had been part of the Mars 96 effort and had expected the Russians to deliver a pair of meteorological stations to the surface of the Red Planet. The Finns had intimate knowledge of the proposed Russian landing system and were throwing their cap into the ring with Lognonné, the French and the latest Network of landers project, bringing the Russian know-how with them.

ESA had been doing their sums and reckoned the Mars Express orbiter would be able to afford 180kg to accommodate landers. Space missions always start life with a consideration of mass. Space engineers always talk about mass rather than weight because the latter depends on gravity. It can be calculated how much a rocket can lift into Earth's orbit. This mass is then broken down into the mass of the spacecraft and its systems, the fuel needed to leave the vicinity of Earth and get to the destination, plus what will be wanted to carry out manoeuvres when it gets there. Whatever is left over is for the science payload of instruments. The first mass quoted by the engineers is never the true number. The real one is always a closely guarded secret because everybody, particularly the Agency, knows the Mission Project Manager keeps some margin as a contingency to solve problems he will encounter during the build. Usually, he will release a bit to allow the instrument builders to overcome difficulties but it is always a big fight. The MEx contingency would turn out to be one of the Beagle 2's greatest obstacles.

It seemed to me that with at least 180kg available we could have the best of both worlds: a lander could be built to include the payload that I needed for life detection experiments and the 'Netlander' people's geophysical package. The instruments could include a seismometer from Lognonné and meteorological sensors for the Finns. I suggested this might be the way to go. No, that didn't satisfy them; they wanted the whole 180 kg. "We require a network of several landers, not one," they said, "to see if Mars is seismically active and for studying its weather." I tried saying "OK, I can understand why you need three landers to pinpoint any seismic event, but couldn't one of them be bigger than the others because it's carrying life detection experiments?" "No," they said again. It then transpired they wanted the whole 180kg so that they could build four not three landers. If one failed to land, or didn't work, they would still have three left. "Redundancy," they called it. It sounded like being greedy to me. The meeting broke up with no agreement "ESA," said Agustin, "will discuss the situation again in a week's time at SPC." SPC is ESA's Science Programme Committee. Paul Murdin was at the SPC meeting; after, he told me "The discussion wasn't very fruitful; ESA were dead set against a lander or landers on MEx." He added "However, in true ESA fashion no decision was made, there's going to be another meeting at the end of September when the people who want landers can state their case."

Somehow the subject of SPC's deliberations about Mars Express, and the hint that somebody British had advocated having a lander, reached the media. Late in the afternoon of 4 June, the phone rang in my secretary's office; the OU's switchboard had put the call through because a journalist was enquiring about Mars. Summoned to the phone, I picked it up and was greeted with the question: "I suppose you know nothing about Britain sending a lander to Mars either?" Because it invited a negative answer I said "No, I know everything about it."

The reaction was electric. I could imagine Susan Watts of 'Newsnight' suddenly sitting bolt upright. She recounted to me how she had spent an unproductive afternoon, ringing around contacts in the space business, trying to find out the story behind a rumour about Britain being involved in a mission to Mars. I explained about martian meteorites, and how I believed repeating the experiments on the Red Planet with the necessary instrument on a lander would answer the question 'Is there life on Mars?'.

She listened patiently, never once interrupting and then said "Would you say this on Newsnight this evening?" "Of course," I answered. "I'll have to speak to my Editor to see if he will change the programme schedule, I'll get back to you." She was clearly excited and it was approaching 5pm by then, but within a minute or two, it may have been seconds, she was on the line again making arrangements for a BBC car to pick me up from home and get me to the studio in time for 10.30pm. It was very obvious we had a powerful weapon. I just didn't know how powerful a story about Britain looking for life on Mars was going to be yet. I had been whisked to Wood Lane to talk about life on Mars before but now the focus was directly on Britain having a mission to Mars to look for it. The stakes had ramped up a notch.

In the next six years I made many chauffeur-driven journeys to news studios. Usually they tried to get me there early and dump me in the 'Green Room' to wait until they were ready for me on camera or in front of a microphone. On this occasion, I was ushered straight into the studio and seated at a table ready for interview. Already there, at another table, was a Tory MP. He was a candidate for the vacant Conservative Party leadership. John Major had resigned after losing in a landslide election to Tony Blair.

Newsnight is basically a politics programme, not an outlet for science stories, so the said MP was obviously anticipating (hoping) that he was the top news of the night. He was wrong. With Peter Snow, a well known technophile, anchoring the programme, the politician was an also-ran. He sat there twiddling his thumbs, no doubt expecting he would never hear of me again or any more about Britain going to Mars. He fumed against a background piece of archive film hastily put together by Susan Watts. As soon as it was over, Peter Snow started firing questions at me. To one about how was I going to pay for a mission to Mars, I famously answered "There's more than one way to skin a cat!"

A follow-up article appeared in the *Observer*; it asked "Is Peter Snow a Martian?" The ball was rolling. I had got through the interview without disclosing Judith's idea for the name of the spacecraft. That was going to be another story, for another day.

In the months since the fossil in the martian meteorite story, we had learned a lot about the value of publicity. It had come about in a rather strange way. We had been researching the history of studying meteorites for a paper commemorating the 200th anniversary of the first recorded meteorite fall in Britain, in 1795. Two hundred years ago people who claimed to have seen stones fall from the sky were ridiculed as ignorant peasants, or worse: not completely all there. Then along came the founder of popular journalism, Major Edward

Topham. He was a man who was always in the news, in fact he made news. His watchword however was 'the truth'.

When Mr Topham made a song and dance about a meteorite that had fallen on his land in Yorkshire, and publicised the event, the world sat up and listened. That, too, as they say, is another story. But as a result of Topham's campaign the study of meteorites, as a science, was born. Without him we wouldn't have been working on martian meteorites; the first one we know about fell only a couple of years after he campaigned. But we owed Mr Topham more than that. Judith and I recognised that if we were going to get Beagle 2 to Mars, it would be a long haul. To attract funding, we would have to keep the project in the limelight and the news, just as Major Topham had kept on telling people about his stone that they didn't believe had fallen from the sky.

To have a British mission land on Mars there would have to be a revolutionary change in the way the Government thought about space. What do serious Revolutionaries do as their first move? Take over the television and radio stations so that they can tell the world about the justice of their cause over and over again. On Newsnight, to use a ship related metaphor, I had well and truly 'nailed our colours to the mast'. I'd made the first move before those in power who didn't want us on their voyage, had mustered their overwhelmingly superior forces.

Chapter 7

MAN WITH A MISSION

So now the public had heard about a British mission to look for life on Mars. Soon we had another opportunity to reinforce the message. Every year the Royal Society has a Summer Exhibition and Soirée. It's been going on since the 1850s. During the day the public, including lots of invited schools, come in and look at about fifteen to twenty exhibits which have been selected by competition from many more entries. It's a prestigious affair because from 7.00pm onwards, the great and the good, politicians, industrialists, Vice-Chancellors and so on, in evening dress, with decorations, get to view the contributions during a buffet supper. It's a must in the calendar for the Fellows of the Society and their wives. For the exhibitors the whole event is exhausting, being grilled by smart kids throughout the day, and at night not knowing who the inquisitor with the wine glass is, because you can't quite read their name badge.

Judith and I had exhibited at the Soirée already a couple of times. On the first occasion it was to show Bristol's lunar work. I made an incredible faux pas during one event; although I'm by no means an expert geologist, I tried to explain lunar geology to the President of the Geological Society and Head of the British Geological Survey. If he wasn't satisfied he was too polite to say. Another year, whilst talking about diamonds, I casually poured quite a large diamond out of a bottle onto the palm of a lady who turned out to the wife of the Royal Society's Foreign Secretary. She dropped it, and before I could stop her was on her hands and knees, in a long dress, grovelling around on the floor searching for it. When she finally returned it to me, I hadn't the heart to tell her it was only industrial quality, worth about two pounds; everybody on the stand had one in their pocket.

We saw the 1997 Exhibition/Soirée as a good opportunity to put over our side of the story on martian meteorites. We had applied before Christmas and been selected, but now we had a chance to talk about the mission to Mars as well. As soon as we opened, it was obvious people still remembered the previous summer's events and many had got wind of my recent appearance on Newsnight. Just to reinforce my belief that the message had reached far and wide, I was approached by a literary agent who told me I was sitting on a big story. She took me to lunch and said "If you ever decide to write it up...".

An innovation Judith had come up with for this Soirée was to publish a project newspaper as a free give-away handout. It was four pages, tabloid-sized, and contained numerous stories about research on martian meteorites, written at a level for non-scientists. It wasn't just about the OU's work but included contributions from the University of Manchester and the Natural History Museum. It was a huge success; we distributed three thousand copies and could have got rid of more.

With the PR campaign well underway, we had to get down to business. The next meeting of the Beagle 2 crew was held in Leicester. I decided to tell them Judith's name, but first things first. We needed something visual, a logo, to put on slides and documents that we would have to produce. We had to start to demonstrate that the project was organised and not just a few people without a coordinated purpose.

We started looking for an image of HMS Beagle that we could convert to a space theme, for example a ship morphing into a spacecraft. Pictures of HMS Beagle are few and far between, just a couple of contemporary paintings. The best known is one of the ship lying on its side for repairs after it had been beached in South America; it was hardly the impression we wanted to give. Eventually we found what we wanted on the cover of a book about Darwin's epic voyage. It was a silhouette, and could be blown up or reduced depending on what it was being used for. Judith made it into an overhead, a picture on transparent film which could be projected onto a screen, and I set off for Leicester.

Most of the people who had attended the meeting at the Royal Society were there; they brought friends and colleagues with them. Also there was Andre Brack. It was the first time I'd seen him since the meeting at ESA's Headquarters in Paris. I don't think I'll ever forget the look on Andre's face when my first move was to project the silhouette and say "We're going to call the lander Beagle 2.". "But, I thought we were going to call it Pasteur," he spluttered, looking shocked. "Andre," I said, "that was before..." I let the sentence tail off. I think he got the message, the French could hardly expect to have Pasteur honoured if they weren't supporting our efforts.

Quite a lot had happened since we had last sat around the table, so everybody had to be brought up to speed. I had to tell them about the ESTEC meeting and how the Finns had shown up armed with lots of information they had from the Russians. I imparted the bad news that the French and Finns had combined forces for a study of a possible Network of geophysical/meteorological stations and worse the French seemed to already have a budget. Of course we certainly had none.

I had also been back to Berlin for a conference on the Moon and Mars. There, the audience had been told that NASA planned to have missions to Mars every two years. Actually it's every twenty-six months. Spacecraft can't travel in straight lines; they have to fly on elliptical paths on an orbit around the Sun. To go to Mars they are aimed at the place it will be when the spacecraft gets there. It's like firing a bullet at a moving target, just on a bigger scale. The best time to 'shoot' at Mars is when the planets are nearest, i.e. on the same side of the solar system. The Earth goes round the Sun once every 365 days; Mars takes 687 days. They are closest together at two years, two months intervals.

NASA's first shot was already on its way. It was due to get there on 4 July 1997. Unlike Viking, which had also been timed for a landing on American Independence Day, but had gone into orbit and been delayed whilst it searched for a safe landing site, NASA's first mission to land on Mars for more than twenty years was flying on a ballistic trajectory. It would enter the Mars atmosphere as soon as it arrived, be slowed down from over 12,500 mph by frictional heating. At lower altitude parachutes would open and finally gasbags, like the airbags designed to protect car drivers in crashes, would inflate and protect the lander from its final impact. This mission, now only days away from Mars, was called Pathfinder. It would be followed by a series of orbiting spacecraft and other landers. They had a focus: 'follow the water' was to be the theme. Everybody from NASA chanted it like a mantra. A programme was all mapped out; the man presenting it said "NASA doesn't want to charge in like a bull elephant." He also made it very clear that if the search for life wasn't already a priority, it was now, thanks to martian meteorites.

ESA's plans were presented by Agustin Chicarro. He had given a good rationale for why ESA should have a mission to Mars, covering all the cultural, political, public interest arguments saying finally "It's the only place in the solar system that might be visited by humans." He didn't devote much attention to looking for life. He made the point that ESA had been trying to have a Mars mission for more than ten years. To have one now, it would have to be

'European'; no individual country in Europe could afford it. He had asked a rhetorical question "What can Europe do that isn't already being done?" He answered his own question with a list of things that might be achieved with a Network of landers. I was left thinking, there's no doubt whose side he's on.

Agustin had also announced "If Mars Express goes ahead there could be an AO in December with proposals due in February," and went on "there could be 120kg for orbiter science payload and perhaps 180kg for landers or a single lander." It was definitely in that order. But it all sounded a bit maybe. A veteran, but vocal, French scientist called Blamont, had disdainfully made the point that whilst NASA now had ten missions, Europe was still blundering about trying to have one.

At Leicester we discussed what we in Britain could do. We anticipated that the Network team would look at the possibility of several small landers. I couldn't see how all the landers in a Network could accommodate the complete set of experiments needed for life detection so we decided we should investigate what was needed for just one to seek evidence of life. We had already guessed 12kg of instruments would be necessary. I wanted sub-surface samples to avoid the oxidation process that might have destroyed the organics Viking was looking for. I also needed a geochemical analysis of any samples studied. To be politic, we would include the essential geophysical experiments as part of our package so our lander could be in the Network.

Some of the people present wanted to consider what could be done with a smaller package, say 5kg, shoehorned on to a Network station. I couldn't see the point since any mass spectrometer would require the whole 5kg and I wasn't going without one. If ESA decided it wanted the best of both worlds, to have a Network and search for life, it needed as a minimum two small landers and one larger one to carry life detection experiments.

Debates about space missions are always like this; there are a few people, like me, that want to do some specific piece of science. Others, often the majority, just want a mission, any mission, to fly a 'widget'. They don't necessarily know what their widget is yet; they listen to the discussion and jump in at an appropriate moment with "We could make one of those." Nevertheless we wrote down what everybody wanted as six bullet points, to be distributed amongst those present. Alan Wells called it a 'communiqué'.

We had taken the precaution of inviting ESA to attend our meeting. They sent Gordon Whitcomb, a long time space engineer from Britain, who was managing the ESA study of what was needed in terms of a spacecraft for Mars Express. He was able to fill us in on what was happening: an AO would be issued on 2 December; responses would be needed by 24 February 1998. ESA would consider what had been offered and announce the results by the end of April. This timescale however would not be confirmed until November when the SPC met again. He was more pessimistic than Agustin about the mass; he thought only 150kg would be available to land on the Red Planet, assuming it was decided to include a lander or landers.

Now that we had a timescale we had to get cracking. Alan Wells volunteered that Mark Sims could spend some time working on possible designs. John Hobbs of MMS said "I can also put in a bit of effort." Alan had some good contacts in Russia and undertook to arrange a meeting with their Space Agency, hopefully to find out about Mars 96 to put us on an equal footing with Lognonné and the Finns who were now calling themselves the Netlander group.

Alan succeeded and two Russians arrived in Leicester for a conflab on 2 July. They brought with them videos to show; unfortunately they were in a format not common in the UK so we couldn't view them. I drove back from Leicester to the OU and got them transferred to a VHS tape. Next day we sat down in Leicester to find out what the Russians were up to.

The first video showed that the Russians were working on a six wheeled rover that climbed over one metre high rocks. It was similar to Lunakhod, the robotic vehicle the Soviets had delivered to the Moon in the 1970s before the Apollo 15 astronauts had started driving around to collect samples. It was a nice idea but totally unrealistic for us given the mass available to put a lander on Mars Express.

We turned to the second video. This was more like it, film of a test carried out to demonstrate how Mars 96 should have landed if it had got to the planet. It would have hit the surface in gas-bags and just in case it landed upside down included a spring mechanism which catapulted it into the air and turned it over. After some questioning we found out the Russians were hoping to have a role in Beagle 2 "Maybe," their leader said, "we can perform the drop tests for you." Looking at their video, this was something I didn't think would impress ESA. The test consisted of dropping the lander from a crane on what appeared to be a building site. The lady in charge was wearing a very fetching headscarf and wellies. Like most things in the Russian space programme I'm sure it worked, but it didn't look very sophisticated.

We discussed another possible role. I asked "What about Planetary Protection?". As soon as it was realised that space exploration was a reality, all the countries interested signed an agreement that they wouldn't transport Earth's biology to other places in the solar system, and, more importantly, they wouldn't bring a potentially dangerous alien life back to Earth. This Treaty was concluded in London in 1965. Landers built to go to planets that could support life have to have paperwork certifying they have complied with what are called PP rules.

Because NASA's Viking spacecraft were looking for an active biology they had been sterilised to make sure they didn't simply detect some terrestrial microorganisms they had taken with them. We couldn't do this with Beagle 2 because the mass spectrometer would detect the dead bodies of any organisms killed by the sterilisation process. Beagle 2 would have to be built ultra-clean.

I suggested maybe the Russians could help us with this from their experience with Mars 96. It got an immediate response from one of them: "How much do you pay. Where do I sign?" It was just a little too quick. Thanks but no thanks, it didn't sound like they'd paid much heed to PP. This was a job that had to be perfect. I decided at that moment it was going to be one part of Beagle 2 I was going to keep control of myself. If we detected life, and I had to stand up and say so, I wanted to be sure I was right.

We pumped them some more about the mass of the spacecraft. It was too heavy for us. The Russians have giant rockets, and their satellites are built like battleships. When I said "Everything is too heavy," the Russian replied "There's a Russian proverb that says the length of a crocodile from its nose to its tail is not the same as from its tail to its nose," implying they could make the mass anything we wanted. This was clearly a recipe for disaster. If we started the project like that we'd soon find we didn't have enough mass.

I had heard enough. The biggest problem working with the Russians at that time was once they had you on the hook, they'd say "We've run out of money and need more." Alan Wells knew all about it. He had an X-ray telescope moth-balled because of such an experience. As if reading our minds the lead Russian said "Mars is a priority after Spectrum X." Spectrum X was Alan's X-ray mission. Spectrum X is still waiting for a launch!

The next day, late in the evening British time, NASA's Mars lander Pathfinder, carrying the tiny rover, Sojourner, bounced to rest in the Ares Vallis on Mars. I didn't know at the time but Pathfinder proved that the landing technology I had just been discussing with the Russians worked. NASA had bought the secrets of Mars 96 and adapted them to return to the Red Planet in 1997. The first pictures from Pathfinder were shown on Saturday morning in a TV slot that the OU, in those days, had in the BBC schedules. It was a bit of a coup and had over a million viewers when other channels were showing children's programmes.

There were a few teething troubles concerning how to get the Sojourner, named after Sojourner Truth, an American Civil Rights campaigner, off the landing platform, but they managed. The little vehicle, connected to its mother spacecraft by a tether, continued to operate for more than thirty days. With NASA roving the Red Planet, our lander would have to have some mobility.

The next time we met at Leicester, it was me, John Hobbs, Mark Sims and Lucy Berthould, a lady who worked for John. The MMS people had brought some computer-aided design (CAD) pictures of a concept lander; it looked a lot like what the Russians had shown us in their video. We sat around and drew up a list of all the sub-systems we would have to include in the design, made a first guess at their likely mass and added 20% to allow for the fact that we might have got it wrong or forgotten a key bit. The total was over 120kg. We needed much better estimates based on real items.

We also had a stab at guessing the cost of the various bits of just the lander, with no allowance for the science instruments – the payload. We were counting on the fact that if people wanted to provide instruments, then they would have to find a way of paying for them themselves. It really was sticking a wet finger in the air; there were just too many unknowns. The total came to just over £20 million, not counting any way of achieving mobility or drilling below the surface. A rover would cost us a lot of mass and probably money. We would have to think about it, so it stayed out of the equation.

There were people developing drills; they caused arguments at meetings of the Rosetta project. Drills were complicated, heavy and there were added problems concerning sticking. Just think about what happens when an electric drill jams in a hole; it tries to break your wrist. Now try to imagine it happening sixty million miles away; the drill will try to turn the lander. Every time there is a landing space mission the Italians turn up and offer to supply a drill. They have a thing about drills. Much as I wanted a subsurface sample I didn't need the aggro of an Italian drill. Nevertheless we pencilled it in and I prayed we could take it out again.

To us £20 million didn't seem too bad a price to pay for a Mars lander; we didn't think cost was a show stopper. Our next hurdle was to prepare for the meeting to be held with ESA at the end of September, when lander teams would present their ideas. We settled on fielding two speakers, me presenting the science arguments for Beagle 2 and Lucy talking about our technical progress.

When it came, the meeting took place at Noordwijk's Space EXPO, a place where ESA has public displays about its activities. It was crowded out considering there were only three contenders with ideas for landers, well four if you count NASA who also sent a deputation. We had first try at convincing the audience. Judith and I had been doing some homework on HMS Beagle's voyage. I started my talk by explaining the name Beagle 2 saying "Darwin was only on board 'to relieve the proverbial loneliness of the Captain' and that's a quote." I was quick to add "Before you jump to conclusions, it's not what you think." I explained "The Captain of HMS Beagle, Robert Fitzroy, felt he needed a companion for a journey of two years. In fact it extended to five." I went on "The previous Captain, a man called Pringle Stokes, committed suicide, in a fit of depression, when the Beagle couldn't achieve the Navy's ambitions. Stokes shot himself, badly; it took him ten days to die." There was worse: "Fitzroy knew he might be subject to bouts of depression, it ran in his family. An uncle had also committed suicide. Fitzroy wasn't taking the chance; he took Darwin along, as someone from his own background, to talk to."

This required more explanation "He wouldn't have been able to socialise with the crew," I said "as Commander of a naval vessel he was in charge of discipline and could even put a man to death. Fitzroy set the tone for the voyage of HMS Beagle by having some of her sailors flogged the first day at sea. Their crime: celebrating too extravagantly the last night on shore." I finished my opening with a joke about being able to flog the crew might be a big help when running space projects. It would as well, if the way the Rosetta mission went about its business was typical. It might seem a wasteful digression but this light-hearted introduction got the audience's attention and they sat and listened to everything Lucy and I had to say afterwards.

The Netlander team were next up. I thought their talk, given by several people, starting with Longonné, was boring. It had too many slides in too small a typeface. There were oodles of data; after all they had been studying a Network for probably ten years without ever being accepted as a mission. It meant they had a start on us and would claim to be a more credible in terms of being ready for launch. The thing that annoyed me about their presentation most was that one of the presenters threw in the comment: "A lander to look for life isn't necessary since the question will be answered by a sample return in a few years." I hadn't tried to knock their project; they didn't need to say anything against mine.

The Netlander presentation included a telephone directory list of partici-pants; everybody and his brother supported the project. I had seen this tactic before: half of the people don't actually do anything. They're part of the 'Dining Club', but claim to be major players. The penalty of having their support is that they want to come to the meetings, make long speeches and get in the way, slowing down progress. ESA however loves these lists; they demonstrate missions are 'European'. The rest of the talk used slides obscured by dozens of logos. Longnonné obviously belonged to the Eglinton school of slide-makers;

it looks like you've done a lot but you can't see the message.

As we filed out for lunch, I was intercepted by Alan Johnstone from the Mullard Space Sciences Laboratory (MSSL). He had been one of the people I had competed against for SERC's Special Replacement Scheme. Like me he now had a Professorial chair, his at University College, London. I knew he was a supporter of Beagle 2. I had seen him standing in the doorway during my part of the presentation. "I thought Beagle 2 was infinitely better," was his comment. "I was looking round the room as you were speaking and felt it went down well."

During the lunch break I was accosted by an ESA engineer called Pierre Coste; sorry about the pun. He had latched on to the fact I wanted subsurface samples. "Do you know about the technology development project I have going with DLR?" he asked. Technology development projects are ESA-commissioned activities with Universities and other Institutes; DLR, Deutsches Luft und Raumfahrt, the German Space Agency, had various establishments around Germany. I said "No," and he offered to take me to his office later. So at the end of the afternoon, he showed me a foot long, inch diameter, cylinder with wires connected to the end. It was sticking out of a milk bottle full of sand. "It's a mole" he said, proudly, "it burrows into the ground." After a bit more small talk he gave me a name of a man who worked at DLR, Cologne. "Lutz Richter, I think you should talk to him," he said, supplying some contact details.

Earlier I had listened to a German called Rudi Rieder of the Max Planck Institute, Mainz. He worked for my meteoriticist friend Wänke, and wanted to collaborate very closely with the Russians. There had to be some ulterior motive, he was so insistent. I later found out that his father-in-law was a mover and shaker in the Russian Space Agency. Still Rieder had some good ideas. He had built an X-ray spectrometer, a chemical analysis instrument, for Pathfinder. Now he wanted to convert it to something called an alpha-proton spectrometer and carry it around on a little tracked vehicle which he described as an Instrument Deployment Device – an IDD. He had learned that whilst ESA weren't keen on landers, vehicles were out of the question. "You just have to get close enough to point it at a rock," he said and added, "it will detect parts per billion (ppb) of carbon."

It was clearly another dig at Beagle 2. I wasn't going to let this one go. It was a scientific error so during question time, I politely asked a question: "On Mars, the atmosphere between the rock and your spectrometer will be 96% carbon dioxide. How do you avoid getting a signal for atmospheric carbon? You'll get answers but they won't mean much, especially for samples where the true carbon abundance is low." Both opposition projects had seen fit to try to attack Beagle 2; they must have felt a little insecure.

Last up was Roger Bourke of JPL, the organisation responsible for NASA's robotic spacecraft. We were treated to the usual catalogue of US Mars missions, including a description of their next attempt to land in 1999. The project would be called Polar Lander. "It will be carrying two instrumented penetrators that will be released during the descent and impact on the surface, returning information about the subsurface of Mars," Bourke droned on, "and we have some spares that we could supply gratis to be part of Mars Express." "Thanks guys," I thought, "haven't you got enough bloody missions of your own?" It was the end of the day; all the contenders had had a say; the next move would be ESA's.

When the Brits are at ESTEC it's sort of traditional, if that's the correct word, to eat at the Tong Ah, a Chinese Restaurant on the sea front, close to all the hotels, so off we went. The 'Tong Ah' has a number of distinctive features: the numbers in the menu are in a random order; they have been the same in all the years I've been going there. Not that it matters, whatever you order, it always looks and tastes the same.

Next morning, Gordon Whitcomb went through the timeline that ESA was following for proposal submissions. We'd heard it all before except that there was to be a briefing in December for people wanting to submit. The major new development however occurred at coffee break. Marcello Coradini drew me and Philippe Longnonné to one side. His message to us was unambiguous: "If you guys can come to an agreement to share the resources," were his words, "I can ensure 230kg will be available for landers." I don't know if he said something similar to Rieder and Bourke, they certainly weren't in earshot when he talked to us. Marcello had been involved when a Network of landers was first suggested. In fact it may have been his idea so I was pleased he didn't seem to be taking sides, unless he was worried looking for life had got its nose in front and was trying to make sure the Network was hung on our coat-tails. Nothing else that was said at the meeting really mattered, but I felt Beagle 2 was in with a shout.

We went away to work on our design and try to make it as advanced as the Netlanders. I spent much of the time trailing around trying to find people who would contribute to the lander. I had two major successes, one with the Germans from DLR, who Pierre Coste had told me about. We had a meeting with them at University College London in early November. They came led by Lutz Richter, he wasn't the expected tall blond Aryan but small, slight, balding, with a designer stubble beard and wore gold rimmed glasses. It was what he brought with him that marked him out: a video of the mole on its four wheeled chariot undergoing some tests. I watched spellbound as it fell over onto its back before using articulated legs to right itself. This thing answered my prayers. Goodbye drill; welcome rover and mole.

Despite Paul Murdin's pessimism, I tried to raise the subject of money with PPARC. It was at a meeting of its Astronomy Committee; we were discussing the forward look budget, the subject of Mars wasn't even on the list. I scribbled a note saying "I want to speak on behalf of an involvement in MEx," meaning Beagle 2, and passed it to the Chairman, who was a theoretical astronomer. He totally ignored my request. It was pretty obvious I couldn't expect much help from this quarter.

After that blatant snub, Judith and I decided we would seek commercial sponsorship. Suddenly what I thought might be salvation appeared on the horizon. Now I was Gresham Professor, I suggested Gresham should hold a Soirée, like the Royal Society, to let the City types, making up its Council, see some of the work the Professors got up to. I was standing by a board describing Beagle 2, when I was approached by a well dressed man with wavy hair and glasses. He introduced himself as "Jack Wigglesworth, a friend of Andy Prindl," and opened up a conversation with "I'm Chairman of the London Investment Finance and Futures Exchange, we call ourselves LIFFE.". "Bingo," I thought, as he invited me to visit him in his City office. Of course I went and discovered he was a neighbour of a well known entrepreneur called Richard Branson!

A few days before Christmas 1997, I was off again to ESTEC for the prospective proposers meeting. My usual way of travelling there was to catch the late evening high speed ferry from Harwich to the Hook of Holland. It got in at midnight, Dutch time, but it was less than an hour's drive through deserted streets to Noordwijk; it was a good way of avoiding traffic round The Hague and Rotterdam which makes the M25 look like a race track. On this particular occasion, I remember the journey as very festive. The Dutch frequently don't draw any downstairs window curtains. I was able to see preparations for the impending holiday all along the route.

The briefing was for everybody who wanted to submit a proposal to provide an instrument to MEx, orbiter and lander alike. The available mass being talked about was 120kg for the orbiter science and 180+30 for a lander or landers. Marcello had delivered nearly what he promised, but of course ESA would still have a little spare margin up its sleeve.

It was a good meeting; it must have been the spirit of Christmas. Philippe was all charm. The optimum for the Network was 3+1 small landers; the plus one was for redundancy. "It isn't the best way of doing it," he said, "but we'll go along with 2+1," i.e. two of their landers plus Beagle 2. He added, as a caveat: "If Beagle doesn't get the money we'll produce additional landers for the 3+1 Network." He clearly believed we had no way of raising the funds. PPARC's attitude was well known in France. Just to rub it in, and to make it clear France was willing to pay for Netlanders, he threw in "We," meaning France, "will complete the Network by launching an extra lander on an Ariane V as soon as possible.". "Bullshit," I thought, "if you've got an Ariane V up your sleeve what do you need MEx for?"

We did some negotiating in the margins about how we could share some items we both needed to avoid duplication, save mass and costs. They would provide items for Communications. In return, we would make room for a seismometer to be supplied by Philippe and some metrological sensors from the Finns who were led by a nice young guy, with the improbable femme fatale sounding name of Ari Matti Hari. We agreed Beagle 2's bid would be for 100kg of the mass available. The Netlander team could ask for whatever they thought the balance was. If it was 130kg, as Marcello promised, they might just squeeze three Netlanders in since they were saying each was about 45kg. To round off the proceedings, ESA introduced a tanned, dark-haired Austrian called Rudi Schmidt as the MEx Project Manager designate. No, he didn't have a red nose, nor did he turn out to be Father Christmas.

Finally, Heinrich Wänke gave a talk about the rock measurements made by Rieder's X-ray spectrometer on Pathfinder. I listened intently; Viking had analysed only soil so it was all very useful data for Beagle 2. But all the chemical analyses of the rocks were identical to the soil; Wänke couldn't say what sort of rocks they were. The true identity of the rocks the mission had called 'Barnacle Bill', 'Scooby Doo' and 'Shark', was still a mystery.

Then we all went home to think about it over Christmas. I drove down to Calais to cross the channel through the Tunnel wondering what pet names we would give the rocks Beagle 2 might encounter on the Red Planet. We would certainly have to clean the dust off them otherwise we would have the same problem as Pathfinder with the X-ray spectrometer Leicester were going to build. X-rays only penetrate less than the thickness of a hair into rocks. Sojourner had just analysed soil blown onto their surfaces by the ferocious martian winds.

There were a couple more meetings after Christmas before the day proposals were due. ESA announced they had chosen to use a Soyuz rocket. This would possibly reduce the mass available. There was talk of the extra 30 kg for landers having to be transferred to the orbiter; however they were considering another solution for getting more mass into orbit around Mars, a technique called 'aerobraking'. NASA had used this to deliver a martian satellite called Global Surveyor in 1997. It involved dipping the spacecraft in and out of the atmosphere and using friction as a brake, saving the need for carrying quite so much fuel. The phrase in ESA's statement was "aerobraking has not been considered at this time." All the experimenters sighed with relief believing there could be some extra margin in the mass budget.

The week before the proposals had to be submitted I spent at Leicester. We had all the information from the technical studies, CAD drawings, a science case to put together and input from the people whose instruments we had agreed to include, as well as the supporting information, like everybody's curriculum vitae with details of the missions they had already flown on. Mark Sims and I, with the help of Richard Cole, who had compiled space mission proposals for the University of Leicester before, licked the whole lot into shape. To check last minute details everybody had promised to be at the end of a telephone. Back at the OU, Judith worked on a cover design with HMS Beagle on it. The whole thing, when it was finished, looked very professional. Taking no chances, the many copies needed were made and the requisite number hand-carried to ESTEC well in time to make the deadline – a few hours before it closed. That's 'well' in proposal submission terms. A copy was sent to everybody who had contributed or lent their name to the effort.

We thought we had been clever, both technically and politically. We packed the DLR mole on its carriage by folding down the wheels on their stalks and squeezed Rieder's IDD with its X-ray spectrometer on top. We had redundant mobility. We had already included Network instruments with our package. The whole deal came to 108 kg, just over the hundred we had agreed with Lognonné, but we still believed there could be at least 210kg and maybe 230kg available. Moreover, we had got Rieder on board. If everybody was happy, ESA would be happy; they like European consensus.

Immediately following proposal submission there was a Workshop at the Geology Society in London. It was a chance for everybody who had submitted proposals to talk to everybody else about the actual submissions; it was too late for anybody to pinch other people's ideas. Judith and I had been looking for more analogies between HMS Beagle and Beagle 2 and had found the text preached at Darwin's funeral: 'Without vision the people perish'. I opened my talk with a slide quoting it. Pleased with myself, I took Marcello for a pub lunch at a little city pub across the street. It was raining, so Marcello was wearing a Mafia style white, belted, trench coat. I wanted to find out if he was happy with the way we had shared out the lander mass between ourselves and Netlander. We looked like a couple of conspirators. So what, everybody knows if you take Marcello to lunch you are conspiring. He didn't volunteer any inside information.

A month later I went to Paris for a meeting with the French about future Mars exploration. If MEx was a success and both Beagle 2 and the Network landed on the Red Planet, the next obvious step was a sample return mission. I was under the impression that the purpose of the bilateral was so that Britain and France could put their heads together with a view to saying "Between us we have technology to go to Mars and bring back samples. Come on Europe, let's get on with it and show NASA they aren't the only game in town." It would be an understatement to say I was a bit surprised when Richard Bonneville, the Programme Director for CNES, France's Space Agency, sidled up to me in the lunch break and said "If you drop Beagle 2 [in favour of the Network], we'll fly it as soon as possible." "Hang on a minute," I thought, "if France can fly Beagle 2 just like that, presumably on an Ariane V rocket, then why don't you fly the 3+1 Network on your own and leave me to get on with ESA?" As politely as I could, I refused this rather transparent attempt to con me. I should have told him where to stick it. My mother would have said "Promises are like pie crusts, made to be broken." I went home thinking Beagle 2 had got the French rattled.

ESA called us back to ESTEC; Mark, John Hobbs and me crammed into a very crowded room to answer questions for two hours about the design of Beagle 2. The room was small and there were probably fifteen people on the Review Panel, each with a copy of our proposal and shed-loads of other paperwork. They said they had already looked at most of the instruments bid for the orbiter. They weren't interested in the science I wanted to do, only the engineering. "Our job," the Chairman said, "is to establish whether Beagle 2 is feasible."

Afterwards, we were sitting outside having a coffee when Agustin Chicarro, who had been in the crowded room, appeared carrying a document in his hand. Giving it to me, he said "Here, you have to sign this." "What is it?" I enquired. "It's the PR agreement," he said. "You have to agree that all public announcements are controlled by ESA." "There's no way I'm signing that," I said, "I have to raise the money to pay for Beagle 2. Judith and I are in charge of lander PR." "You'll have to sign it before you go," he came back at me, "or you won't be on the mission." "Fine," I said and put it in my bag. He never asked me for it before I left. One can only assume he believed Beagle 2 wouldn't be going so it didn't matter whether I signed or not.

The schedule we had been given for the review process, was that the Committee would deliberate, pass their selections to ESA's Solar System Working Group, SSWG, who would in turn make recommendations before the decision would be ratified by the SPC during a two day meeting at the end of May. Impatient for some news after SSWG, I phoned someone called Dave Hall at BNSC, where he was helping Paul Murdin. I knew Dave vaguely, that's to say I didn't know what he looked like. I had spoken to him on the telephone but that had been some years earlier when I reviewed a proposal he had written.

I asked "Is there any information about the progress of Beagle 2?". the answer I got was "There was only enough mass for one 60kg lander. Nobody bid a single 60kg lander so there will be no lander on Mars Express." It was short and to the point. We had been shafted by ESA.

The meeting we'd had with the Russians flashed into my mind. The Russian with a liking for parables had also asked me during coffee time "Do you know why the wives of Russian space scientists wear six metre long nightdresses?" When I replied "No," he laughed and said "Because the quest is better than the result." We had just been led up the garden path and had the rug ripped from under us to mix a few metaphors. ESA had never intended for there to be a lander, we'd been tricked into bidding for mass they could say they didn't have. In other words we had just been through a paper exercise.

I nearly said "********s, I'm not doing paper missions," to Dave Hall. I was a man with a real mission that could look for life on Mars.

111

Chapter 8

EVERYTHING GETS BLURRED

Space Agencies like paper missions: they don't crash, all the instruments work, there are no computer glitches, they're cheap, politicians don't scrap the programme, etc. etc... All in all, in some quarters, paper missions are preferable to the real thing, they keep people in work. Beagle 2 wasn't going to be like that. I wasn't doing it because I wanted a virtual mission to the Red Planet. I had a scientific reason. I wanted to know if there was life on Mars, and I thought I could answer the question by repeating what we had done in the lab with meteorites, if we could get there. In fact we might have found life on Mars already. I went home in disgust.

It was early May; I had the garden to dig. It was boring, I was angry and I wanted time to think. I pondered about what was driving the mass up. The answer came to me in a flash. It was the volume. If you want to make room for things you increase size in three dimensions. If you think of it as a box all six sides get bigger which means the box gets heavier. Beagle 2 had been designed as a truncated pyramid; we thought we would fold the sides down as flaps to expose solar cells to charge batteries. The mole's chariot would use one of the flaps as a ramp to drive off.

Rovers, chariots, instrument deployment devices, whatever politically correct name you gave them had to be sacrificed. I carried on digging, doing mental arithmetic to relieve the boredom of a bit of backbreaking toil. Maybe my labouring ancestors resorted to similar distractions. I figured I could easily dispense with Rieder's IDD. We had only added it as a sop to ESA. But it was only small, it didn't take me long to calculate it wasn't enough. I needed something bigger to throw off. It wasn't going to be my mass spectrometer; it would provide the data we had to have. The mass spectrometer was sacrosanct. But the mole's carrier was also big.

In my mind I went through the likely savings to be made in volume and mass by slinging the mole and its chariot off. Being optimistic it might make the spacecraft as much as 20% smaller, bearing in mind the mechanisms and supports that went with it. It still was not enough, so more spade work was required. It didn't take long. If the lander became smaller and lighter, the hardware to get it to the surface, what we called the entry descent and landing system, the EDLS, could also be scaled down.

I was now out of my depth but I knew I was going in the right direction. There was still another problem. If I chucked the mole and its chariot off we lost mobility and had no way of getting subsurface samples. I was encroaching on the science and soon there wouldn't be any point in going if we were only going to repeat the experiments that hadn't worked on Viking. It was not just mental arithmetic, it needed lateral thinking and it was literally thinking laterally that solved the problem. What if the mole was put down on the surface and the hammering mechanism that drove it started? Would it crawl? I didn't know the answer but I knew the man who would.

I put down the spade and went indoors to phone Lutz Richter. He wasn't in his office at the DLR Institute near Cologne. He was in Berlin. I got another phone number; it took a few calls to find him at a hotel. I explained what had happened and all I had thought about since that morning. I was surprised when he said "I've got the mole with me. I'll try it." A few minutes later he was back on the phone, he had lain the mole down on the carpet and started the mechanism; it had shuffled across the floor.

That evening I sat down and repeated on paper the calculations I had performed in my head. I wanted to be sure I wasn't going to make myself look completely stupid. I wasn't. If we did all the things I had thought of we could shrink Beagle 2, it would become a puppy. If I was right, in a few hours, I had completely upset ESA's applecart. They weren't going to get rid of me and my dog that easily.

It was now the weekend. First thing Monday morning I rang Mark Sims and John Hobbs. They agreed what I was suggesting was plausible but it needed to be worked out properly by engineers with CAD drawings. We arranged to meet up at MMS, in Bristol, and go through the details. It was a successful couple of days. By the time we had finished Beagle 2 had been shrunk by over 40%. Gone were the little vehicles, instead the lander had a robot arm; it was stowed wrapped around the base, like it was giving itself a big hug. The following week I was going to give ESA a headache and it was going to start on Sunday with a little off-the-cuff PR.

Nothing had appeared in the newspapers about our original design for Beagle 2; it had only been submitted to ESA. Now I was going to release the new idea to the press. A journalist who I had known since he worked on the *Cambridge Evening News*, Steve Farrar, was now science correspondent of the *Sunday Times*. Before I went to Bristol I had called him to say "By the end of the week I might be able to give you an exclusive about the UK Mars lander." On the way home, it was late Friday afternoon, I pulled into the Membury Motorway Services car park to spend half an hour explaining the new, smaller, lighter Beagle 2 to Steve. He was very excited and took it to the Editor immediately. By Saturday afternoon I had repeated the details to a graphic designer and received by fax a draft of the accompanying article for checking. Sunday morning it was there in the paper in colour for all to see.

Now I had an excellent excuse to phone Dave Hall again. I explained to him that we had undertaken a rapid reappraisal of our design. "We now believe a lander can be produced within the 60kg limit imposed by ESA," I told him, "I'll write it up as an addendum to our proposal; you can take copies to the SPC meeting in a week's time." It was an order not a request. He agreed to do it, I didn't know if he was humouring me or if he was truly on our side. The document was duly produced, five pages of explanation and a table which showed that despite the greatly reduced size there would be no loss of science. And what happened? The SPC meeting decided to reopen the competition. That's typical, we do all the work and everybody else gets a second chance to beat us. I suppose that's European democracy.

We had until the first week of July to resubmit our proposal. It was done. This time I didn't go to Leicester, we did it mostly by telephone. We ran off all the copies on Friday the 3rd. Next day, Saturday, I was travelling to London; I was going to give the first ever lecture to the newly formed Mars Society at the Science Museum in Exhibition Road. I was sitting on the Royston to King's Cross train when Mark rang me "We've made a mistake in adding up the masses of the parts of the Beagle 2 puppy," he blurted out, "we left something out when we calculated the total; it's slightly more than a kilogram over 60kg." "It's too late to change it now," I said. "Anyway it's only an estimate, we'll tell them we made the mistake but only if we get selected."

The proposal went in with the mistake in it; this time Judith and I drove copies to ESA's Paris HQ. They didn't notice we couldn't add up; at least it wasn't mentioned when we went to ESTEC again to answer another lot of questions. Neither was ESA's PR document produced; either they had forgotten it or thought I had signed it on the previous occasion. I certainly wasn't going to raise the issue. Something else, however, gave me a different reason to be concerned. Rudi Schmidt, now confirmed as MEx Project Manager, came up to me as I was clearing up the papers I had used during the meeting. He confronted me with: "We've been through all your figures.". "Oh, oh," I thought but it wasn't the adding up. "You can't do it for 60kg. You'll need 80kg, and a contingency," he continued, "why don't you drop all this nonsense about looking for life? Just carry a camera to take a picture to show that Europe's on Mars?"

I think he meant ESA's on Mars, but it doesn't matter. "Rudi," I replied, "I can't sell that, people have been to Mars and taken pictures before." And with that, I left. But not before he'd said "As far as I'm concerned, if you exceed 60kg by as much as a gram, Beagle 2 will be off Mars Express." I realised it wasn't going to be easy if we had to work with him. And we weren't going to get any of his contingency if we needed it.

Our fate wouldn't be decided until November, when the SPC next met. We were going to waste six months when we could have been working on the project. It's difficult enough to get money for space exploration out of PPARC when you are selected for a mission; getting funds before you are selected is a non-starter. Judith and I were going to have to spend the time we had to wait doing PR and campaigning.

The first opportunity arose because the Labour Party's new Minister in charge of Science decided to launch his vision for Space to an audience made up of Industry managers and interested academics at the 'Armoury' in Leeds. I travelled up the morning of the event. As I changed stations to get a connection to Leeds, I noticed two bearded men in waxed jackets and carrying school briefcases; they had 'civil servant' written all over them. One of them turned out to be Dave Hall. If he knew what I looked like, he didn't acknowledge me. I'm sure neither of us realised we were going to see a lot of each other in future.

After a couple of corporate speeches the Minister, John Battle, was wheeled out. Like his civil servants he had a black beard; I don't know if he had a Barbour. Instead of embarking on a prepared speech, Battle decided he was going to throw in a few personal touches to show what a nice chap he was. It was his version of me and the comparison of the Beagles. He launched into a discourse about how he had arrived at his hotel late the previous evening. I don't know why he needed a hotel, he was a Leeds MP. I suppose he was trying to tell us how hard he was working for Science and Technology. Then all of a sudden he was saying "I switched on my television and there was an Open University programme on…" The rest was all about encouraging people into Science, what a good job the OU was doing and how the new Government's policy was 'joined-up thinking'.

He eventually got on to his Space policy, and when he finished invited questions. Up went my hand; I was only too pleased to give him the benefit of my joined-up thinking; it all came pouring out "Why don't we have a mission to Mars to look for life? Won't this inspire people? We've performed miracles to get as far as proposing to ESA. We'll do anything to send a mission to Mars, but we need money for Beagle 2. Since you're so keen on the OU, why don't you come and see what we are doing?" I ended.

With true politician's aplomb, he brushed it all aside. He was very busy with his new Ministry but "Of course my office will arrange something in the future," was his get-out to the final bit of the question. He never came but back at the OU I updated the VC, Sir John, on developments and told him the new Minister was likely to be 'OU-ophile'. Sir John's response was "I think we might be able to pull this off," and added that the University would back me with some money.

After listening to Mr Battle, I was standing in the lunch queue when I was tapped on the shoulder by the man behind. I turned to face the fourth bearded man I had encountered that day. I looked down at his badge: 'Dave Whittle, Vega Systems' was printed on it. "Did you mean it when you said you'd do anything?" he asked. I could hardly back out now so I said "Yes." Clearly unconvinced and probably believing I wouldn't do what he was about to suggest, he went on "Would it extend to being involved with a pop group?" "Why not?" I answered, looking quizzically at him. Pop groups don't scare me, I had met some when I was at University in Swansea, I had organised doormen at Saturday night hops, employing my mates from the football team. It was the mid-sixties and the groups we booked for peanuts, like John Mayall's Bluesbreakers and the Moody Blues, became household names. "OK, I'll be in touch," he said. We moved off with our trays, to join different tables.

I thought no more about it until a few days later when he phoned me. The question he asked now was "Can I bring some boys from a band to see you?". "Fine," I said, not wishing to appear over keen by avoiding the obvious question "Who?". We arranged a day – Wednesday 10 June. I still hadn't asked who it was; he ended the conversation with "By the way it's Blur, have you heard of them?" Had I heard of them, the band that won the battle of Britpop? The poster advertising their album 'Parklife' had greeted me every morning from above my son's bed when I woke him up. Dave rang off before I could get more details.

I now had some research of a different kind to do, and the place to do it was Tower Records on Piccadilly Circus. They sold books there which they didn't keep in the University Library. I found one that said that Damon Albarn, the band's leader and singer, had said in an interview with the *New Musical Express* (I used to buy it a teenager): "Blur are the best band on Earth," adding "and probably the Moon and Mars as well." Maybe he was trying to make his claim come true. I marked him down as probably coming with Dave Whittle. Going through the catalogue of Blur songs I found one about the satellites of Jupiter and Saturn. It was written by the bass player, Alex James; he obviously knew something about planets, he had to be a certain visitor. I couldn't find any connection to the other band members: Dave Rowntree, the drummer, or Graham Coxon, the lead guitarist.

On the appointed day, I awaited the guests in my office. Judith and I hadn't told anybody who was coming, not that we knew. We didn't want it to turn into a festival for autograph hunters or a damp squib. Judith fetched them from Reception. To get to me, whoever was coming would have to walk half-way across the Campus and through the Department of Earth Sciences. Even at the OU, where people believe the lecturers are stuck in a 1970s timewarp of flares and kipper ties, the members of rock bands would not be entirely unrecognisable. Nevertheless Alex James and Dave Rowntree, but no Damon, made it without being accosted.

Entering my office, Alex thrust out his hand saying "I'm Alex James, you're famous!" We sat for several hours discussing their interests in space. They weren't yet in the category where their back-collection of songs was worth hundreds of millions so they weren't looking to buy a mission to Mars. They said however, "Perhaps the band can help you get some good publicity for Beagle 2 with an important new audience."

They had got to us via the time-honoured process of a man who knew a man, who knew another man. Whilst on a tour of the US, somewhere in the Mid-west, far from light pollution, and looking at the night sky, their conversation had turned to "Why doesn't Britain have a space programme?" The band's accountant was listening and wonder of wonders lived next door to Dave Whittle's Managing Director. Even more luck had landed them with me, who had asked the same question of Mr Battle: "Why don't we have a space programme?"

We had lunch; both were vegetarians. Fortunately we had the right sandwiches. Then we toured the labs, where students were working. Dave Rowntree, who had been a computer programmer before joining the band, asked lots of intelligent questions about resonant frequencies. Drummers know about such things and they were relevant to the ion trap mass spectrometers that my people were building. Nobody twigged who they were; in fact my students thought I was interviewing prospective new researchers. One even said "That ginger bloke, who asked all the questions, seemed pretty bright!" The visit wasn't entirely incognito: halfway through the day a head suddenly appeared above my window sill. The owner, who was cleaning windows, almost fell off his ladder at what he saw. I bet that night in the pub his mates thought that he was having them on about seeing Blur; his usual stories about intruding on some dolly-bird's bath time were probably more credible.

I went home; it was the start of the 1998 World Cup and on the way I bought a football anthem, 'Vindaloo', by Fat Les, aka Alex James and Keith Allen, to put me in the mood. It went in my bag with my son's copy of Parklife already signed and dedicated. My enjoyment of the World Cup was rudely interrupted. Early Sunday evening, Judith received a phone call from Addenbrookes Hospital, in Cambridge. The owner of the autographed CD had broken his neck. "Not to worry," the informant said. We broke more speed limits. With other students, Joe, re-enacting World Cup drama, had dived to stop the ball falling into the Cam but instead fell in himself and hit his head on the bottom. Only the presence of mind of a punt pole-wielding tourist and the proximity of an ambulance saved him. At the hospital, they put the budding Gordon Banks into a scaffolding-like structure and prevented him from sitting up. He watched four weeks of football, lying flat on his back, looking at television through a pair of prisms which allowed him to see round corners.

Whilst talking to Dave and Alex, plans for more PR activities began to emerge. Judith and I had been thinking about how to draw the attention of more of the Aerospace Industry to Beagle 2. The Farnborough Air Show was taking place in September. I had already been visited by two senior managers from MMS, Mike Rickett and Peter Truss. John Hobbs had told me that one of them would be promoted shortly because their current Division Head was retiring. Judith and I took this pair of visitors to lunch in the garden of the 'Leathern Bottel', a pub with a pleasant garden, local to the OU. Both said they were willing to support Beagle 2. We came away thinking that Pete was more enthusiastic but got it completely wrong. Mike, the less ebullient one became the new MMS boss and an absolutely key player in the Mars mission saga.

Judith and I now went to Bristol again to discuss how we could exploit the Farnborough opportunity. There we brain-stormed with Ray Merchant, MMS's PR guru. He was somebody, like me, who had a thick Bristol accent. He thought it wasn't smart to be on an Industry stand, it would convey the wrong, 'loadsamoney', message. Better to blag our way onto the back of BNSC's display. If we generated enough interest, we might be able to impress them. MMS would direct people to us from their Pavilion. More importantly,

The "there is (sic) no data for you" phone call from NASA's Jet Propulsion Lab (Christmas morning, 2003)

An unusual team: Alex James, Damien Hirst and Dave Rowntree, with the first clam shell Beagle 2 model and spot paintings at the Royal Society (July 1999)

PLATE 1

Stephen Pillinger, the man described as a saint who said he didn't know where he came from; the earliest picture of a Kingswood ancestor (around 1870)

Levi (in characteristic pose) and Sarah Honour in front of Townsend's Farm; Pem is the child on the right (ca1895)

My father and mother on their wedding day (1 August 1931)

On the right (Alfred) Jack Pillinger, my father, and a hole in the road some time in the 1960s

PLATE 2

With big sister Doreen, aged less than one year (1943)

Aged three (1946)

Aged 5 or 6 with Pem, touring the streets of Bristol (1948–49)

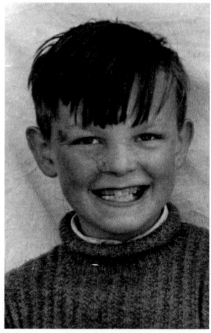

School photo aged 8 (1951)

PLATE 3

Me, second from the left on the back row, aged thirteen, Kingswood Grammar School class 2B (1956)

With my boyhood inspiration, *Journey into Space* author Charles Chilton, right, and David Jacobs, who played thirty-two parts in its sequel *The Red Planet* (2000)

PLATE 4

Pony trekking on Rhossili beach,
Gower Peninsula (spring 1966)

University College of Swansea first eleven football team, Universities Athletic Union
Champions. I'm the one with the watch on the left at the end of the front row; as
substitute I got to wear the watches (1967–68)

PLATE 5

Me on the day the Apollo 11 lunar sample was opened at Bristol University (October 1969)

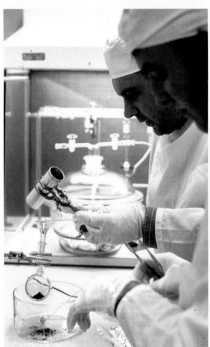

With James Maxwell, opening lunar sample 10086

Geoff Eglinton monitoring contamination with a 'differential sniffometer' during the sample opening

PLATE 6

Queuing to see the Moon, Bristol University Wills Memorial building, Park Street (1969)

With Paul Abell dissolving an Apollo 11 lunar sample in acid, note the trade mark sideburns also visible on previous page (December 1969)

Reminiscing with Sir Patrick Moore on 40th anniversary of the Apollo 11 mission (2009)

PLATE 7

On a trip to Houston a lady in a coffee shop said to me "Do you play for the Perfumed Garden?" (1972)

Shusy and Joe with Sputter dressed to go out at Sunavon (1979)

Shusy and Joe more typically dirty

With Shusy and Joe, receiving a DSc from the University of Bristol (1984)

PLATE 8

Down on the Farm – all mod cons – the toilet over the ditch

Filming with John Macnish (on the left holding Rachel, the horse)

Explaining the Beagle 2 model to Keith Allen during filming for the documentary 'Beagle to Mars'

PLATE 9

Everett Gibson, NASA, on a visit to the Open University (1985)

Signing 'the book' at the Royal Society as an FRS (1993)

Everett Gibson presenting the plaque saying asteroid 15613 is named Pillinger (2005)

PLATE 10

EETA79001, the meteorite containing a trace of the martian atmosphere that showed we had samples of the Red Planet on Earth, with organic matter possibly the remains of 'recent' life on Mars

ALH84001, the meteorite from Antarctica containing a tiny fossil suggesting 'ancient' life on Mars

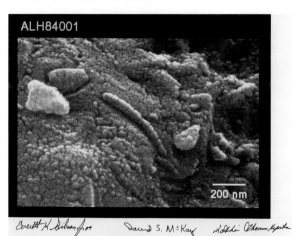

The fossil that put the World in turmoil, its picture autographed by the discoverers

Science Minister Ian Taylor holding the martian meteorite, Nakhla, which fell in Egypt in 1911, with Ian Wright and Monica Grady (1996)

PLATE 11

At the Mansion House with the Lord Mayor of London. On the left Mike Rickett and on the right John Hobbs

Enjoying lunch with Mark Sims on the day we selected the instruments to fly on Beagle 2 (August 1998)

Founder members of the Beagle 2 Lander team with (from the left) Ian Wright, TC Ng, John Hobbs, Mark Sims, me and Jim Clemmet

With, from the left, John Underwood (Martin Baker Aircraft), Mike Rickett and John Thatcher (Astrium) and the Beagle 2 clam shell model visiting the House of Commons

PLATE 12

Sir John "I think we can pull this off" Daniel, Open University Vice-Chancellor

Paul "I can't tell you to go on, then again I can't tell you not to" Murdin pictured at the second launch of the European Space Agency's Cluster mission

My first meeting with Lord Sainsbury at the Farnborough Air Show (1998)

PLATE 13

Miles Hedges, Finance Director, Open University

David Leadbeater, Deputy Director, British National Space Centre

Me with Matthew Patten, M&C Saatchi, and the £1 cheque

Friends of Beagle 2: (from left) Alan Wells, Director, Space Research Centre, University of Leicester; Colin Hicks, Director of the British National Space Centre; John Casani, Jet Propulsion Laboratory, Pasadena, California

PLATE 14

Some of the people involved in building Beagle 2 (Christmas 2000)

PLATE 15

Dave Barnes rehearsing the movements of Beagle 2 robotic arms for operations (2003)

Lutz Richter in Redland Aggregates' Sandy Quarry with the mole

Damien Hirst creating the Beagle 2 calibration target

Andy Spry (right) and Dave Moore celebrating Beagle 2 leaving for Astrium Toulouse (Febuary 2003)

PLATE 16

Ray would carry the costs from his budget. Ray said "I'll get Martin Baker to contribute." It was my turn, "I'll get the Blur boys to come along, they're both keen flyers; they should pull the crowds in."

Martin Baker were Martin Baker Aircraft, MBA; it's a company that makes ejector seats for fighter pilots. It got the idea when the Baker half of the partnership, who originally built planes, was killed in an air crash. Since then they've saved the lives of more than seven thousand flyers. The main reception at their factory is decorated with letters from grateful beneficiaries. Martin Baker supplied the entry, descent and landing system for ESA's Titan lander called Huygens. It wasn't due to be tested in anger until 2005 when the spacecraft got to Saturn, but when we visited Steve Lingard of MBA at a factory near Denham, just inside the M25, he and his colleague John Underwood thought they were well qualified to take charge of an EDLS for Beagle 2. Steve was yet another person with a Bristol pedigree. After the visit MBA joined the infant Beagle 2 Consortium being assembled by the OU and MMS. A Memorandum of Understanding was discussed but it was never signed.

We didn't just have to convince engineers, I also had scientists to impress with what Beagle 2 might be able to achieve on Mars. Judith and I had found the right place to do it: the Meteoritical Society's annual meeting in Dublin. This would be a chance to show our hand to an international audience and enjoy a pint or two of Guinness, a taste acquired by Judith when breast-feeding babies.

Judith now had another brainwave. "We need a model to show how small it is," she said. Next question: how to get one in the short time available. Answer: cardboard, scissors, loo rolls, glue and so forth, Blue Peter style. Enter daughter Shusanah, reading Engineering at Cambridge, to create the first Beagle 2 full scale model on the kitchen table of the flat she shared with friends in Portugal Place, a few doors up from the house with the golden helix outside, once owned by Francis Crick, another player in the story of life on Earth.

Off we went to Dublin with our cardboard pride and joy in a black plastic bin liner. I revealed Beagle 2, like a rabbit out of a hat, during my paper on what we were hoping to do on Mars. It impressed Leo Enright, a giant, shambling, freelance, Irish science correspondent, who immediately pitched it for a piece from the Conference for BBC News. They went for it, so later that morning a troop of people was seen crossing Trinity College's cricket pitch looking for a filming location It must have looked bizarre, Leo at the front, me following, then a camera crew and Judith bringing up the rear clutching the aforementioned model in its black plastic shroud. We repeatedly committed sacrilege as we criss-crossed the wicket in search of the right place.

119

Ray Merchant liked our first Beagle 2 representation and said "We have to have a professionally made one for Farnborough." The job was given to Adrian Porter, MMS's model maker, adding yet another Bristolian Beagle team player. We also had to have some animation video to show how the lander was supposed to get to Mars. To cope with that little embellishment we recruited Anthony Gambier-Parry. With a shiny new toy, including a mole on a string, a round table, a bucket of red sand from Redland Aggregates' quarry at Sandy, Bedfordshire, some polystyrene boulders and a loop of video tape we descended on the BNSC stand at Farnborough.

If you think you know about traffic jams, you don't until you've tried to get into the Air Show on the first morning, but it was worth it. We worked like dogs; sorry couldn't resist that pun. The BNSC personnel deserted their side of the stand, where they were being ignored, to help us cope. Leo was partly to blame because anybody who had seen us on TV wanted to see Beagle 2 in the flesh so to speak.

Farnborough has around 200,000 visitors; it felt like Judith and I spoke to them all. We recognised it was essential to give exhibitions a personal touch. People come to see the project, but they feel they have got much more out of the experience if they've actually spoken to somebody who is working on it. We made it policy to populate stands with guides who could speak authoritatively. We never allowed the yellow-costumed dolly-birds, favoured by motor car manufacturers, who thrust carrier bags of meaningless propaganda into the hands of passers-by. We did give the masses that came something to take away, our latest newspaper, now called the *Beagle 2 Bulletin*, the first of our newspapers with its permanent name.*

We were surprised by the number of people who wanted to be photographed with the model and/or me (Judith won't be photographed, ever). In our turn we got photographs of some of the celebs including 'British' astronaut Michael Foale, who stopped by. One person we didn't get was Peter Mandelson, Department of Trade and Industry Minister at the time. Judith and I got lots of good ideas from his little guidebook on how to spin a story, but BNSC kept us at a safe distance. Judith talking to him might spell disaster; he might even have learned a trick or two.

We did get a safer Minister however. Lord Sainsbury had inherited, perhaps

*Footnote: We continued printing newspapers periodically throughout the Beagle 2 project under the title *Beagle 2 Bulletin*, usually bringing out a new *Bulletin* to coincide with some special event or project milestone. In total we published seventeen editions; the print run rose to 10,000 copies. They were avidly collected and posted out to schools and Societies, as well as being made available at lectures or pressed on anybody who stopped to look at the dozens of exhibits or demonstrations we put on.

acquired is a better word, the responsibility for Science from the never-to-be-heard-of-again Mr Battle. Lord Sainsbury had only been in the job a couple of weeks when I first spoke to him as we posed behind the model of Beagle 2 for the paparazzi that followed him around. Although he'd only been in office a short time Lord Sainsbury had already learnt Minister-speak and delivered the lines given to him by civil servants well. In answer to the inevitable question from me "What are the chances of some money for Beagle 2?" he replied "It's a PPARC issue." It wasn't; PPARC only funded the science on space missions. It wasn't in their remit to pay for industry to build a spacecraft. That would be down to a Government Department or it had to come from ESA. Britain's annual subscription goes to ESA who redistribute the money through contracts to industry.

Despite the new Minister's Pavlovian response, it was soon apparent he was really interested. He wasn't a career politician using the science portfolio as a stepping stone to some perceived better (in my opinion less important) job in Government. You won't find a scientist who cares how he got the job; he was a good advocate for science. He was in it for the long haul, whereas the usual Science Ministers were only interested in keeping their noses clean. They would believe making promises of cash to upstarts such as me as suicidal.

Alex and Dave arrived to do a stint on the stand but I had another more important job for them. Ray had found what he thought was a potential sponsor, an engineering company in Bristol who did a lot of business courtesy of MMS. He had invited a senior manager to have lunch in the MMS chalet. At Farnborough the chalets are where the deals are done. They face out over the airfield where around 2.00pm the flying displays start; well-oiled clients sit on the verandas with their after-lunch drinks for a close-as-it-gets view of the military and civilian hardware screaming down the runway. It's one of the treats of the show.

The first time I saw it my mind returned to the time I was seven: my primary school teacher, Miss Handel, gave each pupil a little notebook and pencil to keep a daily diary. I misplaced my pencil by sticking it in the improbable place of the top of my sock. It started an inquiry into why thirty-five pencils rather than thirty-six were handed back. Before I lost my pencil (I've been putting pens in strange places ever since) I wrote a page about an air crash at Farnborough which killed a lot of people. It probably wasn't what she intended but I realise now that, even then, I was more interested in technical things in the news than the mundane details of everyday living.

Ray's select little lunch party had a crash of a different kind. One of the guests, not the one who had come to hear about Beagle 2, was delighted to find he was sitting with Blur; he eventually left clutching an autographed menu for his teenage daughter. The man Ray wanted me to impress wasn't interested in rock stars so I was able to give him a good ear-bashing about the science and technology of the Mars lander. The meal finished, the guests stood up, some going straight outside, others visiting the gents beforehand. Ray's 'mark' caught my sleeve and said "Can I have a word with you privately?" In the corridor of the chalet he treated me to a blistering lecture on the subject of wearing ties and how he couldn't possibly introduce me to his Managing Director so improperly dressed.

I was used to people telling me to wear ties. Look at any of my old school photographs and you'll find there is always one person not wearing a tie – me. I was always getting into trouble for it. I hate the damn things; I think it's silly to tie a piece of string around your neck. I've never thought of myself as a fashion trend setter but I suppose I was. These days Presidents and Prime Ministers favour the casual look trail-blazed by me.

Back in time for the flying, I found Ray waiting for me. "What did he say, what did he say?" he greeted me. I related the details of my recent dressing down, another pun, with Ray squirming with embarrassment. All he could say at the end of the story was "Prat!" and he didn't mean me; more than ten years later he still apologises whenever I see him at cocktail receptions. Me, I just laughed, Alex and Dave had come to Farnborough still wearing boots, muddy up to the knees, obligatory for summer Festivals, important events in Rock's social calendar. The epitaph to this story: every time I visit my sister in Bristol, I pass a derelict factory; Mr 'Not-dressed-properly's' company soon went bust. Maybe he always berated customers who didn't wear cufflinks as well.

Farnborough ended as a big success for us. I already knew lots of the players in the space industry, many of them stopped by the stand. There were a whole host of companies I didn't know who expressed an interest in being involved. Judith had a collection of business cards for invitations to an event we had up our sleeves. Only two companies were stand-offish: SSSL, Space Science Systems, a software outfit; and SSTL Surrey Satellite Technology. The latter's business is small satellites, perhaps they thought we were encroaching.

One of the other places where I started to make important contacts was meetings of the Parliamentary Space Committee at the House of Commons. Steve Lingard introduced me and took me as a guest to their annual dinner. I even wore a suit, but no tie. Earlier in the day I had met balloonist Don Cameron. I was toying with the idea of having a tiny balloon as part of Beagle 2 to lift a camera to look down on the landing site. I also thought the idea might appeal to Mr Branson if Jack Wigglesworth could put it to him. Conversationally, I had asked Cameron how to go about approaching potential sponsors. His reply sticks in my memory: "You've got to kiss a lot of frogs before one turns into a Princess." Tell me about it, I've just related a story about a warty old toad.

At the Space Committee dinner I looked across to the far side of the room. Sitting there was Ian Taylor, the former Conservative Science Minister I had got on so well with at the time of ALH84001 and life on Mars in meteorites. As I looked, he got up to leave early, presumably for another engagement. "Pity," I thought, but instead of heading for the door, he circumnavigated the room to reach me. He asked me how things were going so I started to tell him about Beagle 2. He stopped me in mid-sentence with "We must have lunch," and left.

Not knowing the etiquette of these situations, I searched for a restaurant in Westminster and invited him, but he insisted it had to be in the Members' Dining room at the House, in case a vote was called. Over lunch, Ian suggested some companies I could contact as prospective sponsors. One was run by a former internet pioneer, Clifford Standford, who had realised a packet when he sold Demon Internet, the first provider company, in the UK. He was about to set up again as an outfit called Redbus and was looking for investments.

Redbus and the Red Planet had a nice ring to it; it would keep Redbus in the news for over five years. They could become a brand like Virgin with Beagle 2's help. If he then sold it, he would make a nice profit and we would have had a Mars mission. I visited Cliff, a large man with red braces, another good sign, in his office in Regent Street to make a Beagle 2 pitch. Nothing came of it, perhaps just as well. In 2005 Cliff pleaded guilty to industrial espionage and hacking into somebody else's emails. Judith and I weren't having a lot of luck with potential sponsors.

Ian Taylor had other suggestions like "I'll ask a question at Prime Minister's question time." He duly did, and he and Tony Blair famously debated who they might agree on to send to Mars. It ended with the Prime Minister saying he'd write to Ian; it's a euphemism for "I don't know what you are talking about, I'll have to ask my advisors." Another approach, this was one I hadn't heard of, was to put down an Early Day Motion, an EDM. It's a device, a sort of petition, used by MPs to draw attention to an issue they feel strongly about. Beagle 2's EDM attracted twenty-eight co-sponsors.

Come September I at last thought I was making progress on the money front with PPARC. I was phoned by Sue Horne; she's the formidable lady who controls space related budgets for them. Sue said "We're casting around for things to bid for at the forthcoming CSR." CSR is the acronym for the

Comprehensive Spending Review; it's a bun-fight between various Government Ministries for future budget allocations. The jockeying for position starts at the bottom; various sub-departments make bids, these go up to the next tier and so on until Cabinet Ministers fight it out with the Chancellor. Nobody ever gets what they ask for so it comes back down the chain with more battles at every stage. It's a long drawn out process, often for little or no gain, a bit like the Battle of the Somme. Still, if you don't play you don't win. I said "Beagle 2 will need £25m," upping the £20m Mark Sims, John Hobbs and I had come up with. "Time is marching on," I added, "if we don't start soon, we'll be playing catch-up and paying more people." We were already wasting time whilst ESA continued to deliberate.

On 24 September, she rang me again. "I don't know how to tell you this," she began, "PPARC's senior management have decided not to put Beagle 2 forward as a CSR bid. They think Beagle 2 has such a high public profile already, that it will undoubtedly get funded!" She continued "They had higher priorities." I said "Non-attributable, what higher priorities?" She answered: "No point in it being non-attributable, everybody will know where it came from anyway." She rattled off a list of Astronomy projects which were being supported. I said "I don't see how those scientific priorities were assigned; Beagle 2 has never been reviewed scientifically by PPARC."

I went on to catalogue the number of times I had suggested and, point blank, asked for a review of the project. After badgering Paul Murdin on one occasion he had refused, saying "No point!" But that was the problem with the British Space programme – defeatism. People had stopped trying because they thought there was no point in trying. Too many good ideas ended as just dreams. But, I'd obviously made my point forcibly; less than a week later I got a phone call from Eric Priest of St Andrews University. He was the Chairman of PPARC's Science Committee. He said "We're meeting in Edinburgh to consider suggestions for what projects might be added to PPARC's 'Roadmap'. Come and give a fifteen-minute presentation."

I had a week to think what to say, but I was already preoccupied elsewhere. Courtesy of Gresham College and the Lord Mayor of London, Judith and I were being allowed to use to Mansion House, the Lord Mayor's official residence, for a Reception to promote Beagle 2. I had invited all the companies who had visited the stand at Farnborough and a few more. The venue was not the sort of place you can get into every day, so all the companies sent their top men, like James Martin, one of the twins who owned the family business of MBA. It was clear that he was a supporter; he would later say the company would invest some of its own resources in Beagle 2. I was hopeful of seeing Lord Wolfson, whose fortune supports science projects. The Wolfson Foundation had been good to me in the past, but, as it was the 'Day of Atonement', in the Jewish calendar, and his Lordship was a strict Jew, he didn't make it. When one of his staff told me the reason for his absence, I thought "What an appropriate choice of date."

There were others who didn't attend. One was the Provost of University College London, UCL. When I tackled him afterwards about UCL meeting some of their own costs, he was quite rude. He was another who believed it was a PPARC responsibility. "I want money for research, I don't provide it," he said. I told him PPARC had informed me they didn't have any money earmarked for Beagle 2 and he replied "Can't be very good science then." That really ****ed me off. I told him if he didn't cough up, the MSSL, who had joined the Consortium to be in charge of the cameras, could go hang (that's the toned down version). He must have got the message because MSSL carried on working, so I relented. I felt I owed it to Alan Johnson, who was from MSSL, for his support the previous September at ESTEC. Sadly, Mansion House was Alan's last involvement in Beagle 2; he died of a brain tumour shortly afterwards. The role he would have had was taken by Andrew Coates.

Alex and Dave also came to Mansion House, they were now a regular part of Beagle 2 events but Paul Murdin hadn't met them. Judith introduced the pair to the top man in the British Space programme. The conversation went as follows: Judith, "Let me introduce Alex and Dave, they're from a famous rock band." In response, Paul, "Hello, I'm Paul Murdin, I work for BNSC." Alex: "Who are BNSC?" Dave, quickly, "You know Alex, they were on the back of the Beagle 2 stand at Farnborough." It summed up BNSC's profile in Space – not quite as recognisable as NASA.

We did have one more success at Mansion House. Judith and I were standing in the street trying to hail a cab to transport the model to King's Cross when we were joined by Chris Lee of SSSL. He was heading off to the Underground to Paddington for the Bristol train. He parted company with "I don't think you'll make it but there's no way we are going to miss out, in case you do." We almost had a full house of Bristol Mafia.

Next stop Edinburgh. I lugged the model all the way there on my own for a fifteen-minute attempt to convince PPARC of our worth. I made a pitch for £5m to get us on the road map. I actually meant get the show on the road. The guy who was making the next presentation said "Gee, that's a hard act to have to follow," as I handed over. I don't know how he got on but Eric Priest told me next day that only he and one other member of the Committee had wanted to support Beagle 2. The rest, all astronomers of some description, rejected the bid. Eric refused to accept the decision and eventually cajoled a grudging £1.5m offer. It proved illusory. When the results of CSR were announced PPARC had got a bad settlement. Paul Murdin said to me "Any hope of even £1.5m is out of the question." I had struggled with the model for nothing.

We still had one more chance of money from a Government source as the end of the year approached. There was a scheme called the Joint Infrastructure Fund, JIF, running. Essentially it was for Universities who wanted money for new buildings or lab space. You had to submit bids for matching funds, that is, shared costs. We thought, maybe with a little creative thinking, we could describe the Beagle 2 EDLS as the 'Infrastructure' needed to carry out science on Mars. Accordingly, together with Martin Baker, I wrote a proposal asking for about half the cost of Beagle 2, claiming that with such an award we would be able to raise the other half from a variety of sources. The JIF committee didn't buy it.

The end of the year was fast approaching. We still didn't have a go/no go decision about landers, or if it would be the Beagle 2 lander, from ESA. Rudi Schmidt had already told us the decision now couldn't be taken until February. Another ESA pass the buck or cop out was in progress. The reason given this time was that the bids from various companies competing to build the Mars Express orbiter were still under consideration. ESA had to wait until a selection was made and then see if the winner had included the costs of adding a lander or landers to the orbiter. Talk about a chicken and egg situation: if ESA wanted a lander couldn't they have told the bidders their tenders had to include the costs of adding the extra components for attaching a lander or landers? Sometimes I think I am just too logical for ESA. In retrospect it was probably part of an 'if we delay long enough perhaps Beagle 2 will go away' policy.

The fact that Blur was involved with Beagle 2 was now well known, the story having been broken in the *Daily Telegraph* by Roger Highfield. Actually we gave him an exclusive at a West London recording studio. The photo shoot with the ubiquitous model of Beagle 2 took place in a children's playground just along the street. When the article appeared it seemed to consist entirely of an interview with my daughter.

Other parts of the media read it anyway. That weekend's 'News Quiz' included a question "Why won't there be an Oasis in sight when Blur land on Mars?" After the usual bit of banter, it was answered by Alan Coren who began with the familiar "This is the story about..." It was now taken for granted the public knew about Britain's space mission to Mars and Blur had made it a household name, but what was going to happen was still very blurred.

Chapter 9

NOT NEIL ARMSTRONG

Far from being an Express, MEx had so far crawled along. Now entering 1999, it began to pick up speed. Beagle 2 had heard that MMS Toulouse, the French division of the company, had got the contract to build the orbiting spacecraft. Mark Sims and Jim Clemmet from the British division of MMS, at Stevenage, went to Toulouse to make initial contact. MMS Toulouse had included provision for a lander in their bid to build MEx.

The reason Jim made the trip and not John Hobbs was that GEC, the General Electric Company, who owned MMS, had sold the space part of the business to British Aerospace. The work in Bristol was being transferred to a different site, in Stevenage. Old friends of Beagle 2, John Hobbs and Ray Merchant in particular, had decided not to up sticks and move; in Ray's case literally, he walked with sticks. It was a big wrench and I missed them. John now had to work on Airbus, something to do with the rear part of the wings. He was teased unmercifully about having gone from the cutting edge of technology to the trailing edge.

It was a shame to lose the Bristol connection but at least my journey to MMS was now only twenty miles rather than a three hundred mile round trip. On that visit to Toulouse Beagle 2 made a dramatic shift. Mark, Jim and others were talking in a bar about the problems the pyramidal Beagle 2 might have because of all the mechanisms and hinges that had to operate before the lander could be opened. Its sharp corners and edges made it vulnerable to knocks when landing. If it came down on any of its four sides, then each hinge would have to be strong enough to turn the lander into its correct orientation.

After several drinks, and much head scratching, a new improved design appeared at the suggestion of a Leicester mechanical engineer, Shaun

Whitehead. Mark sketched it on the back of a beer mat. We now had a clam-shell or pocket-watch Mars lander. Mark still has the four inch square piece of card so he can prove that Beagle 2 was designed 'on the back of a beer mat'. The brewer – that remains a secret until the company coughs up the sponsorship money.

I first met Jim Clemmet, a slightly balding, bespectacled engineer, yet another person with a beard, at Leicester on 22 January 1999. He became Beagle 2's Engineering Manager for the entire duration of the project. Beagle 2 could not possibly have done without his phenomenal efforts and dedication. The first thing I did at the meeting was to inform everybody that from here on we would be videoing everything that happened in Beagle 2. Everywhere I went, I was going to have a cameraman following me. Well not quite everywhere, but the principle was that we would video the story of Beagle 2 for posterity in the style of a fly-on-the-wall documentary. If I was on the way to becoming a television star, I would have to watch what I said and did because I would frequently be 'miked' for sound and have a camera looking over my shoulder.

On Monday 18 January, Judith and I had met Steve Wilkinson, a BBC Executive science producer, who worked at the OU, in the Commissioning Unit. We had never come across him before although we had, like many at the University, been exposed to television cameras as part of the OU's unique teaching methods. Steve walked into my office dressed from head to toe in his preferred outfit colour scheme, black: black jeans, black shirt, black socks, black shoes and so on. He had come to discuss an idea for a new series he was commissioning to be called 'Final Frontiers'. It would be an Astronomy/ space exploration magazine covering the latest research. He had heard that my group were involved in lots of projects and he wanted to be kept informed if there was anything that could be filmed for his series.

He got more than he bargained for. Judith asked him "Have you heard of Beagle 2?" He hadn't, but soon we were discussing the filming opportunities that it would present and Final Frontiers was forgotten, except that if we filmed everything that happened, as the British Mars project progressed, then bits of the recordings could be dropped into Final Frontiers as news items. If we did this, Steve said "I can hide the costs of filming you in other budgets." He then wanted to know "When's the first event?" I told him "We're having a meeting at Leicester on Friday."

The Leicester meeting was to discuss Beagle 2 as a 'system'. We had to consider the lander in its entirety, rather than as a series of component parts. All the bits of Beagle 2 had to work or the whole thing wouldn't. The new clam-shell idea was exposed to the gathered team, but we certainly weren't going to tell ESA yet; they still thought we were building a pyramid.

Since we were all in Beagle 2 together the meeting decided that there would be no individual mass allocations for the instruments or other bits, Jim would be in charge of whole mass allocation. That having been said we went through the possible masses of the various bits. The sort of mass we would need to produce the mass spectrometer came out about 0.6kg less than we would have liked. Ian Wright and I sat pondering the difficulties which lay ahead as Ian totalled up the masses of the various components on his napkin in the lunch refectory. Like the beer mat, it was kept for posterity.

France had now announced it was joining with the Americans to explore Mars so just over a week later, Mark Sims and I went to Paris to attend a meeting where they would announce their plans. We almost didn't get in. Just as we arrived the French Science Minister, Claude Allegré, turned up. France had a Science Minister who was a real scientist, I knew him well; he even worked on isotopes in meteorites. Mr Allegré arrived with a convoy of black Citroens and a posse of Gendarmes. They ushered him into the Hall and slammed the door behind him in our faces. We quickly nipped round the back and got ourselves into an overspill room with a closed-circuit television feed.

Everywhere was full with smirking French and Americans. They were going to have a joint venture programme. The jewel in the crown was going to be a Mars sample return (MSR). The mission would take off in 2005 and be back with pristine material from the Red Planet by 2008. Whenever we mentioned Beagle 2, the answer we got was "No point in trying to search for life with a robot space craft like Beagle 2."

They were going to launch an Ariane V provided by the French. There would be sufficient space for a bunch of Netlanders to go along for the ride. To upstage MEx and Beagle 2, as part of a PR extravaganza, in 2003, the Americans were going to send a mission carrying an aeroplane that would fly around in the martian atmosphere taking pictures. It would commemorate the 100th anniversary of the Wright Brothers' first flight on Earth which had lasted for a whole twelve seconds. To pay for all this the US was going to spend $300m/year over ten years; the French were matching it with an eight year budget in francs equivalent to $2.5 billion. It was little wonder Allegré ran around with armed guards. Lord Sainsbury, the British Science Minister, needed only his secretary, the delightful, and delightfully named Sandra Desir, to protect him.

Every time they (ESA, the French, NASA, PPARC, the Editor of *Nature*, etc.) did something like this it just increased our resolve and fuelled the 'us against the World' mentality I was building with Beagle 2. I looked at Mark; so far we had almost no money. "If this is what we we're up against," I said, "we'll have to think harder." It's a phrase the famous atom scientist, Lord Rutherford, was fond of saying when strapped for cash.

ESA was still trying to find things we'd overlooked. Early in February Judith and I went to ESTEC to discuss Planetary Protection. Judith, as a microbiologist, was going to take charge for Beagle 2 which would have to be built such that it didn't have more than an agreed number of spores (dormant microorganisms) on it. ESA had called in a man from NASA, Perry Stebakis, conspicuous at the meeting because of his shiny domed head, to explain the rules. We didn't need him to tell us what we had to do; it was paramount as far as I was concerned that Beagle 2 didn't take with it things that would confuse the experiments we were trying to perform. Planetary Protection has various classifications: Beagle 2 would be in the second highest, category IV. We told Perry that we were prepared to go further than the rules required. We would invent a IV 'plus' standard and minimise the amounts of non-biological carbon-containing contamination on the lander. He was well satisfied we were on the case.

After that we were allowed to attend MEx Science Working Team (SWT) meetings run by Rudi and Agustin. At SWTs Principal Investigators had to report progress. Just as I expected, at the first one I attended every other instrument was further advanced than those on Beagle 2. But of course unlike us, they all had their money and were employing the workers they needed. We were still doing what I called 'Mars-lighting', our manpower was being filched from other projects. Work on Beagle 2 was clandestine and done by people being paid to do something else. The meeting kicked off with Rudi telling us that MEx would be launched sometime in an eleven day window starting 1 June 2003; it would reach Mars by Christmas. The lander would leave the orbiter on 21 December to land on Boxing Day. He said "NASA will be flying its plane on the 17 December."

MEx was going to take nearly seven months to fly to the Red Planet. He gave some details about the orbiter: it would be an approximately cube-shaped box (spacecraft don't need to be streamlined like in the minds of science fiction writers) measuring 1.6 × 1.7 metres. The solar arrays would give it a 'wing span' of eleven metres. They could be used for aerobraking; this had still not been eliminated, but Rudi said "If we do it, it will take an extra six weeks to slow MEx down."

There was lots of discussion about the orbit that MEx would fly. The people building the ground penetrating radar didn't like it because they wouldn't get any data until two years into the mission. None of the orbiter instrument groups liked the fact that the orbiter would have to communicate (telecommunications, exchanging radio signals) with a lander; they were pacified a bit when Rudi said "Lander Communications will take place at four day intervals." It was nice to feel so welcome. I could just imagine NASA sending a lander all the way to Mars and then only talking to it occasionally. It was immediately apparent that Beagle 2 was considered to be a hitch-hiker with no say in what happened when we got there.

The debate about Communications went on and on, especially after it was announced that a new radio receiving dish in Italy probably wouldn't be ready in time. MEx would need to ask the Americans for access to the Deep Space Network, DSN (a series of radio telescopes all around the world so that as Earth turns it's always possible to communicate with far away spacecraft). Now Rudi said "NASA will want something in return." He looked at me before continuing "Perhaps the lander can accept some American co-Is [co-investigators]." This was terrific, they didn't want us but they wanted us to accept some dining club members on their behalf.

"And of course," Rudi announced, "the budget for MEx is nearly spent. Beagle 2 will have to pay for the extra manoeuvres needed to target its chosen landing site, and for the costs incurred in operating." He elaborated; he expected me to pay 8.4Meuros to the European Space Operations Centre, ESOC, at Darmstadt in Germany. He was going to have to get real, if Beagle 2 was part of this mission; Britain was paying its £40m subscription and didn't have anything else on MEx. When I got back from the meeting, I told Dave Hall, "Finding the funds to build the lander is one thing but, paying to communicate with it, is another. Rudi can kiss my arse!"

I thought there was just one plus for Beagle 2. I had found out at SWT we had inherited a piece of equipment called MARESS from Netlander that didn't contribute to our mass or cost. MARESS was on the orbiter, it had been the electronics package that would have talked to, and received data from the Network. The Italians, who were making it, said they would still supply it for Beagle 2 instead. There was however a downside that went with it, a Belgian experiment called NEIGE, on the orbiter. It would study the ionosphere and geodesy, the shape of Mars. Without batting an eyelid Rudi said "I'm allocating NEIGE 0.6kg." We'd have to see what happened if we asked him for the extra gram he told me that Beagle 2 was going to get over his dead body.

The only people who seemed to want Beagle 2 on the mission at all belonged to the High Resolution Stereo Camera (HRSC) team. Their leader, Gerhard

Neukum, I knew. I had played table tennis with him when we both spent time at the Lunar Science Institute at Houston during Apollo. He hated losing, but then so did I. If he'd been a film actor he would have become typecast as a POW Camp Commandant. His colour camera had already cost more than our entire lander was likely to. He wanted Beagle 2 because it was going to measure an absolute age for rocks whereever it landed. This would give Neukum a reference point to calibrate a method for giving the relative ages by counting impact craters at various places on the martian surface he would photograph.

The last presentation at the SWT meeting was by an Italian, Fulvio Drigani, who thought he knew everything there was to know about PR. He treated us to the benefit of his advice about the MEx strategy for the Public Understanding and 'Outreach'. "ESA will target 'Decision Makers', Ministers, first," he said, "then the science community, and lastly the Public."

This was totally back to front according to Judith's strategy. If you get the Public to show an interest then Politicians will; MPs and Ministers owe their jobs to the Public. Even if, like Lord Sainsbury, they were unelected, somebody who is elected appoints them. I was glad I hadn't signed ESA's PR document, to get Beagle 2 flown we were going to make sure Politicians heard that it was 'the will of the People'. PR for the science community wasn't on our radar; they were big boys, they could find out for themselves.

One of the most important aspects of a space mission is the software. There are more missions that have ended in disaster because of some error with the computer code than because some piece of hardware broke, for example Cluster. Back in England I turned my attention to software. There is more than one company in Britain that specialises in this area. For a start the company SSSL, who the sceptical Chris Lee worked for, was one. The giant business software house, Logica, has a specialist space division. It was common knowledge that these two organisations didn't get on. When Beagle 2 began to discuss its software requirements both sent representatives, they wanted to know the bidding process. "There is none," I said. "There's nothing to bid for. Beagle 2 doesn't have any money." With that they went outside in the corridor and came back with their own solution: Logica would write the code for the EDLS; SSSL would put their effort into operation of Beagle 2 on the ground. Mike Rickett told me afterwards, "An amicable settlement between those two is unprecedented; they don't even speak to each other, never mind discuss a sharing arrangement which pays nothing." I think he thought about putting me up for the Nobel peace prize.

That Logica were on board there was no doubt. First of all I got an invitation to a social event they held at the Science Museum. Lord Sainsbury was there to do a bit of meeting and greeting. To me, he said "I will give you what support I can, certainly moral support." Moral support I didn't need. Fortunately it turned out to be much better than that. Next, I received an invitation to speak at the dinner arranged to celebrate Logica's twenty-five years in the space business. The event was held at a Victorian Royal Shooting Lodge just outside Darmstadt. Judith and I had a second good reason for going; we could give ESOC the once-over with free travel and dinner thrown in.

The Shooting Lodge had been given a makeover so it was now a top of the range Hotel and Conference Centre. On entering we were greeted by a large painting of the German aristocrat who had built the place. The portrait showed him with his favourite hunting dog; it certainly looked like a beagle to us. Later that evening, as guests of honour, we made our way into the dining room between two lines of traditionally lederhosen-clad Germans, fan-faring us with hunting horns. The last occasion a Pillinger had mixed with the hunting fraternity, it had cost him a pound fine.

The dinner was great, some good relations were cemented. There was just one snag, ESA were signing the contract with MMS Toulouse, the following morning in Paris. They had it down as a PR event, although clearly not one to impress the public. They wanted all the MEx PIs there for press interviews. I was expected to be a part of it. At 4.00am Judith and I slipped out for a rapid drive across Germany and France. We weren't the only ones creeping around in the dark. Logica's management also sneaked out en masse. The night porter must have wondered if there would be anybody left to settle the bill.

After ESA's corporate PR event, we had a bit of local PR to do. Marcello had let us in on a little secret: ESA's Director of Science, a short, volatile, grey-haired Frenchman, Roger Bonnet, had a friend who was an artist; this friend had a piece of artwork he, and Bonnet, would love to see on Mars. "If you can deliver," said my Machiavellian friend, "it will get Bonnet on side with Beagle 2."

We had our own ideas about art on Mars so reluctantly agreed to talk to the French artist. He duly turned up at ESA's event but he wasn't an artist at all, but a French geophysicist who had designed a sculpture from shaped memory alloy. This material is used a lot on spacecraft; it is made into a particular shape at one temperature then bent to a different shape at a different temperature. When the temperature changes back, the substance reverts to the original shape as well. It's like black magic and has lots of uses.

The artist's sculpture, called 'Mars Ball', would respond to the diurnal temperature cycle of the Red Planet. On Mars, it's −70°C at night but near

133

zero during the day. The Mars Ball was going to change shape on a daily basis. We were going to be asked to show it happening; it was a nice idea but there was no way we could afford the mass, or more importantly the volume, which meant mass to us, to fly his art. Once it was on Mars, we wouldn't be able to show it in motion anyway because the only pictures we could send would be stills. Nevertheless he insisted that we should come to his studio; "It's only a few minutes away," he said.

To show willing, and placate Bonnet, we agreed to go with him. He got into the front seat of our Land Rover, to act as guide. We set off; it was soon pretty obvious that he didn't know his way around Paris. Not surprising really, wise Parisians don't bother with cars, there's nowhere to park them unless like Marcello you have a Corps Diplomatique plate. A quarter of an hour later, we passed in front of the Eiffel Tower heading north. I regularly drove in Paris and even in traffic jams could reach the Eiffel Tower from ESA Headquarters in five minutes, and the Peripherique in ten. It was nearly an hour later when we left the City on the south side by the Porte du Lyon. If this artist had any sense of direction at all he never used it, he was too busy telling us all the reasons we should relent and fly his sculpture.

On the road towards Bordeaux, we enquired politely how much further. "Just a few kilometres," was the answer, "perhaps you would like to look at my scrapbook of press cuttings." A massive volume of pictures was produced and handed over. It occupied the time as we travelled for another thirty minutes. We were now at least forty kilometres in exactly the opposite direction to the one we wanted to be headed. Getting a bit more irritated, I said "We are going rather a long way out of our way." At that point, he produced the Mars Ball out of his bag! It was at least the size of the DLR rover we had sacrificed to get Beagle 2 down to 60kg. I swear he came very close to being pushed out of the passenger seat into the fast lane. Fortunately for him our destination lay at the next exit.

His studio was in a Metallurgical Institute, and he had lined up a smiling Director, who greeted us for a tour of his establishment. No doubt it would have occupied another two hour interlude whilst the artist continued to press his case. We refused a coffee and left him and the disappointed Director standing in the street. We headed for home. It's well known you have to suffer for your art but not that much, even to have ESA's Director in your pocket. Bonnet never supported Beagle 2 but of course that may have had nothing to do with this little diversion.

Boy, were we pleased we had already signed up Damien Hirst. Judith's PR-savvy brain had slipped into gear whilst watching a TV programme about him. We realised that after sitting at the top of the Soyuz-Fregat rocket for a while, being shaken up by the launch process, and then spending six months in space, some of our instruments would need recalibrating when Beagle 2 got to Mars. Isotope geochemists are well used to the problem, they always measure a standard, then a sample, then a standard, sample, standard and so on, for the best results. We decided we should apply the same principle to the cameras, and our various spectrometers. Very soon the concept became a calibration chart, an array of test targets, in fact a trademark Damien Hirst spot painting. So we made the long trek to Devon to see Damien after Alex James had put us in touch.

Just as well we took the model in a four-wheel-drive vehicle; Britain's enfant terrible artist lived at the top of a hill, reached by a rutted track. Damien says he thought Alex was winding him up when he told him we were coming to talk about a space mission. At any moment he expected Jeremy Beadle to appear as we explained what was needed for Beagle 2. But he soon got the message we were deadly serious. Spot paintings came in all sizes; ours was going to have to be uniquely small, and make minimal impact on our mass and volume budgets with no power needed. Damien's miniature fitted all the criteria, whilst fulfilling an essential scientific need. As a bonus we would get all the hype which went with Damien, worth the trek any day. We celebrated on the way home by buying a beagle doll from a garage; we called it Fulvio and he travelled everywhere with us, on the car's dashboard, throughout the Beagle 2 project.

Incidentally, I did meet Jeremy Beadle after the end of the project. He had been a Beagle 2 follower throughout and would have definitely been up for any spoof we came up with; we could have had lots of fun with ESA.

I thought we had come across a French version of Jeremy when cravat-wearing Alain Clochet, the MEx Industrial Project Manager, turned up for our next meeting with MMS Toulouse. It was for what was called the Requirements Review. We had to 'freeze' the interface between Beagle 2 and MEx; essentially we had two spacecraft, each needed to know what the other was doing so that a mismatch did not occur and wreck the mission for both of us. Since MMS Toulouse were the Prime Contractor, they issued all the RIDS (documents asking for information). Clochet arrived with a lever-arch file full of them for a meeting at Leicester. All day Jim, Mark, and I answered his questions until at six o'clock in the afternoon he dropped his bombshell: "Astrium Toulouse require you to deliver the flight version of Beagle 2 to us at the beginning of June 2002," he said. This was a whole year before it was due to launch. We thought he was joking, "No, I'm not," he said and trotted off to his hotel for the night.

The rest of us went our separate ways, leaving Mark to clear up the thrown-away bits of paper. It was as well he did, rather than leave it to the cleaners. Amongst the stuff Clochet had put in the bin Mark found a rumpled up copy of the real schedule, with us pencilled in for 2003. We let Alain have his little joke. He was an amusing character who had another idiosyncrasy: he always posts his Christmas cards after 25 December. We still get them usually about the second week of January.

For the Requirements Review, Beagle 2 introduced its own full time Project Manager. Mike Rickett brought in one more beard, John Thatcher. With Beagle 2 being a spacecraft in its own right it was important to have somebody in command that had been in charge of similar scale projects. John had exactly the right CV; he was repatriated from a US project to become a new Beagle devotee. The first thing he said to ESA was "Beagle 2 is a spacecraft in its own right, so treat it like a spacecraft." They ignored him. Until now, Mark Sims had more or less acted as Project Manager and had made a brilliant job of it. Alan Wells was a little put out when Mark stepped aside, but we created the new title of Mission Manager for him; it meant that he would retake control once Beagle 2 was on its way to Mars. He would run the mission on the Red Planet. None of this affected me; I was the Beagle 2 front man, the face of the project, its driver and motivator. I had more than capable people in all the right places doing the managing. John Thatcher and I lived at opposite ends of a mobile phone connection, with Mark attached to both of us by an umbilical cord.

Beagle 2's target for landing on Mars was going to be a region which we hoped was a bit of dried up sea or a lake bed. So far I had only seen the mole's abilities tested in a milk bottle and heard about the impromptu trial on the floor of Lutz's hotel room. We decided to run a test in the quarries of Lafarge Redland Aggregates at Sandy Heath, Bedfordshire, a few miles from where Judith and I live. Sandy could easily be described as a fossil beach. It was another chance to gather material for our embryonic documentary and get a bit of news coverage as well.

We had, for the most part, only been on the BBC, so to spread the coverage around a bit we invited Lawrence McGinty, the ITN science correspondent. For the documentary, we would film Lawrence filming us, filming the mole. In keeping with the doggy theme of Beagle 2, Lutz had christened the mole PLUTO standing for Planetary Underground Tool. The tiny, cylindrical, eight inch long, star of the show, and his handler, flew in for the day from Cologne.

With Judith taking pictures for the *Beagle 2 Bulletin* and a 'trekky' digger driver, who the quarry manager, Vikky, had set to guard us, it made a team of twelve to record the antics of a device with a total weight of only 600g and power consumption of only a couple of watts, equivalent to a small torch. Like all good days at the seaside, it ended with fish and chips, before setting out for home.

PLUTO was kept on a lead, a wire to supply the electricity to the hammering mechanisms that drove him along the surface, or into the ground. As the mission went on, PLUTO's lead got shorter and shorter because every centimetre meant more mass and a bigger motor to wind up the cable. It started at ten metres and ended up as three.

But it was the demonstration of how the mole worked on various television programmes which caused most fun. Its forward movement was created by a weight inside. A motor was used to compress a spring until, after a few seconds a catch slipped; the spring was released throwing the weight and the mole forward in a jerky fashion. After seeing it work, TV presenters would invariably grab the mole to explain the operation during a piece to camera, mimicking the motion with their hands. Male presenters were very careful with how they did it; women weren't, so a demonstration of the mole, in their hands, very often became representative of an indecent act. The lovely Phillippa Forrester was guilty of it during filming for Tomorrow's World, reducing the entire male studio crew to giggling hysterics. I tried not to join in but it was difficult standing pretty close to her; the Director had apoplexy. Fortunately there was a fire alarm at that moment and, in the enforced recess, somebody must have tactfully explained what it would look like to the viewers.

Sandy Quarry wasn't the last time we used the Beagle 2 puppy pyramid. We had a couple more engagements. One was on 'Blue Peter'. As we sat on the set with the model and of course the ubiquitous Blue Peter dog the current incumbent of the role got up and stalked off in a huff across the outspread solar panels. It was clearly aggrieved the presenter appeared to be paying too much attention to somebody else's dog. I went home with a Blue Peter badge.

The final appearance of the pyramid model, before its honourable retirement, was the Chelsea Flower Show. We were asked by a horticultural college at Hadlow in Kent to join them on a stand at the most prestigious event in the gardening calendar. Everybody who's anybody attends on 'Members' day. Our offering was about 'hydroponics', a way in which astronauts could be fed by growing vegetables without soil during a space mission to Mars.

On the opening day you stand by your display to answer quetions from an official judging panel; you have to watch out for the undercover judges

137

who sneak about making secretive notes. We obviously passed muster because there, on Tuesday morning, pinned to the Exhibit was the coveted gold medal certificate. It was the first time in my life I had been honoured with a gold medal. Judith, who had done all the work for our contribution, myself and the Hadlow gardeners, who really deserved all the credit, cracked a bottle of champagne over the Beagle 2 model. Later I eaves-dropped Bob Geldof giving a very passable explanation of the Beagle 2 project to a companion. Unfortunately, we didn't get it on camera but it least we had the satisfaction of knowing our message was reaching where other space missions weren't.

We now had a new model of the clam-shell Beagle 2 and planned to reveal it to the public at the next Royal Society Soirée. Damien wasn't ready yet to produce his calibration spot painting, nevertheless, we visited him in his studio/workshop; no, factory would be the best way to describe it. Judith and I were treated to the sight of a man filling in spots with paint on a new work which occupied the wall for the entire length of a warehouse. It was for a New York show.

When she was tiny my wife, who had been badgering her mother for something to do on a rainy day, was told "Go and colour in the spots on the wallpaper." She did exactly as she had been told, using her best, different coloured, crayons. She remembered doing it when she had to make me slides for the meeting we went to at Davos. She could clearly have claimed precedence over Damien in some respects. Had she continued to demonstrate her artistic talents, or patented the spot painting idea, maybe we wouldn't have been searching for funds.

We took Damien information and pictures of the Beagle 2 spacecraft and asked if he could create something we could display to attract attention to our stand at the Royal Society. You might think that was taking a bit of a risk. Who knows what might arrive: half a cow being towed behind the mole or a pickled Beagle or two. You can trust Damien to deliver the unpredictable so we couldn't claim to be surprised when the 'Red Planet' he created from scores of red-winged butterflies arrived. Nor should it have been a shock when we got two works instead of one. The spot painting entitled Beagle 2 was a 5 × 5 matrix with the Beagle 2 probe replacing the centre spot. It was an immediate success especially as Damien, and Alex and Dave, attended the opening ceremony. Lord Puttnam, who did the honours, made a bee-line for the stand almost before the sound of the words "I declare this Exhibition open," had died away. We have a wonderful irreverent photo of Damien yawning behind Lord Puttnam's back, as the movie mogul enquired about the drugs scene instead of Mars science. Blur were just as much of a hit; they must have wondered just how many autograph collecting nieces the Royal Society's Press officer had. Later that evening we were visited by Jenny Page, who was the Chief Executive of the upside down wok being built on the Isle of Dogs; she enquired about putting Beagle 2 in 'the Dome'. This was a question we had to follow up.

By this time we knew Lord Sainsbury was up for giving Beagle 2 some money. The key player in getting to the Science Minister was MP Tony McWalter. He was the member for Hemel Hempstead and Robert Hutchison, my meteorite curator friend, was not only in the constituency but active in local Labour Party politics. Knowing Tony was a keen member of the Parliamentary Science and Technology Committee, Robert had arranged for a visit to the OU in the autumn of 1998. Very shortly after seeing the Beagle 2 model and going round the labs, Tony had been hammering on Lord Sainsbury's door demanding an audience to press our case.

In early May, there was an ESA 'Ministerial' in Brussels; this get-together of the Science Ministers decided they were going to back Mars Express. Christine McGourty, for the BBC, took a big gamble that they were going to say yes because she announced the result whilst the meeting was still going on. It was in order to be on air before the end of the six o'clock news. I know she was ten minutes premature because, as I listened to her report, I was talking to Dave Hall, who was still inside the meeting, on a mobile. It was now obvious Beagle 2 was sufficiently newsworthy for the media to take risks to be first with any information about the mission.

Lord Sainsbury was interviewed by James Naughtie, another Beagle 2 media ally, next day on the 'Today' programme, and confirmed the Ministerial's decision. I did an interview with Christine outside the Royal Society. A group of mountaineers had just found the body of George Mallory on the lower slopes of Mount Everest. It's still a mystery whether Mallory actually reached the summit. Many believe he did, beating Edmund Hillary and Tensing by 25 years. When his body was recovered, Mallory was hardly equipped for an ascent of the world's highest mountain. Like Beagle 2 he was rather under-resourced, so I have a lot of sympathy for this 1920's climber. I referred to the other main story of the week by saying "Only the Brits would send somebody out to climb Everest wearing brown boots and a tweed jacket." I had more than a passing interest in Mallory's expedition. Noel Odell, the last man to see Mallory alive, used to come into my lab in Cambridge and sit at a desk in the corner. He once showed me his hand-painted lantern slides of the Expedition; he was at least fifty wears ahead of Judith with the technique.

The announcement by the Ministers had upstaged ESA's May SPC meeting; the delegates from the ESA member states just had to play second fiddle by confirming it. Paul Murdin phoned me from the corridor outside SPC immediately he had the good news. It was in the middle of another fire drill; all told, during Beagle 2 I rehearsed fire evacuations on the sites of six different organisations. Perhaps the most blatantly opportunistic were Logica: seeing us filming during the practice, they immediately produced signs bearing their company's name and logo.

But back to Paul Murdin: I moved away from the crowd outside the OU's Earth Sciences Department to listen to the detail. "BNSC," he said, "want to have some kind of special announcement about Beagle 2 in the next couple of months. Do you have anything positive to say on the sponsorship front?". "Not yet," I answered. "In that case, Lord Sainsbury is likely to give you something from the DTI," Paul informed me. After a few more minutes talking, it was pretty clear that this was a 'sprat to catch a mackerel'. If we could show progress on the money front, ESA were going to be asked, at the next SPC Meeting, to contribute £6–8m.

I found out later that Britain was 'under-returned', meaning that we weren't getting our fair share of work in respect of ESA contracts given to the Space Industry. ESA works on the basis of a policy of 'juste retour' which means that the member states pay their 'subs' into a pool so that projects bigger than any individual country can afford can be undertaken. When the projects start, each nation gets a share of the work in proportion to the amount they put in. Britain was 'under-returned' because it hadn't got a fair share from a number of projects, not just Mars Express. To put it bluntly, ESA owed us money. Beagle 2 was going to be used as a way of getting some back. It was going to be a pawn in a political game. But if Beagle 2 was going to be the beneficiary, then so what; I had said it was so important that somebody would pay and I was being proven correct.

The message that we had to be ready for the Science Minister obviously filtered down the system. Our request for money to fund the instruments: the mass spectrometer gas analysis package, Leicester's X-ray spectrometer and MSSL's contribution to the cameras, had been submitted to PPARC on 22 December the previous year with a special Beagle 2 Christmas card. It had been festering in their system, presumably, because they claimed they had no money. Now it was dusted off. Sue Horne asked us to attend a funding review at Cosener's House, an historic mansion PPARC use for meetings in Abingdon.

So on a bright early July morning we duly arrived to do battle. The proposal had received a positive peer review; I wouldn't have believed them if they said it hadn't. Now it was a question of how much was it worth, or more accurately, how much was PPARC willing to scrape together. Alan Wells and I fought valiantly but £2.6m was all Sue could muster, split three ways: £1.2m to the OU, £1.1m to Leicester and £0.3m to MSSL. It wasn't anything like enough; the mass spectrometer we were building for the Rosetta comet mission had a budget of over £7m, but I was going to use some of the same people so I hoped Sue would look the other way. We tried to push the Panel to £3.5m but we couldn't shift them; they presumably had been given a ceiling they could go to.

After the Soirée, Judith and I headed for the sunshine. We had a list of places in France where meteorites had fallen over the last two hundred years and it was a good way of choosing obscure places to visit. We had made it to a place called Apt, on the edge of the Luberon; it was Bastille Day when I got a call from the lab telling me to phone Paul Murdin. Throughout Beagle 2 my mobile was always on, in fact it would have had to have been surgically removed from me.

When I tracked Paul down, he wanted to say "Lord Sainsbury is going to show his generosity to Beagle 2 at the beginning of August. The DTI will give some money to Beagle 2," Paul went on, "as soon as July is over. Parliament will be in recess, it's an opportune moment for Lord Sainsbury to unveil his Space Plan." He was right, August being a flat month for news, it would mean a lot of coverage for Beagle 2. OK by me, Judith and I would be back from France by then. I phoned the OU's VC to suggest he might like to put somebody on the case. What I really meant was "Offer the Minister the OU as a venue." I knew it wasn't likely to be taken up; journalists don't stray north of Watford unless the circumstances are exceptional. But it was worth a shot since the Beagle 2 money chase was good copy and just might attract the media.

Leaving somebody else to get on with it, we went for a beer to celebrate. From here on we never had one day's peace, not even when we were supposed to be on holiday. It was 24/7 for Beagle 2; in fact holidays seemed to be the most hectic time with crisis after crisis occurring in July. Perhaps the opposition's strategy was to attack when Judith and I were away.

The OU didn't get a chance to stage the launch of Lord Sainsbury's Space Plan but Beagle 2 got the best of the deal. I was driving home late on Friday afternoon 31 July. Again I was disturbed by my mobile in the car but by this time I had a 'hands-free'. On the line was Robin McKie, the science correspondent for the *Observer*. He asked a lot of questions about Lord Sainsbury giving £5m to Beagle 2. I knew the DTI's story for the Minister's press conference had leaked.

Sunday newspaper journalists get very annoyed by the fact that news always goes first to the Dailies. The Sundays will break embargoes on science press releases but it was pretty clear that Robin had a controlled, and probably exclusive, leak. Another journalist, the following week, told me somebody from the DTI had tried to plant the story with him.

The *Observer* broke the 'Beagle 2 gets some money' story on its front page on 2 August. The report read "Tony Blair wants Beagle 2 to have a Union Jack on the spacecraft." It started another media scrum at the OU; I was alerted to what was going to happen when I was phoned by Lawrence McGinty, with what sounded like a washing machine in the background. Maybe it was a tumble dryer and he was drying his shirt which had been soaked with sweat. The weekend had been a scorcher; Monday 3 August was the hottest day of 1999 and Beagle 2 was the hottest property and story. Lawrence said "I'm on my way to the OU post haste." And the OU is north of Watford!

There were six satellite trucks on the Mulberry Lawn outside the VC's office when I got there. I don't know whether some alert cameraman captured Sir John hanging out of his first floor window demanding to know what all the commotion was about. He joined the throng at lunchtime and brought with him six pints of lager from the Cellar Bar, one for himself and some for Beagle 2's crew.

Although we had already had all the media coverage, Lord Sainsbury went ahead with the press event to launch his Space Plan. Actually I was still doing interviews as he arrived at the Science Museum, which had been chosen as an appropriate London venue. To enter the room the Minister had to pass me standing in the doorway, on the phone yet again. As he smiled a greeting, the radio presenter at the other end of the line asked me a question, something probably about money, which only Lord Sainsbury could answer. "I don't know," I said, "here, ask him yourself, he's standing next to me." And with that I handed the Minister my mobile. It wasn't clear who was more surprised, Lord Sainsbury or the presenter; probably his minders from BNSC. It was all part of our strategy of surprise to wrong-foot people whereever possible.

I sat one side of Lord Sainsbury at the press conference; on the other was the Director of BNSC, Colin Hicks, a civil servant transferred from the Post Office to run the British Space Programme! Colin turned out to be very helpful to Beagle 2, but I can't say I was optimistic at first, considering where he came from. After that, I frequently sat alongside the Minister. His minders didn't seem to realise this always presented me with the chance of a private word. Judith and I used to think up succinct one line messages I could deliver. It was a sort of subliminal brain washing.

I always annoyed the organisers of these carefully orchestrated events, because I would never rehearse or give them a prepared script. At this press conference I remember interjecting, into one of Lord Sainsbury's answers to a question from the press, the reason he got on so well with the Beagle 2 team was that like him, we weren't paid for what we were doing. The Government had just published the salaries of the various Ministers. Lord Sainsbury never drew his, but no doubt he didn't need it.

After the press dispersed, Judith and I spent the afternoon in the Museum, near their Apollo exhibit with our Beagle 2 model, talking to visitors, answering questions and handing out *Beagle 2 Bulletins*. Judith had also devised a series of postcards, giving out a new one each time the project progressed a bit. Her logic was that they could become collectors' items but, if they were used for the purpose intended, as they went through the post, our message was going to be spread even further. They were relatively cheap and certainly went down well with kids. On this occasion, one kid decided to have his postcard autographed by me. Pretty soon they all joined in and a queue formed. I put my name on everything I was offered until a little lad, grabbing back his postcard, looked down at what I had written. At the time we were sitting right underneath the replica of the Apollo lunar module; the kid's face dropped, as he turned away and loudly said "Oh! I thought he was Neil Armstrong."

Chapter 10

SOME DISTANCE LEFT TO RUN

We were totally eclipsed by that small boy. Speaking of which 11 August was the day when a total eclipse was viewable from southern Britain. By the time it can be seen again in Britain I expect men to be walking on Mars. The trouble was the weather forecast for 11 August was diabolical; it had been overcast for a week already. Then salvation came in the form of a faxed invite from ESA to attend an eclipse event at Noyons, Northern France, right in the centre of the corridor of totality. They were expecting eight thousand guests, half of which would be media. Late the evening before, Judith and I decided to pack up the Beagle 2 model and head south. We left our decision late but as soon as we got across the channel we started looking for a hotel. It was like Christmas Eve in Bethlehem – no room at the Inn. We slept in the car in a motel car park and moved off at dawn the next day.

The roadside signs announcing 'See the Eclipse courtesy of ESA in Noyons' began to appear forty kilometres away from the town. When we got there, it was closed with traffic diversions in force. Eventually we parked on the pavement outside the cemetery at least a kilometre away from the event. There was no chance that we could carry the model or several packets of *Beagle 2 Bulletins*. We walked back into town feeling surely, as invited VIPs, we would obtain permission to drive on to the site to put the model of the lander going on ESA's Mars mission, on display for some good ESA PR.

The local heavies recruited for the day, led by a formidable lady, had different ideas; they weren't having us at their precious event, let alone our model, without an ESA ID. After lots of gesticulating and some very loud "Nous sommes avec Agence Spatiale Europeene," repeated slowly, we went away.

I said to Judith, "These clowns are so thick they'll accept anything with a photo on it as long as we're brazen enough." So at another gate, I marched through waving my University of Cambridge Library card. That card is magic. Believe me, if you can get into the Cambridge Library with it you could gain access to Fort Knox. I once used it to travel right across Europe after leaving my passport at a hotel. Access gained to ESA's event, the first person we encountered was Paul Clancy; I hadn't seen him since the day Judith named Beagle 2. "Hi Paul," I greeted him, "wish you had come along before. We've been having trouble getting in." The retort came back as quick as a flash, "I'm trying to get out."

Frankly we weren't surprised, we had got into what looked like a badly levelled building site. It had all the trappings of a cut price pop festival; Blur would have recognised it immediately from their early days: the sea of mud, the fans sheltering under makeshift polythene tents and the single portaloo with a queue which stretched to infinity. If we had stuck around, sooner or later someone would have asked if we had any toilet paper, only I wouldn't have understood, my French doesn't stretch that far. I might have offered a nice shiny *Beagle 2 Bulletin*.

Everything was staked out in pitches for exhibitors, most of whom had taken one look at the weather and decided to watch the eclipse on telly. This was certainly the case for the thousands of journalists, we could see only one intrepid Japanese TV crew, probably hardened by filming Japanese game shows. We beat a hasty retreat, drove outside of town and joined a crowd of locals amongst the stubble and straw bales in a newly harvested field of wheat. The sky was completely overcast until just before the moment of totality when the clouds obligingly parted for us to experience the sudden drop in temperature when the Sun completely disappeared. We departed for home leaving a few mystified Frenchmen clutching our newspaper and their children with postcards. Once again we had discovered we could do better public PR than ESA, certainly better than the French.

We didn't get the £5.0m from Lord Sainsbury straight away. Once BNSC had had their PR hit from it we realised we were only going to get the money in dribs and drabs. It was designed to make sure that we kept on searching for sponsors. Towards the end of August, John Thatcher and I met with Dave Hall and a payment plan for Astrium and Martin Baker was worked out. They would share £1.5m about 50:50 until the end of the year. During 2000, they would get another £2.5m and the rest after 1 January 2001. The £2.5m was supposed to keep them going up to the time the spacecraft was delivered. Only then would the final £1.0m be handed over. We reckoned it was about

10% of what we needed during the time we should be all out to build Beagle 2. We couldn't really complain; we had started this knowing we had to get the money.

The PPARC £2.5m for the instruments was to support the OU, Leicester and MSSL until the launch date at the beginning of June 2003. Although it wasn't enough, it allowed me to recruit the team I wanted. Some of them: Andrew Morse, our mass spectrometer and software expert; Simon Sheridan, who worked on valves and the vacuum system; and Taff, he was christened Geraint, Morgan, a chemist, who designed the gas processing systems. All these people were doubling up working on Rosetta. The new money would allow me to bring in a CAD engineer, an electronics man and someone to manage them as a team. This crew would work together throughout the project. For the most part they lived in a thrice-condemned 'portakabin' we called the Beagle 2 Dry Dock.

We could also place outside contracts, one of which went to Denis Leigh. He was someone I had known for years working for a variety of companies that bored him. He had set up a number of businesses of his own, pioneered some mass spectrometer product, got bored again, sold out and set up anew making something else.

Ian Wright and I were already paid full time by the University. Judith, who was employed as a technician, was also fully committed to the PR, and the fund-raising campaign. In the spare time she didn't have she was my minder and as a microbiologist, she was getting to grips with the problems of Planetary Protection. We had lots of meetings about this with the engineers involved in designing the spacecraft but PP was always getting shelved. "Let's get a design that works first, we'll find out how to build it sterile later," was the conclusion the engineers at the meetings always came to. Only John Dowson, who worked for Mark at Leicester, realised we might be storing up a problem. He helped tremendously by compiling a list, the declared materials list, of things that might be used during the build phase.

After the eclipse debacle, Judith and I considered it high time Beagle 2 relieved the 'proverbial loneliness of the Captain' Lieutenant Commander Jamie McMichael-Phillips, Captain of the current HMS Beagle. Our namesake was back from duty in the Indian Ocean so a trip was arranged to Devonport. Again it rained all the time, an inch in twelve hours. We complained, the locals said "You should be here when it really rains," presumably like the Swansea of my undergraduate days. We began to think we knew how Darwin felt when, because of the weather, his ship was unable to sail for nearly a month.

We toured the pubs in Plymouth's Barbican, the 'Ship', the 'Navy', and the 'Distillery' etc. Some we got trapped inside because it was raining so hard, that's our story anyway. We wondered whether Darwin, or the unfortunate Christmas merrymakers who got flogged for returning drunk from their last night on shore, had visited any of these. Instead of receiving a flogging we lunched in the Captain's cabin: traditional Navy fare 'cheesy, hammy, eggy' with a nice red wine. Our hosts were allowed to drink some because HMS Beagle's hand guns had been removed on account of they expected the public at the weekend for a Navy Day. They said "We have guns because there are still pirates in the Gulf!"

Everything was steward-served by a man with white gloves, even the coffee, and everybody called the Captain "Sir". You simply don't get your due respect leading a space mission. After lunch we toured the ship, fixed to return for some PR filming, and having seen the chart-making activities, which was Beagle's current purpose, suggested that perhaps one day they should make a map of our martian landing site. We had found out that Beagle 2 should have been Beagle 10. If being a spaceship counts as being a ship of the line, our Beagle was the 10th vessel to carry the name. We left a pile of *Bulletins* for the crew to distribute during their planned open day and headed for home with a foot square souvenir HMS Beagle crest; when it was offered, I said "It's no good; the Project Manager will never let me screw it to Beagle 2's bulkhead!"

Back home, we thought, as my father would have said, our ship had come in. I had asked Jack Wigglesworth to put me in touch with Richard Branson. One day my secretary rushed in bearing a letter with a Virgin logo on the envelope. Frantically I ripped it open to find inside a cheque for £14.00, a refund on a ticket I had bought for a Virgin train from Milton Keynes to London in April 1998. I'd sent in a claim and forgotten about it. It took so long to come I can only believe they didn't reimburse passengers for their breakdowns any faster than they ran their trains. At that time, to go to London from Milton Keynes you didn't look up the time table, you just turned up at the station and got on to the next train. Incidentally, I still have Richard Branson (Virgin)'s cheque; I'll give it back to him if I ever get the chance.

At the time we were offering a sponsorship deal along the line that anyone who signed with us could have all the PR hits until November 1999 when we hoped to be confirmed on board MEx. Thereafter for 50% of a substantial fee, £10m or more, they could be the exclusive main sponsor up until we entered the martian atmosphere at Christmas 2003. If we landed, the other half would fall due and they would be the sponsor throughout the rest of the mission including all the fanfare with finding life on Mars, if we found any. We had a scheme, called 'the pyramid', that went from the top down or the bottom up sometimes, for smaller involvements.

The scheme depended on exposing logos on Mars. We had an ideal place to put them on the gas-filled bags. I remember talking one day to James Wilkinson, the BBC man who broke the news of the martian fossil and our follow-on story concerning the isotopically light carbon. He was due to retire and was doing the rounds of people who'd given him good stories to say goodbye. But the journalist in him would undoubtedly spot the last big exclusive if he tripped over it in the process. Casually I said "James, to raise funds for Beagle 2, I'll probably have to have logos on the lander's gas-bags." His ears pricked up. "You'll actually do that?" he asked. "Sure," I replied, "why not?" "Can I run it as a story?" he wanted to know. Again I told him "Why not?" Within minutes he was off back to Wood Lane with a copy of the Beagle 2 animation he was going to doctor to make his point. That evening the 9 o'clock News showed pictures of the gas-bags with 'Put your Advertisement here' scrolled across them as free advertising for me from the BBC.

There were three gas-bags; that meant another two sponsors after the main one. If we could get £5m each for these secondary sponsors it would be for another quick profit of a cool £10m for very little effort. The bags were already designed to stay inflated so they would pop off, drop the clam shell lander and roll away. The logos would be there to be pictured by the cameras. We couldn't see any problems with the strategy. Surely some advertising manager would recognise the value of such a prominent position.

Whichever way round the pyramid worked, the tip was a single sponsor, or person, the wide base was the public, thousands or even millions of small donations. We were forever being told by somebody, who claimed to have a good idea for funding Beagle 2, that the way to do it was to launch an appeal 'have your name on Mars with Beagle 2' or some such slogan. We had to explain firstly that NASA were already doing this for free and secondly we didn't have a system to handle collecting thousands of small donations. "Maybe if a Bank or a Building Society wants to be the sponsor they can arrange it," I would say. Despite never launching such a campaign, we had children offering their pocket money. We always sent it back with some gift or other.

We received some crazier suggestions. One day I was phoned by a Dutchman who offered himself as a fund raiser. I asked him "Why should I give you the job?" He told me "In the past I have come up with imaginative ideas for sponsorship programmes." "Like what?" I said. He proceeded to explain how he had devised a scheme whereby men, for a small fee, could nominate a star who they would like to see photographed in the nude. When he had collected enough pledges he approached the most popular names and tried to negotiate the photo shoot. If he was successful, the star could have half the money. He said "If we do it again, Beagle 2 can have whatever is left over, after I've taken my expenses cut." I said to him "Maybe if the people who subscribe to the scheme nominate Alex James, he'll donate his fee to the project and we'll win twice." He said "I never thought of that." Needless to say we didn't employ this genius.

But there were also some very promising leads. Lutz Richter phoned to say that he had mentioned that Beagle 2 was looking for sponsorship to the representative of a large company that made power tools. They had come back to him asking for more information for a forthcoming Board meeting. A Board meeting, this sounded serious. The company was Hilti and registered in Leichtenstein, presumably for tax purposes; we hoped so anyway. I offered to give them a presentation. Because video conferencing was just becoming the in vogue way of holding important meetings without the hassle of travelling half way round the world or, in this case, across Europe, we suggested I should address their Board by satellite to give the pitch a space feel.

There was just one video conferencing suite in central Milton Keynes. We booked it for a morning and I addressed a room full of suited men sat around what looked like an appropriately expensive mahogany table. We had just recruited an extra pair of hands to run around behind me, a diminutive dark haired girl called Becky. She did the honours during the video conference and everything went splendidly. I answered all the questions they threw at me. I thought I had done well until they phoned a few days later to say that they had decided their image wasn't quite space-age yet.

This wasn't the answer I wanted so we tried again with Black and Decker, whose name is synonymous with electric drills. We were having a drill on board Beagle 2; just it wasn't an Italian one to obtain sub-surface samples, it was a rock drill being supplied by Dr Ng, a Hong Kong dentist. Because we couldn't pronounce his name we always called him by his initials: 'TC'. Black and Decker had been involved in supplying the drill used first by the Apollo 15 astronauts on the Moon to obtain a soil core. I had also adapted a Black and Decker hand drill to make a circular diamond saw capable of cutting lunar rocks in half when I had worked at Bristol. I still had the photos of the results and even some film of the drill in action.

I knew Black and Decker hadn't had any exposure from their lunar activities. "This time," I said to a marketing man who agreed to see me, "it could be different, if you sign on with Beagle 2." As I gave him more details he listened very patiently, indeed I detected he was enthusiastic for the ideas I suggested for promotion campaigns with the first martian pictures on their power tool boxes, in DIY stores everywhere. He said "I'm going on holiday this evening; someone will get in touch." They never did. We had one more try with tool companies by approaching Bosch. It didn't get very far. Our Hong Kong dentist friend TC shrugged and philosophically said, "I'll just have to pull more teeth."

Black and Decker's offices were on the London road just outside of Reading. The most famous company in Reading, who everyone thinks might have in interest in sponsoring a Mars lander, was Mars chocolate. Getting Mars to pay for Beagle 2 was just about as popular a suggestion as believing Richard Branson would be gagging for it; David Bowie of 'Is there life on Mars?' comes in third; the song is nothing to do with the Red Planet, the title is a euphemism for an unlikely event. Judith and I didn't rate our chances with Mars very likely. I'd been told even though Helen Sharman had worked for the company they had wanted nothing to do with her flight in space apart from allowing her to take the time off as unpaid holiday! A man I spoke to at Mars confirmed that the confectionery company didn't see planetary exploration as its image. "Plenty of people have asked," he said. Moving on I tried him on the subject of dogs. Mars own Pedigree pet foods, makers of 'Chum', but he wasn't impressed.

For another video conference presentation, I went to Hewlett Packard's UK headquarters in Bristol. It was an enormous concrete and glass complex occupying a place that used to be all fields when I was a kid. I remember cycling through them to get to Filton, to stand with other kids, watching the planes take off at the end of the longest runway in Britain. It was the place they had the Bristol Brabazon, the Jumbo jet before its time; alas it was abandoned, another example of the Great British Government's lack of foresight.

I gave a Beagle 2 lecture to the Hewlett Packard (HP) staff. It was at 5.30pm and beamed on to California. David Hewlett, who owned most of the shares in HP, was interested in extraterrestrial life; he picked up the tab to fund 'SETI', the search for extraterrestrial intelligence, when the US Government ended their support. It seemed a good bet if he was prepared to gamble on finding life by sending 'anybody out there?' messages, surely he would be up for something closer to home even if it was only microscopic. I knew HP was developing a tiny digital camera. We had already chosen Beagle 2's main cameras; they were being provided by Jean-Luc Josset from a Swiss company called Space-X. There would be two of them to take stereo pictures of the scene around Beagle 2 at its landing site on Mars. But the most exciting picture of all would be one that showed the lander sitting there; that would be the one the press wanted.

Of course it couldn't be taken by an on-board camera.

But I thought there was another way to get the iconic picture of Beagle 2 on Mars by putting tiny cameras on the gas-filled bags. If it could be done then we could certainly take pictures of the surface of Mars as the lander descended. We might even get some more as the bags bounced around, they would be invaluable for understanding the stresses involved in the landing. All these images would have to be stored on Beagle 2's computer and transmitted back to Earth later. To get the pictures of Beagle 2, taken from the gas-bags, they would have to be radioed to the lander. It would add complexity but looked do-able. If it needed more mass maybe the prospect of such a fabulous PR picture would persuade Rudi to relent on his 60kg ceiling and give it to us.

But first the carrot of sponsorship and massive advertising impact had to be dangled in front of HP. They could supply the cameras for the gas-bags and pay for the privilege of putting them there. It was another of our brilliant ideas to get Beagle 2 paid for which came to nothing. Maybe their miniature camera was a product that wasn't developed further; I don't recall anything like it coming onto the market. We didn't pursue the concept with our existing cameras; they would have been too big.

We moved on to the financial giants. This time, it was the accountancy company Price Waterhouse Coopers. They were being taken over by Coopers Lybrand, based in Holland, nothing to do with my friend with the foolproof scheme, I hoped. They must have been seriously contemplating the opportunity we were offering for sponsorship because they sent two people to London for a meeting with me and John Thatcher. After an afternoon of us detailing all the possibilities, they rushed away to catch a plane back to Amsterdam. I found out later they were also considering sponsoring the cricket on television's Channel 4. I think landing on Mars was just a little wide of the wicket for accountants.

I remember once relating this story to some complete stranger I was talking to at a business reception organised by a cruise ship company. He had approached me with the novel cocktail party opener, "I've seen you on the television, how's fundraising for Beagle 2 going?" I didn't know who he was or what he did but he laughed and said "Tut, tut!" in all the right places in my tale, so I threw in "I suppose it could have been worse, they might have been actuaries. And what do you do?" I asked him. "Actually," he said "I'm an actuary!" Such are the hazards of making pitches blind.

On another occasion, I was offered an introduction by someone who said they knew of a man, a member of their sailing club, who was a partner at accountants Ernst and Young. "He's the only person I've ever known," said this intermediary, "who was walking past a Ferrari showroom, stopped, went in and paid cash out of his bonus for a shiny new 'Testarossa'." I didn't get any money from this city slicker but at least I got lunch at a smart London restaurant.

One of the favourite questions at all these encounters was "What happens if it all goes wrong? Have you got insurance?" Space missions are seldom insured as the premiums are prohibitive. Self-insurance is the name of the game for satellites and robotic missions. Organisations like ESA expect that some missions will go wrong and therefore they will have to mount rescues. Mars Express was a rescue for Mars 96. This gave us the idea of looking for an insurance company as a dual sponsor, that way if any thing went wrong the primary sponsor could expect a re-flight, a second bite at the cherry, with all the attendant publicity. There's no such publicity as bad publicity and this was a no-brainer for the insurance industry, I thought.

I floated this idea at a lunch given by the Mercers' Company with a man who said he was big in the City in insurance. The response to my idea, however, didn't come from that gambit. Instead it happened when I was in a Beagle 2 payload meeting with all the groups who were providing instruments. I was halfway across the OU campus away from my office in the only room available. The discussion going on was the perennial one about cutting a bit off PLUTO's lead to save some mass, when my new PA, Michele Lightfoot (her dad's the famous jazz musician) burst in. "There's a man on the telephone," she said, breathless, "he's from the insurance company Abbey Life. I've told him you are in a meeting but he said interrupt you. I tried telling him you are miles away. He said he'd wait."

I left the others to it and hurried back to my office. I picked up the telephone and asked what he wanted, anticipating it could only be about sponsorship. I needed someone in insurance and now they were phoning me. He must have heard about the opportunity for insurance from the man at the Mercers and was getting in before someone beat him to it. This man, whoever he was, began "I suppose you realise you are an important man." Well that was a good start. "You realise you are on lists of the most important people in Britain," continued the disembodied voice. This was getting better and better. "Have you considered taking out a policy on your life? Can we advise you on making a will?" I put the phone down. If I had got my hands on him it would have been he who needed the services mentioned.

I thought about what prompted his call. I had just been listed in a *Sunday Times* supplement as the 99th most influential man in Britain. Someone, whose handwriting I recognised instantly, Ian Wright, had ripped the entry out and posted it on the Department notice board with 'Should try harder', scrawled across it.

At least the opportunities for PR were coming along better. At the end of August 1999, Blur celebrated the ten-year anniversary of their formation. They put together a collection of memorabilia for an exhibition called '3862 days'; it opened in a gallery in Hoxton Square with a Beagle 2 model included. It was the first chance for Judith and me to meet Damon Albarn, the Blur front man, lead singer, song writer and driving force. We were also introduced to Blur's management, CMO: Chris Morrison, Niamh and Selena. Throughout the project they patiently obliged us when we asked the band to do silly things on behalf of Beagle 2.

There was a private party on the opening night. It was our first experience of what it's like to arrive somewhere and have to push in through a throng of adoring fans and paparazzi hoping to catch sight or a picture of the celebrity guests. If we found life on Mars, could we be the first celebrity scientists?

In addition to meeting Damon, we met his dad, Alex's parents and his sister Deborah. Lead guitarist Graham Coxon's parents grabbed us the minute we got inside the door. I had already spoken to Damien Hirst's mother when I phoned him at home one day; this lady is responsible for naming the artist's latest masterpiece, the diamond-encrusted skull, 'For the love of God'. I know rock musicians and wild artists must have mums and dads but I'm sure nobody expects them all to be very nice normal people. As Dave Rowntree told me "Blur are at the pipe and slippers end of Heavy Metal."

Then there was Keith Allen who wanted to ask if he could be involved in Beagle 2. We didn't know it at the time but we'd see a lot more of him. And somebody else we found wandering around was Jerome Blake, a giant, shaven headed film actor who specialised in roles as a baddy. You will have seen him if you've been to one of the 'Star Wars' movies; he's always one of the nasties dressed in uniforms that conceal their faces or who are made up to look like the Director's interpretation of a cosmic warrior.

We had lunch with Jerome a few days later. We were surprised to find he was another member of our ever increasing Bristol supporters' club. He came from Hanham, about two miles from Kingswood. Hanham was where I'd played most of my teenage football. Jerome was in the mould of Darth Vader (Dave Prowse); you've guessed Dave Prowse too was from Bristol, he started out as a bouncer at the Glen Ball Room, scene of many a Saturday night out during my mis-spent youth.

Jerome had some serious advice, "You are sitting on a valuable story for TV and the movies. Don't let anyone nick it." At the time they were casting the next episode of Star Wars, Jerome promised to make sure George Lucas knew about Beagle 2 when he visited the Producer's ranch. "Tell him, he already gave us a mention in 'Jurassic Park' when somebody said about our diamond evidence for an asteroid killing the dinosaurs," I said. I thought I might as well get in a hint that George Lucas must have heard of the science I did. Jerome remained a firm fan of Beagle 2 throughout the project, attending events when he was in Britain. There were times during the mission when I felt I needed the back-up of large men like Jerome or better still Blur's heavies, who in addition to keeping over-enthusiastic fans off the stage 'guarded' Mike Tyson when he came to Britain!

Maybe I should have taken them one Friday at the end of September when Mike Rickett and I were called to ESTEC to meet with John Credland, a bluff Yorkshire man, Head of the Space Projects. He might have been a space engineer but he had big hands that looked as though they could never have built anything smaller than a steam engine.

It wasn't a friendly meeting even if it started amicably enough. We began by discussing various things ESA had left over from previous missions that Beagle 2 might acquire; Mike and I hoped they would be for free. But then Credland threw in what I guess was the real purpose of the meeting, "ESA want their logo on Beagle 2." The story in the *Observer* that Mr Blair was expecting a Union Jack must have precipitated this. I said "John, I never started the business about flags on Beagle 2; in fact, until I get somebody to pay, nobody is getting their logo or flag on the lander. I have to keep the best places to sell. The sponsors may not even be British."

It provoked a thinly veiled threat which began "If you want ESA support..." If he meant money from ESA, I didn't. It would put the lander under their control. That would mean they could cancel us, not that they couldn't prevent us flying already. The Beagle 2 lander would be the first casualty if the going got rough and their money started to get tight. Rudi had as good as said so.

All I wanted from the Agency was for us to have fair treatment; a share of the MEx payload for the Brits in return for our annual subscription. As it stood, Mars Express would carry two experiments from France. One was an infrared spectrometer to study the surface features of Mars and another was for looking at the atmosphere using UV/visible wavelengths. The martian atmosphere was also being studied by the Italians and they had a ground-penetrating radar instrument. The Germans were responsible for the main-PR grabbing piece of kit – the colour camera – and had an experiment which required no mass but used the spacecraft's radio transmissions to investigate the shape of the Red Planet. Even the Swedes had an experiment. Need I go on; without Beagle 2 the Brits had b*****-all except some dining club memberships.

All these countries had work from ESA as well: Germany was going to be the location of the Operations Centre, the French were assembling the orbiter, using a Swiss-made structure, and a radio telescope ground-tracking station was in Spain. There wasn't anything that British Industry was doing.

Nevertheless I couldn't afford to be in hock to ESA; I just shrugged. This started Credland off in another direction. "ESA are not sure that displaying commercial logos on a space craft is legal. The Science Director is consulting lawyers." I had expected this red herring; sooner or later, somebody would come up with this show-stopper. I informed him "There's a precedent, the Russians launched a rocket with 'Pizza Hut' written down the side." I knew all about this and was trying to find a way of getting to Pizza Hut.

Don't ever think the Brits who work for ESA show any favouritism to the old home country; they've all been brain-washed by Europe. I wasn't surprised by his next attack. He gave me a lecture about how all ESA's launches had the ESA logo on the rocket. I retaliated "I'm not stopping you putting an ESA logo on the rocket." This meeting was soon going to become a full blown row, despite Mike being a pragmatic peacemaker. I had better things to do than fight with John Credland. By 10.00am I was on my way back to Calais and home. The OU's Council were having their annual weekend get-together; I was expected to go and butter them up.

And there was the interest being shown in Beagle 2 by Jenny Page, Chief Executive of the Millennium Experience, aka 'the Dome' to deal with. John Thatcher and I went to meet some Dome people in an office across the street from BNSC in Buckingham Palace Road. We were greeted by a man called Martin. All I remember about him was he was smiling and wore a brown suit. He called in a colleague whose name I didn't note and they proceeded to tell us how important it was to have Beagle 2 in the Dome and how prominent a position they could provide. It was at this point that John and I realised they were expecting us to pay for the privilege. "Hang on a minute," I said, "I thought the boot was on the other foot; we tag on to an existing Dome sponsor, who after the year 2000 is over will continue to support us through until 2004 when we've landed on Mars."

That definitely was not what they had in mind. The man in the brown suit stopped smiling and said "But you could get the money to be in the Dome from the Government." To which I replied "No, and we won't ask. If there's more money to be had from the Government we need it to build the lander, not rescue the Dome." At this he got quite shirty and said "We'll ask the Government then for support to have Beagle 2."

I didn't need parasites. As soon as I got back to Milton Keynes, I wrote to Paul Murdin saying "If you get any requests for money from the Millennium Dome on our behalf, it isn't with our consent; we didn't put them up to it. If the Government feel inclined to give the Dome even more money, we can't spare the time or our manpower to support activities unless the money comes direct to us." I was pretty mad. That was the end of story, Jenny Page was fired soon after and maybe the man in the brown suit was sent packing too. 'PY' Gerbeau became the Dome supremo and nobody from Beagle 2 wasted Millenium Eve trying to get to the Isle of Dogs to be with our dog that night.

An event in early September had brought home to us the hazards of going to Mars. NASA took advantage of the opportunity for flying to Mars that 1999 presented by launching two spacecraft. The first was a cut-down version of a much bigger project called Mars Observer, which had inexplicably gone missing in 1992. The second shot was a lander, the successor of Pathfinder, that would attempt to visit a region near the polar ice cap of Mars, never before considered, but extremely interesting because of the prospect of encountering frozen water ice. These two missions were called Climate Orbiter and Polar Lander respectively. The largest cost of a space mission is the marching army of workers involved so these projects had been built quickly and thus cheaply. Cheap for NASA is relative; Dave Rowntree, asked during an interview for Beagle 2 about the amount of money needed to build our spacecraft compared to NASA, replied "Twenty-five million quid." When challenged by the interviewer with "Isn't that a bit expensive?" he retorted "You couldn't get a screwdriver in NASA for that!"

Maybe a slight exaggeration, but NASA's latest two missions were part of a new philosophy, brainchild of Administrator Dan Goldin, called 'smaller, faster, cheaper, better'. Judith and I were crossing Tower Bridge, on our way out of London to Dover, and another ESA meeting, when we heard no signal had been received from Climate Orbiter after its attempt to go around the back of the Red Planet.

Nobody from NASA was celebrating that night. In contrast, a few days later I was invited to join in a celebration of things that had happened to Britain since 1900. I went, along with 399 others, who were said to have been the 'Makers of the 20th Century', to a lunch with the Queen at Mansion House. I actually hoped I would be a maker of the new Millennium, and Beagle 2 would still be remembered by the people living on the colonised fourth planet in the solar system, as that adventurous little spacecraft that came a thousand years ago. Although some of the Brits who made the 20th century, Churchill for one, were dead, it was a chance to meet some interesting people. I queued on the stairs behind Andrew Lloyd Webber who was talking animatedly to Richard Attenborough, so there was no chance to launch the idea of 'Beagle 2 – the Musical'. Believe me, I would have tried.

The highlight of the event, for me, was telling Bobby Charlton about Beagle 2. He and Geoff Hurst, the only man to score a hat trick at a World Cup final, were there. Shame it was too late for Bobby Moore, the greatest defender to put on a pair of boots, I could have asked him for a few tips. Maybe I should have sought help from Sir Bobby about running rings around European opposition.

Then it was back to fund-raising. Judith and I had thought up a way of circumventing the problem of something going dramatically wrong. It was frightening off too many potential sponsors. We came up with a way they could pay by instalments, the equivalent of buying my bike on the 'never, never'. Plus it would make use of something we had already invented which had proved to be a success. First we had to find a newspaper that would play ball. Likely candidates were the *Telegraph*, where Roger Highfield had given us exceptional coverage, and the *Daily Express* who had Michael Hanlon, another Beagle 2 fanatic, as science correspondent and features writer. Roger is a new generation reporter; he looks more like a business man and uses all the latest technology. Michael could easily play the part of the old fashioned newspaper hack, complete with slept-in look suit. Their newspapers were as different as chalk and cheese too and had different circulations, which meant they could share our idea.

What was the idea? The papers could each publish a supplement – a continuous documentary of Beagle 2's progress. We would let them have the copy for nothing; it ought to boost circulation as Beagle 2 got closer and closer to Mars and should peak during the post-landing experimental phase. The supplements would carry advertisements and we would get a hopefully large share of the advertising revenue. Again we thought it looked foolproof; we could even argue with ESA it was not compromising anybody. It was part of the 'Outreach' policy.

We rated the *Daily Express* as the more likely taker because we visualised their version being named 'Mars Express and Beagle 2'. Michael liked it and made the initial introductions. After several visits to the *Express* we got to the real power, Editor, Rosie Boycott. Then it all went downhill and pear-shaped. The newspaper was sold to top shelf magazine magnate, Richard Desmond. Rosie and the rest of the editorial staff were axed in favour of a new team. We could imagine what ESA's response would have been to having its mission classified as soft porn.

Back in June, the MEx Science Working Team had noted that MARESS, our radio link, had not made much progress. By the end of September it was no better; no, it was worse, nothing had happened. It was looked at again in November at what was called a Preliminary Design Review or PDR. By now it was critical. Since the package was being supplied by the Italian Space Agency there was no individual to wave a stick at. Perhaps I'm too cynical, but I believed that the Italians weren't taking the lander seriously. Perhaps they were voting against us at ESA meetings, so believed we weren't ever going to be approved. Accordingly they weren't putting in any effort unless they had to. Somebody had to take responsibility and an agreement to deliver MARESS signed with Astrium Toulouse.

The other problem to do with Beagle 2 communicating with home was the time the orbiter was going to take to get into orbit. It was pretty clear that ESA didn't want to try aerobraking. MEx was their first venture into planetary exploration so they were opting for the simpler, less risky, way of slowing it down by firing the propulsion system. Because this was going to be the way of things, I was told Beagle 2 would get five and a half minutes of radio communication on MEx's first orbit. Then the team would have to wait ten days until MEx got into its final orbit to send commands and receive information. To run the lander immediately after we reached Mars all the instructions needed would have to be stored in the on-board computer. It was hardly satisfactory but typical of ESA's attitude – MEx came first, Beagle 2 was considered to be an add-on, a bonus, fine if it worked, but if it didn't would they care? We were a hitch-hiker so what could we do? Not much, if we wanted the ride. We had to accept the situation and hope that the PR we would bring to the whole project would make them decide to burn a bit more fuel to get into orbit faster.

As this was being discussed by SWT, I decided it was time to take a walk. I got about half way to the door when my mobile began to ring; it was very obviously me being called. I answered but waited until I got outside to talk. It was Selena from Blur; the band were going to release their next single the Monday following the next ESA Science Programme Committee meeting. SPC would be making another ruling on Beagle 2: on or off MEx. CMO knew we were expecting some kind of decision. "It will be an opportunity for a bit of mutual publicity," Selena said. "Alternatively, we can make a stink if ESA say no," I replied, thanking her for keeping me in the loop.

We had already done a deal with Tomorrow's World; they were going to bring the news, good or bad, to the Nation about whether Beagle 2 was to continue as the British mission to Mars. The SPC meeting would take place on the afternoon that Tomorrow's World was broadcast but we recorded the piece in advance on 5 November, with me, Dave and Alex, at the Science Museum. We hoped the only fireworks that week would be at the bonfires we were going to that evening. Because we didn't know the outcome of SPC's deliberations, Peter Snow, who was presenting, recorded three versions: Good news, Beagle 2 is still going to Mars; Bad news, it isn't; or as Peter insisted calling it, the ESA have 'funked it', no decision version.

It was the first one which went out on the Friday night. On the following Monday, Blur's new record hit the streets. One of the tracks was called Beagle 2. It had been written and recorded back in the summer. I had been summoned to Damon's studio, on a scalding hot day, to listen to the at first strange, but ethereal music which was destined to be the Beagle 2 call sign if we ever got to Mars. Also on the CD as the main track is 'No distance left to run'. It really should have been Peter's last version of the recording that was broadcast. The final decision hadn't been made. ESA thought they had Beagle 2 on a string and the story had some distance left to run.

Chapter 11

IN FOR A POUND, OUT FOR MILLIONS

B eagle 2 was still alive but ESA hadn't given us the unequivocal endorsement that other instruments on MEx enjoyed. Of course, they could be cancelled but it would have to be on technical grounds. Beagle 2, as always, had the 'Sword of Damocles' hanging above it: we had to demonstrate we could get funding. Alex and Dave were happy, they treated Judith and me to lunch at 'The Ivy'; some scientists ought to be regarded as valued customers, worthy of being granted a table there the same day when they ring up out of the blue.

At the end of 1999 in addition to Beagle 2, I still had responsibility for two instruments on ESA's Comet chaser mission, Rosetta. I had to go to the SWT meetings for this mission as well as running around chasing money to go to Mars. In the middle of November the Rosetta mission held a meeting in Germany. It was at Schloss Ringberg, a castle owned by the Max Planck Society, Germany's equivalent of the Royal Society. The place was just south of Munich. Before we set out Judith checked the weather forecast for the area: it was going to snow. "That'll be nice," I said. "I like snow." "What if we get stuck?" asked the more sensible Judith. "We won't get stuck, it's only November. Europe's roads don't grind to a halt like ours when a few flakes of snow fall," was my response. "But the cars have chains," she warned. "But we have a Land Rover," I replied. Judith learned to drive in a Land Rover; her father, Jack Hay, was one of the eight founder members of the Land Rover owners club in the early 1950s. She practically had Land Rover bits in her pram.

We set off and got as far as Stuttgart before the first sign of snow; by the time we reached the village of Tegensee, overlooked by the Schloss, it was already pretty thick. We booked into a hotel, thinking tomorrow night we'll stay up at the castle. We reasoned it would be nice to have a meal and go up the last few miles early the next day in time for the start of the meeting. I say up because Schloss Ringberg is a fairy tale German castle at the top of an alp. It's only a small alp but nevertheless it's an alp. We got up to find thirty-two centimetres of snow had fallen during the night. Nevertheless, off we went. It was just as well we had a Land Rover. To get to Ringberg involved some off road driving up at least a mile of snow covered track through a forest, but we got to the top thanks to four wheeled drive.

I attended the first day of the meeting. Always the optimist, I said to Judith "Don't worry, at this time of year, like in Britain, the snow will be gone in the morning." But it wasn't, at least as much fell again during the night and a blizzard was raging when we got up. It was a foot thick on top of the Discovery. Some of the hardy Germans at the meeting had thoughtfully brought their skis; they had no intention of talking about comets that day and disappeared cross-country skiing. They could say they were discussing the problems of operating a spacecraft on an icy snowball and were quite prepared for it to be a long discussion. Much as we would have liked to stay, we went gingerly down the mountain, carefully avoiding a stuck tractor trying to get up with relief supplies.

By the time we got home there wasn't any sign of our Arctic adventure but we had pictures of our downhill slalom and lots of slogans we were going to offer Land Rover for a sales campaign arising from a sponsorship deal with Beagle 2. "Would you set off on a voyage of 'Discovery' to Mars in anything but a Land Rover?" might sell a few 4x4s. The company published our story in their magazine; another PR success, but no money. When I later did a launch event for the Milton Keynes Land Rover franchise, I was promised a sweet-heart deal when I traded in that Discovery. It did 200,000 miles for the cause, during Beagle 2, by which time the showroom's manager had gone and his successor knew nothing about the arrangement; I really must get some of these promises written down. That or get some professional negotiators in.

That brings me to our next move, and a reason I had to get back from Ringberg. As a result of the publicity we were now receiving, everybody knew we were on the search for a sponsor, or sponsors. Several companies, to be more accurate individuals, who had set themselves up as agents approached us. I had read about other wheelers and dealers in the business pages of the papers and had chanced upon a few more likely representatives.

I came across at least one who became very famous – Mel Goldberg, a lawyer, who negotiated deals for sports stars. I met him in the Green Room of a television studio. He was about to give an interview about Nike signing up Tiger Woods for $90m over five years. I went to see him afterwards in his offices and suggested he might offer the same sports giant a deal whereby Beagle 2 would make an impression of Nike's distinctive 'tick' in the soil of Mars, rather like the Apollo 11 astronaut's boot print on the Moon. That picture is still the one always shown when talking about Neil Armstrong's 'one small step'.

I metaphorically explained to Mel "I'm just like somebody who plays for the team and does every Saturday as long as I don't get injured." I said "Even if I do, my convalescence and comeback will be worth money." I meant if we didn't reach Mars we could always try again; I was keen to avoid "the what if it goes wrong?" question. I don't know whether he put it to Nike; I certainly didn't get any follow-up phone calls.

Another possible agent I talked to was Derek Draper, who had worked as a parliamentary lobbyist. He claimed to have access to the Blair inner circle, which the media eventually decided was an unfounded boast. Derek had set up an agency called 'Farm', in Tottenham Court Road. I talked with him and his partners in the proverbial no-frills office, a table, a bare light-bulb and a filing cabinet. He was more interested in PR 'farming', hence the name. He was going to 'farm' out commissions to his creative team of contacts working on the client's image, rather than sponsorship deals. I felt, in Judith, Beagle 2 already had all the creative PR talent it needed. She had already done pretty well in promoting my image. I wished him well. Unfortunately the name Farm and the concept were claimed by an existing company. Enough said, Derek Draper retrained as a psychotherapist only to reappear, much more recently, in a political email scandal.

Before making our next move, I had another meeting with the VC. He had, perhaps misguidedly, suggested that the OU would match whatever I raised elsewhere. It wasn't quite a complete match but he was now thinking about giving me £2m. Henceforth, he wanted me to liaise with Miles Hedges, the OU's Finance Director. I think liaise meant he had delegated his own role to Miles, not that he didn't believe I was doing a good job. He just wanted somebody senior in the OU hierarchy to hold my hand if I needed it because his tenure was running out. Better still, from Beagle 2's point of view, Miles would have financial clout.

If you walked into a bank and were greeted by Miles in his pinstriped suit, sober shirts and ties, horn rimmed glasses and clipped moustache, you would feel immediately that your money was safe. He was definitely a huge asset; Miles gave an air of respectability. He would be somebody I could offer as a representative on the Beagle 2 Steering Committee which Paul Murdin now felt was a necessity. Miles became Chairman of the Beagle 2 Steering Committee which was constituted from the partners who had put some money up to get us this far. There were representatives from the OU, Astrium, BNSC/PPARC, Leicester and Martin Baker. Even though Miles was on my side I sometimes had to work hard to convince him to convince the others on that Steering group.

Miles had another attribute that turned out decisive. He had a chemistry degree. ESA, when Miles was dealing with them, thought he was just an accountant rather than a chemistry graduate who had changed his spots. It was an advantage that they believed he didn't understand them when they were doing a little bamboozling on technical issues.

Judith and I were now ready to play our trump card in the search for money. We had selected the company who would take over the role of sponsorship hunters. I had spoken to Damien Hirst, who had invited Charles Saatchi and me to lunch. It didn't happen but I talked to the advertising legend on the phone and a meeting was fixed for me with Matthew Patten, Head of Sponsorship for M&C Saatchi, the agency that had succeeded Saatchi and Saatchi.

Accordingly, we met Matthew, late one Friday afternoon, in a boardroom matching the company's status, in offices occupying half of one side of Golden Square, Soho, a stone's throw from Piccadilly Circus. Matthew was very blond, in fact white haired, and all the things you would expect somebody in charge there to be. He was already a Beagle 2 convert when we met him. Just for a change, we did something to officially take him on board. Judith gave him a cheque for a pound, and photographed it, just to prove it. He said "I'll keep it as a souvenir." I hope he didn't spend it when we went for a drink in a plush wine bar across the street to cement the relationship. I imagine however the agency had an account there.

It was designed to, and did, boost the confidence of the Steering Committee. I rang around to tell them the good news. The VC's secretary asked to deliver the message said "Super." Ian Wright, cynical as ever, said "It did for Mrs Thatcher." Alan Wells rang after Mark had filled him in; his comment was "I hear you've got a bit of a coup. Congratulations." Perhaps the one we most needed was from Paul Murdin "I don't suppose they'd be doing it if they didn't believe they'd be successful, but excellent. I'm off to tell Colin Hicks." Colin, presumably, informed Lord Sainsbury. Miles, who had obviously made a complete transformation from chemist to accountant said "Are they doing it for altruistic reasons?" as he anticipated more of his money disappearing out of the window in fees.

As a consequence everybody had a good Christmas, which wasn't the case for the NASA engineers who had worked on their second Mars spacecraft of 1999. On 3 December, when it was supposed to transmit an 'arrived safely' message, there was silence. It wasn't just a single spacecraft lost, it was three Mars landers. The soft lander had been carrying two penetrator projectiles, like those offered by Roger Bourke to MEx in September 1997. They hadn't answered attempts to contact them either. Presumably ESA were glad, for a change, that it was Beagle 2 that made it through the competition so far.

The newspaper cartoonists heaped derision, undeservedly, on the Polar Lander engineers. They had largely left those involved with the Climate Orbiter, who might have expected it, alone. Their embarrassing mistake was to have two teams, one working in imperial units, feet and inches, and the other in metric. What's more it had been going on for ten months. Every time they fired some small thruster motor to correct for the tiny pressure exerted by solar radiation on the spacecraft they noticed a slight discrepancy but did nothing about it. At least we wouldn't have to worry about such a mistake; we would be struggling to pay one team let alone two. One NASA manager said "We knew it was going to happen twelve hours before it did." Another added "People make mistakes." A third said "The fault was that our checks and balances didn't pick it up." And finally, to look on the bright side: "It only cost $125m, it could have been one of those big missions we used to do that took ten years and cost a billion bucks. Be thankful for 'smaller, faster, cheaper'."

The arrival of the Saatchis brought ESA scampering to London in the form of a Mr Jagtman, their Head of PR, who reported direct to Science Director, Bonnet. He asked two questions, "What do ESA stand to gain?" I told him "A Mars lander." Then he wanted an answer to "What does Beagle 2 insist on?" "At last", I thought, "we've got the 'Stone of Sisyphus' over the top of the hill."

The feeling didn't last long. The dreaded MARESS had failed its PDR. It was hardly surprising, the Italians hadn't designed anything. John Thatcher, Mark and I went to ESTEC to discuss alternative strategies with Rudi Schmidt. We went through all the options for communicating via orbiters: ESA's or NASA's, direct to Earth, perhaps using the same system as Rosetta? All of them had advantages and drawbacks. One of the advantages was that since the Italians were in default, ESA were going to have to pay to build an alternative system. Rudi said he would give a contract to a British company, QinetiQ, the privatised Defence Engineering Research Association. Astrium, that meant John, would have to manage them. I thought Rudi was being very helpful until we got on to the subject of the long delay in communicating with us immediately after landing.

In fact it was the period immediately before landing which distressed me most. NASA had held an Inquiry into what had happened to their Polar Lander; they thought the computer had got a spurious signal when the landing legs clicked into place. The software interpreted it as the moment to shut down the motor and the spacecraft simply dropped out of the sky. They had no way of knowing for sure. Pathfinder had had a radio beacon to demonstrate that the lander was still alive throughout the descent. A similar device had been thrown off Polar Lander, a casualty of the cheaper-not-better philosophy. One cartoonist changed the slogan to 'smaller, faster, cheaper, <u>BITTER</u>'. The NASA Inquiry document stated "Never again, it's false economy, not to know how far we got." They realised it saved more money in the long run if you knew for a fact how near to success the spacecraft had come. There never was an explanation about where the polar ice penetrators 'Scott' and 'Amundsen' went, but NASA stopped working on penetrators.

We had got the message about beacons; it's a pity ESA didn't. We decided we had to have one on Beagle 2 as it came down through the atmosphere to the surface of Mars. An engineer at Stevenage came up with a clever 'if you don't have the resources you'll have to think harder' solution. Since the spacecraft would have to be spinning for stability when it entered the martian atmosphere, like a rugby ball thrown by a scrum half (I knew my old Headmaster's insistence on playing rugby would help me one day), it would have to be spin-balanced like the tyres on your car.

The clever idea was to build a transmitter into a balancing weight. Mars Express could listen to Beagle 2 throughout its entry and descent; "If the signal stops," John told Rudi "we'll know how far down we are." "But MEx isn't going to be risked by having to turn its antenna towards Beagle 2" Rudi replied. I know it was still the Pantomime season but I thought he was kidding. In fact I said "You're ****ing kidding, Rudi." MEx not being available to communicate with us for days after landing was one thing, we could get round that, but not monitoring the descent was ****ing lunacy, bordering on criminal neglect. He then compounded it by saying "It doesn't matter, you won't be there!" In his mind MEx wouldn't be taking us. I thought "If I ever write my Memoirs and need to explain why we didn't have a radio beacon, Rudi, you, and this conversation, are going to get special mention."

As a result of Mr Jagtman's visit, Judith and I went to ESA Headquarters with Paul Murdin to explain our PR and funding modus operandi; they had wanted to hear it for some time. I had always told them "We'll tell it to ESA's top management when we're ready." They not only had senior people at the meeting in Paris, they also brought a lawyer.

We spelled it out for them: the flight model of Beagle 2 will carry logos in places negotiated by the project. They will be seen in the course of science operations, and logos will be on all publicity pictures, animations, graphics etc. Through Judith's foresight we had bought the domain name www.Beagle2. com as a project asset; it would be hosted by the OU.

We explained that by last autumn we felt we had made sufficient progress with our PR strategy to believe we were capable of raising the shortfall in funding. The opportunities for a family of sponsors existed during building, testing, delivery, launch, flight, landing and operation of Beagle 2. All the sponsors would be ethical.

I went on with the explanation: "To reap the maximum rewards for our efforts the time has come to place the responsibility for raising funds in the hands of a professional organisation that can bring sponsorship negotiation skills, management and maybe some additional ideas. If Beagle 2 is not already a household name it is destined to be one. We now also have a household name, the Saatchis, to manage the portfolio. We started at the top; we never had to work down our list of potential agents." It was a pity the meeting dealt only with PR and money. I should have laid down a few conditions with respect to engineering decisions. I had tried to think of everything but as the NASA man said "People make mistakes." Mine was not to insist, at that meeting, that Beagle 2 was treated as an autonomous spacecraft with adequate mass and communications resources.

On 25 January, M&C Saatchi announced their involvement with Beagle 2 to the Press. The next day, with the news in the papers, the International Mars Exploration Working Group (IMEWG) met at BNSC. All the countries with an interest in the Red Planet attended this ad hoc meeting which moves around the nations on an approximately six month cycle, according to who offers to play host.

IMEWG was the opportunity to discuss with the Americans strategies for communicating with spacecraft. With more and more attention being paid to Mars there was lots of enthusiasm, on all sides, including with ESA, for an 'industry standard' for telecomms. It would mean that everybody's orbiter could send messages to, and receive data from, any Mars lander. Because communication with Mars is only possible when the transmitters and receivers can 'see' each other, it's not always possible. If everybody was using the same method the number of opportunities would be increased. There would also be a sort of international rescue network for SOSs between spacecraft, a long way from home, when things went wrong.

Here was a method of tiding Beagle 2 over whilst MEx got itself into a stable orbit and ESA started thinking about communicating with us. Although NASA had lost four spacecraft in a row and its next lander might be postponed, it had already started building an orbiter for a 2001 launch. At IMEWG, the engineers attending from JPL promised to look into whether they could change the way the orbiter communicated, simply by altering the computer software. It looked like a lifeline for Beagle 2.

Relieved of the job of fund raising, Judith and I were able to concentrate on PR. Our still rising media profile meant Matthew Patten would have plenty to offer for sale to potential sponsors. We were constantly gathering video footage for a possible Beagle 2 TV documentary but in March 2000 an early opportunity to use it presented itself. Steve Wilkinson had commissioned an 'Indie' TV Company, Circlevision, run by John Macnish and his wife, Jane, to make a pilot for 'Final Frontiers'.

I met up with Circlevision and discovered they were also making a series of six programmes for the BBC to be called 'Personal Passions'. The concept was that the subject of each programme would be filmed involved in some activity he/she was well known for, side by side with coverage of his/her hobby, which the audience probably wouldn't know anything about. The company had already made a programme with Max Clifford, the man who places sensational stories with tabloid newspapers. Beagle 2's was not quite in the same category but going to Mars was up and coming. Circlevision asked me to be a subject in Personal Passions. I jumped at the chance and said "I can talk for ever about cartoons; I've been interested in them since my sister bought me Roy Ullyett and Giles annuals when I was about ten."

At the time, Judith and I were preparing an exhibit for what has become known as SET week; it's a week in March when various organisations, including Universities, try to promote Science, Engineering and Technology. We agreed that Circlevision would film me talking about Mars to the school kids at the event at London University's Imperial College. We would then go round to the British Museum to see some Regency comet cartoons, to allow me to plug ESA's Rosetta mission. Finally, we'd go out to the *Daily Telegraph* at Canary Wharf to interview cartoonist Matt about his love of space missions, particularly ones to Mars that crashed or disappeared for other reasons.

Circlevision got more than they bargained for; we had found out that Princess Anne was going to open the Exhibition at Imperial so we asked the organisers to put Beagle 2 on the route of her walk around. "No," they said, "there is a strict protocol to these things." My children said "Boring, boring," when I told them about strict protocols during events for schools.

What happened? I saw the Princess coming my way, so I simply stepped into her path and said "Would you like to hear about Britain's effort to land on Mars?" Far from being non-plussed, she let me guide her to one side and spent several minutes asking questions before moving on. It was all captured for Personal Passions on video. I wish I had been due a fee for repeats of Personal Passions, men who serve petrol in all night garages are always telling me they've seen it. Actually I didn't get anything for it; like everything else it was done for nothing to increase public awareness of Beagle 2.

Astrium, who had paid for the stand to put Beagle 2 on were delighted; they challenged me to get the rest of the Royals interested in Beagle 2. It was a challenge I couldn't resist and would have succeeded if Prince Charles hadn't cried off a visit to the Royal Society when I was due to be at the forefront of a welcoming party. The Society's Executive Secretary told me "If you can't get him to take an interest in science nobody can."

The organisers at Imperial College, who behaved as though it was all part of their plan when Princess appeared happy, gave me a b******ing, but it was too late, I'd done it. Judith would plot these serendipitous opportunities and I would grab them. We believed live action with Beagle 2 was infinitely better than the scripted and stage managed events favoured by ESA. We were prepared for anything that came our way and something positive would come out of it, even if sometimes things went wrong.

During a period of just a few weeks, after Personal Passions we managed a host of novel PR events. I was a guest at a Star Wars event, filmed a documentary for Hungarian TV and gave a lecture at a public school. The biggest announcement, however, was that McLaren, the motor racing team, were going to make the carbon fibre shell of Beagle 2; we now had a Formula 1 lander.

We were constantly badgered by journalists who promised banner headlines if we gave them an exclusive about Beagle 2 sponsorship arrangements. Judith and I were choosing whose turn it was to get first chance at a media story and we tried to spread it around for maximum impact and to make sure all the journalists got a turn. There was only one who complained, the rest thought we were giving them a fair crack of the whip.

It was clear we had a different view from ESA for the targets for what they called Outreach. For example, we were sitting on a story about Keith Allen making a video for the Euro 2000 football anthem; I was going to be in it and the choir would be wearing badges bearing the slogan 'Mars or bust'. On the more serious side, I attended a Parliamentary Inquiry into the workings of BNSC. Inquiries like this occur in upstairs rooms at the House of Commons. There is a long corridor of rooms where they take place and the Interrogators sit around a horseshoe shaped table. I was asked to give evidence, as was the Chief Executive of PPARC. I don't know what he thought he was doing but he showed up with a pile of slides to show on a projector.

When the question of Outreach came up he leaped in with both feet believing here was a subject he could get some brownie points for. He explained "PPARC are reaching out to the best science students," and with a smug look on his face, anticipating much praise, he threw in "our goal is to find the next Stephen Hawking." At this point the Chairman turned to me. I said "I have an entirely different approach. I want to tell everybody about science. My favourite audiences are the ones who don't know anything and think they don't want to. I'll talk to anybody; I want to reach the rough kid who sits at the back of the class." It was no contest; every MP on that Committee had constituents whose children were my target audience.

Somebody then asked "Why haven't PPARC funded Beagle 2 already?" He got the response "We didn't realise immediately that the science was so good!" I was feeling pretty good now as I stepped outside. Walking along the street I made two phone calls. The first was to John Thatcher, he told me "Astrium have run out of money and will stop work if more of Lord Sainsbury's £5m isn't released." The second was to Judith, who said "Buy a paper, Damien's had a spat with Marco Pierre White." Grabbing one from the kiosk at Piccadilly Tube station, I read that the chef, who was in partnership with Damien at the time, had claimed that butterfly paintings were his idea. 'Mars', made up from red butterflies, displayed at the Royal Society, was at the centre of the punch-up and had been destroyed. Nothing much I could do about that, but I would have to sort Astrium out.

As soon as Paul Murdin had got his Steering Committee, he wanted it to be given a presentation from M&C Saatchi and he wanted it soon, on 7 April. Matthew Patten and I prepared his material very carefully during the week running up to the big day. It coincided with my last Gresham College lecture. In the coming weeks I would no longer have this monthly event as a commitment.

My last Gresham lecture finished, I met Matthew on the platform of Kings Cross station for the journey to Stevenage. The showdown would be at 3.00pm. We still had two hours for last minute adjustments and trying to anticipate the questions, but more importantly preparing the answers.

Saatchis might have the reputation but Judith and I felt we knew what we were doing. Put it this way, we had an enormous hand in what Matthew said but he delivered it with aplomb, and of course his audience wanted to believe that everything they were hearing was Saatchi speak. Paul had asked for evidence of our PR successes. I think he thought he would get a one maybe two page list of newspaper articles. We turned up with the newspapers, not just the cuttings either but the whole paper and magazines so the Steering Committee could see the size of the headlines, the prominence given to the article, the neighbouring stories and what was the big news of the day to indicate the likely sales figures. We did a very thorough job. What we took filled a whole crate.

For the occasion, which took place at Astrium, Matthew's audience was Paul, Miles, Mike Rickett and Steve Lingard. Because fund-raising was being discussed Alan Wells wasn't invited; he was searching for money for the National Space Centre (NSC), a Millennium Outreach project in Leicester, and Miles didn't want a conflict of interest. John Thatcher was waiting outside the room.

There was no doubt that the crate did what it was supposed to when Paul said "Because of the way the PR has been done, Beagle 2 is as near as damn it unstoppable. This meeting is virtually the last time it can be stopped." He wasn't correct, there were a lot more meetings where it might have been ended but it was a good way to start the discussion. I couldn't resist asking him "Have you brought the cheque with you then, or would you like to phone a friend?" If he had asked the audience the answer would have been a forgone conclusion.

Matthew, bless his heart, did us a real favour by immediately removing any aspirations the Committee might have for managing the PR. "If it's not broke don't fix it then," he said. It was my nightmare scenario, having to consult with everybody before we did anything to make sure the logos were in the right order. I've often said "I bet British adventurers didn't have too many management meetings when they painted the map of the World pink." We were already having enough without PR debates.

I had the impression that the meeting was hoping to get a message from Matthew along the lines: "Saatchis have a list of clients who are sitting gagging to be offered a sponsorship opportunity." So all he would have to do was ring around and ask "Would you like this one?" Instead he asked a rhetorical question: "Why are you in such a hurry? You still have more than three years to go until the big payday." Then he explained what he meant "For every project Saatchis have handled, when the money has been accepted early, we have said to ourselves, when it happened, we could have got more!" I don't remember whether this was one of the responses we had rehearsed or whether it was a spur of the moment idea, but it was absolutely vital; it led to the Steering Committee discussing the possibility of 'underwriting' the project by way of a loan to which they would all contribute. Paul went away to consult; John Thatcher's threat that Astrium had run out of money was likely to make him consult faster.

Whilst everybody on the Steering Committee were thinking, consulting or otherwise not committing themselves, Matthew and I went about the business of trying to find sponsors. Matthew produced a list of possibles and started to contact them. If any looked hopeful he suggested a meeting about Beagle 2 at Golden Square. If that looked promising I was wheeled out for a follow-up or we would go round to the candidate's offices. For each potential sponsor we would think up a Mars angle unique to Beagle 2. One thing that Judith and I would never concede, however, was the name Beagle 2. Matthew kept on about wanting to offer naming rights, i.e. some company would be allowed to choose the name for the mission; usually something like their own brand name. We argued this was silly. Beagle 2 was now a household name in its own right. If Richard Branson had come up with the cash we would have accepted the name being changed to Virgin Beagle 2, but not just Virgin.

I don't think this was a show-stopper with any of the people we talked with, who around that time included the National Westminster Bank, Air Miles, Logica and Swatch, a branch of the Omega watch company. They all seemed to recognise that they would be paying to have their name attached to something which already had enormous momentum. I had already talked to Sony about sponsorship after we had found Beagle 2's battery was similar technology to that used in Sony's video cameras. Matthew and I revisited them several times; even though they were preoccupied with Play Station they always seemed to be teetering on the brink of saying "Yes."

One of the wilder visits we made was to a nascent digital, web-based, TV company called Network of the World, NOW for short. They had a slogan 'The Future is NOW'. The company seemed to emanate from Hong Kong, certainly from the Far East, somewhere around the Pacific and its owner appeared to have billions to invest in new media. I'm not sure whether the billions were pounds, euros, dollars or yen, all that mattered to me was that there were billions of them. M&C Saatchi wanted a big piece of the action with NOW.

A short taxi ride from Golden Square took us to a glass sky scraper in west London. Everything was chaos. They were installing TV studios and God knows what else in this building. The focal point of the organisation was a paunchy American who was trailed everywhere by at least eight minions all carrying mobile phones which they thrust at the boss man periodically, saying things like "So and so from Los Angeles..." No call lasted more than fifteen seconds before it was replaced by another. They all consisted of some barked order to a person in a far away place.

We followed him with all the others, Matthew's arguments usually being answered "Yeah, yeah." I'm sure Matthew told him we wanted £10m. I wasn't quite so clear whether he agreed; it was impossible to distinguish one conversation from another, but I'm pretty sure I was going to have my own digital TV channel for Beagle 2 and Mars news. But the only thing which comes up if you 'Google' Beagle Channel is information about the relatively safe sea passage our namesake charted for the purpose of avoiding Cape Horn. So I guess I must have dreamed it. In which case I think we had probably just avoided similar stormy waters because I've never been able to find out what happened to NOW then or in the future. Google only has one cached page on NOW.

My days were pretty full but so were the nights. On several evenings, my son Joe and I went to a recording studio in London along with Fat Les and a cast of thousands, to make Keith Allen's latest football anthem, 'Jerusalem'. At least I didn't have to learn the words, we had sung it at school at the end of every term before whoever was Head Boy would ask for three cheers for the staff to be followed by the Head Girl leading three cheers for the holidays.

I tell everybody I played drums, actually drum, on Jerusalem. There were five drummers; Dave Rowntree, Justin Welch of 'Elastica', record producer Ben Hillier, TV and radio presenter Roland Rivron and me with a big bass drum to beat time. At the end of every video take, in best rock band tradition for excess, we were expected to trash the set; we didn't have a big budget, so we pretended and had to keep rebuilding the drum kit.

Jerusalem was adopted by the FA as the official song for the Euro 2000 tournament. Fat Les got to sing it live on 'Top of the Pops'. It only reached number eleven in the hit parade but holds the record for the biggest band ever on TOTP; we collapsed the stage when we were all on it. We also did a 'Live' at Wembley. I got to fulfil every little boy's dream of walking up the players' tunnel as part of a team led out by the captain (Keith) and into the sunlight, in front of a hundred thousand fans. Only it was raining, we weren't allowed to go into the centre of the pitch to sing and the crowd was restricted to seventy thousand. Ah well, you can't have everything – I lived the dream, with just one match to spare before they started to pull the old Wembley down. And we subliminally brain-washed another few million people about Beagle 2 in the process; if you'd looked closely at the coverage of the match you'd have seen that the choir are all wearing the 'Mars or Bust' badges we gave out during the recording.

We were actually doing some work on the spacecraft and the instruments and had been getting a handle on various aspects of the mission. Beagle 2 was expected to enter the martian atmosphere at about 13,000mph (5.75 km/sec). It was going to be pushed off MEx by springs using what we called the Spin Up and Eject Mechanism, or SUEM, being built by Hunting Engineering of Ampthill. When I went there to see a gangling grey-haired Steve Burnage, our contact, it was seriously secure, all the walls and gates were topped with coils and coils of barbed wire. The SUEM seemed to have some Cold War heritage; I didn't ask what it was.

The spinning Beagle 2 probe would be slowed down by frictional heating due to atmospheric resistance. When it reduced to about one and a half times the velocity of sound, Mach 1.5 (350m/sec, 700mph) an accelerometer would tell the computer to fire a mortar to deploy a pilot parachute. This was expected to open to slow the probe down further. Every step after that would be decided on the basis of time elapsed since deployment of the pilot chute. Pyrotechnic devices would break bolts that held a cover on the lander and in the process release a second, bigger parachute. With the bolts gone the heat shield, which protected everything from the frictional heating during entry, would drop away. The exact times for these events had yet to be worked out using a model of the martian atmosphere. We were planning for Beagle 2 enveloped in gas-filled bags to hit the ground at 100mph (30m/sec). When it did, the force would be over two hundred times that of gravity (200g) and the bounce might be a hundred metres back off the surface but across the landscape with some horizontal velocity depending on the slopes involved. After lots of additional bounces over which we would have no control, the final drop out of the gas-bags, providing protection during all the fun and games, would be from a height of one metre. When the lander hit the surface it would experience an even greater shock, we thought about 350g.

The instruments inside the lander, not just the lander itself, were going to have to be built to survive all these extreme conditions. The lander body, made from carbon fibre, would probably be black and look a bit like the material popular for making non-scratch kitchen sinks. So we were throwing everything including the kitchen sink at this project. Jim Clemett's best estimate for the whole box of tricks, now he knew more about the various components, was 30.084kg; with the items to get us down to the surface, the EDLS, it went up to 59.569kg without the SUEM. Since MEx was supposed to be built to deliver a lander or landers, the mass of the SUEM would have to come from the orbiter budget.

The team also had some ideas about how to build Beagle 2 to survive the low temperature on Mars particularly at night when it would drop to minus 70°C. This was an area of expertise for Simon Peskett from the Rutherford Appleton Laboratory. One of the solutions under consideration was to include a material that would give off its latent heat of fusion as it froze. It's the trick fruit growers use when they spray water onto apple trees in blossom to protect them from frost. The water gives off heat as it changes to ice; it's been known for centuries, there's nothing new in science.

Things were becoming clearer about the instruments to support the mass spectrometer. In the early models of Beagle 2 we had envisaged picking each instrument up with the robotic arm and putting it down again to select another. We very soon decided this was too dangerous, if the plug for one device got stuck then we couldn't subsequently use another. Each time we would have to make and break electrical contacts. Even in your own living room you tend to leave electrical equipment plugged in, switching it on and off as you need it. We decided Beagle 2 would do the same.

At Leicester, Mark Sims, several engineers and geologist Derek Pullan designed a system that had stereo cameras, a microscope, X-ray and Mössbauer spectrometers and TC's corer grinder all together at the end of Beagle 2's robotic arm. To switch instruments and devices simply required the unit to rotate by a fixed amount. This was a big advantage because it would be certain that all the instruments pointed at exactly the same spot. All it lacked was a good name. A competition was organised in the Leicester coffee room. The assembly of instruments at the end of the arm became known as the Position Adjustable Workbench. Now the dog had a PAW.

The Steering Committee had more meetings. Numerous ways of obtaining the bridging loan were suggested. Astrium already had a loan from BNSC which could be rescheduled. What pleased Miles most was everything was going through his accounts. Alan Wells was now attending and had an idea, maybe the Millennium Commission could be persuaded to couple the money the NSC expected with an involvement in Beagle 2 if they were given something high profile for their visitors. "Perhaps putting the lander together?" Alan tentatively suggested; it was more of a question.

I wasn't prepared to let anybody else be responsible for ensuring Beagle 2 was not going to measure a false positive. I was going to oversee PP. Miles and Paul were more pragmatic. The former didn't want Saatchis fund-raising for two projects; the latter didn't want Lord Sainsbury to think Saatchis were raising money for two projects. It was the same worry with a different slant. As a compromise I agreed that the working model of Beagle 2 that we would need for rehearsing operations could go to NSC. The public could watch Beagle 2 practising, not being built if the Millenium Commission coughed up.

Attention turned to getting some money for work from ESA. ESA's projects always ran late so they must have cash in hand, maybe they could contribute. Paul had already got word that Bonnet and Rudi Schmidt wanted to join the Steering Committee. Miles said "Not without a large donation." "Anyway," he said "I'm now calling it the Board in keeping with its newly acquired financial status."

Paul had heard NASA was impressed by all aspects of Beagle 2, the science, the engineering and the concept of a private/public partnership to pay for a spacecraft. NASA's own programme was in a bit of a jam. With 'smaller, faster, cheaper' dead, things were going to be more expensive. It was rumoured that there might be an orbiter in 2001, but a lander would have to wait to go head to head with Beagle 2 in 2003. Somebody on the new Board suggested "We could solve our funding problems by selling a Beagle 2 to NASA for the price that it would cost us to build two. That way we would get ours for free." I'm sure it was a semi-serious suggestion. Shortly afterwards, NASA announced they would have a lander, called Athena, in 2003. As for NASA's grand plans of a Mars sample return with the French, Everett Gibson told me "JPL has closed the MSR office and laid-off a hundred and fifty people."

The Board continued to meet throughout the summer until July when we had the first of what would be our annual July crises. The first hint that all was not well was when Steve Lingard didn't turn up for a Board meeting. Mike Rickett and Paul spent twenty minutes outside in the corridor whilst the rest of us sat around twiddling our thumbs. When the meeting eventually got going Paul told us that to get Government money for the Underwrite I would have to go with Colin Hicks, to see a man called Jim, who seemingly controlled the DTI's purse strings. Miles decided to refer to him as 'Jim'll fix-it'. In due course we met 'Jim'll-fix-it', who came accompanied by another man called Gavin Costigan, from the Office of Science and Technology (OST), because it was his budget that was about to be raided. They both wanted to meet Matthew and hear the Saatchi pitch first hand.

A couple of days later, Mike Rickett and I took Jim and Gavin to Golden Square at 8.30am. It was a chance for Matthew to tell these new players what he needed to make his life and the fund-raising easier: "I want a statement from the Prime Minister supporting Beagle 2, emphasising the science and technology aspects for educational purposes; an appearance by Lord Sainsbury in a video that I can show when talking to potential sponsors, and most important, we have to move away from the indecision about Beagle 2 being a part of MEx," he said, "the message has to be clear; Beagle 2 is happening, otherwise people will never put their money in." He got none of them. The last one was critical for him; he could have lived without the others.

Almost as if it was a planned strategy, Mike's secretary rang on his mobile to say the BBC website was carrying a story headlined "Lord Sainsbury has to bail out Beagle 2." Our agreed party line to any questions about this was to be "The OU and Lord Sainbury's office are having talks." Jim and Gavin went off to talk to Lord S so it was absolutely true.

They must have persuaded him it was a good idea, because Miles heard from Paul that the Underwriting plan was go and that he, Paul, was telling everybody the good news. The price of Beagle 2 was set at £29m with four partners sharing the cost. Then Miles had a call from Mike Rickett to say that Martin Baker weren't going to contribute. Miles was angry; he said "It's all Paul's fault, ringing round everybody with a 'Happy days are here again' message!" One thing about the decision that made Miles most happy was the DTI hinted that if Matthew raised more cash than was needed, they wouldn't be able to share in any profit. They'd been told the Government couldn't accept money so any extra would be a windfall for the OU.

Mike told the story of what had happened with MBA, presumably as related to Paul in the corridor at the Board Meeting. I remember Paul being particularly crotchety after that. He had laid into me and told me I would have to choose between the Comet mission, Rosetta, and Beagle 2. I wouldn't be allowed to do both. I had chosen Beagle 2 and handed over being the PI of Rosetta to Ian Wright.

But back to Mike's tale of woe: Steve Lingard had been confident MBA would be in, so Mike had spoken to their Finance Director, the unbelievably named Mr Badman, who said "Our Board can't make up its mind, it's not our main business." "You're withdrawing then," said Mike. "No, but I'll write a paper for the MBA Board to consider," was Mr Badman's answer. Frustrated, Mike said "Do you realise the timescale we are working on? Surely you can get a response quickly; you're a private company." On 2 August, Mr Badman rang Miles to say "MBA's Board don't want to take the risk." The same day he told John Thatcher "I'm sorry MBA ever got into Beagle 2."

The rest of the crew sailed merrily on sharing a debt of £29m. It may be that the result displeased ESA. John Credland was said to be very unhappy at the way the finance had been arranged. Rumour had it, he'd told somebody "ESA are so keen on Beagle 2 that they have been contemplating putting it to the

SPC that I take the project over lock, stock and barrel." Word reached John Thatcher that they still might be prepared to buy the Underwriting out. John had answered "It's not that simple," because it was obvious they thought it was only Government money.

Not long after, all the players in this little drama were together at the Royal Society for the launch of the rebuilt Cluster mission aboard a Soyuz-Fregat rocket. If it was successful, MEx would be the next spacecraft on the launch pad. They must have been queuing up outside, Mike Rickett said: "When I got there at 8.15am, Credland, who was supposed to have £10m burning a hole in his pocket, was trying to do deals with Paul Murdin and people from PPARC."

Everybody was wearing suits except me and Paul, who arrived in a baseball cap. Asked why, he said "I'm in my launch gear; we have to be more adventurous now we're in the entertainment business." Some of the attendees were counting the proceeds of the sponsorship fund-raising already. If ESA gave £10m, money that was ours already, it wouldn't have to be paid back and it would be easier for Matthew to make a surplus. One of a contingent of PPARC bureaucrats had apparently said "Any share we get will be cycled through the OU's research programme." If Miles had been around he would have commented "Too right it will, but what makes you believe PPARC are getting a cut?"

The Cluster launch was a huge success but it wasn't the only thing being celebrated. Judith overheard Colin Hicks boasting "I have been named Civil Servant of the Month on Number 10's website." This must have been a real feather in his cap and made him pleased that he'd left the Post Office for BNSC. His next promotion though was probably going to depend on how many millions M & C Saatchi put in the Beagle 2 kitty.

Chapter 12

WE'RE HERE TO HELP YOU

I got the impression John Credland was not happy when he rang me at the beginning of September to tell me that ESA were going to send somebody to review the progress of Beagle 2. "We can help you," he said. It was enough to send a shiver down my spine; I thought to myself "With assisted suicide you mean, don't you John?"

It soon became apparent to me that there had been an attempt at a sell-out, to off-load some of the costs, if not all the costs, of Beagle 2 to ESA. Credland was certain that he had done a deal. I protested I didn't need any reviewers turning up until we had had a chance to put in some real effort. Having only just got our hands on a promise of money, we had to get cracking, not waste time preparing a pile of paperwork for a review which was going to be a forgone conclusion. It was intended to rubbish everything we'd done on Beagle 2 effort, and conclude ESA needed to rescue us.

Review or no review, he was sending Rudi and an accountant, Torstin Switsur, to see me and John Thatcher next day about ESA's role. As promised (threatened) they arrived, Torstin in a very thick woollen suit; he must have come from somewhere cold. We already had a plan about what to offer them. Martin Baker hadn't withdrawn from Beagle 2. Steve Lingard told me "Mr Badman is back in his box, MBA are going to remain as a sub-contractor to Astrium rather than as a partner." This was going to be a strain on John's management so we suggested that ESA could buy in by taking over the EDLS lock, stock and 'two smoking barrels'. They could pay for it, they could manage Martin Baker. As recompense they would acquire the IPR (Intellectual Property Rights) for future ESA attempts to go to Mars.

We were surprised how easily they accepted it. We were down the pub before 12.00 noon for an 'all pals together' lunch. The visitors were on an early flight home. Mike Rickett was even more surprised, in fact he didn't believe it when we told him "John Credland wouldn't have sent Rudi without some brief about what he could or couldn't accept."

But he hadn't briefed Rudi. Next day I had an irate Credland on the phone, they didn't want just the EDLS. He began to give me chapter and verse about how they, ESA, had needed to rescue MBA when they got into technical difficulties with the parachutes for the Huygens Titan lander. For Beagle 2 they wanted the whole project. We should hand over our budgets to them. They would manage the building of the spacecraft, Astrium, MBA and all the sub-contractors. "PPARC can manage the science instruments," he said. It was now transparent who had been double dealing. It was just an opening gambit; "Bonnet himself has rejected your proposal for the buy-in to Beagle 2," Credland said. And there was more, "He wants a review of your PR arrangements. ESA have to be in charge of PR and there's not going to be any before launch." It's little wonder the public believe we don't have a space programme. When I later told John Thatcher about Bonnet's intervention he immediately suspected a wicked French plot. "Bonnet is French," he said "he only wants to ensure that the French beat us to Mars." He was becoming paranoid.

As the conversation with Credland proceeded it became apparent he didn't even have the money he was promising Beagle 2. He was going to have to bid for it to the ESA Industrial Projects Committee, IPC. This could easily go pear-shaped and surprise, surprise, Beagle 2 would be cancelled.

His next item on the agenda was "ESA want Lord Sainsbury to sign a letter written by the OU, asking for ESA to take over Beagle 2." We were to infer that Astrium were incompetent. When Dave Hall later showed me a copy of what ESA had drafted, it was indeed the anticipated suicide note. I told Dave "In his dreams, there's no way Lord Sainsbury should sign this, let alone send this crap."

Whoever orchestrated this little bit of skulduggery clearly wasn't party to the nature of the Underwriters agreement because they didn't know Astrium were equal partners with the OU. I knew who not to suspect: it wasn't anybody near Lord Sainsbury, I remembered Paul Murdin once saying at one of the early meetings "The fewer people who know the details of any financial dealings the better." I guess he hadn't bothered to tell PPARC so I suspected it had been the funding agency who had been courting Credland.

I was clearly able to antagonise John Credland ever so easily; all I had to do was say "No chance, John. I don't care how many meetings you've had or how many deals you think you've cut, if the OU, i.e. me, wasn't there, they aren't worth a light." That precipitated some real threats. He said "The review will be by NASA people, Rudi has told me your data are an embarrassment." I said "I thought it was one guy coming to help, not a whole bunch of NASA people." I was now convinced "help" meant "NASA will find you've not made much progress and provide the excuse ESA needed to cancel or take over the project."

I obviously had to report all this to Miles. I laid it on pretty thick: "ESA management means more paperwork and incessant reviews, all to no avail. Eventually Beagle 2 will slip into oblivion – all your money will be down the drain." I know how to jerk an accountant's heart strings. But every word was true. Miles soon got the message; it would be better to lose the money if Matthew didn't succeed than allow somebody else to throw it away. Miles was really beginning not to like ESA.

If this all sounds pretty bad there was worse to come. NASA had already said they would have a Mars lander in 2003, now they decided they would make it two landers with the same design and launch them separately to Mars to reduce the risk by doubling their chances. One US scientist, when asked "What about Beagle 2?" commented "Beagle 2 is like trying to hit a home run off the first ball." I think that translates to "six". Another scientist, from JPL, had the affront to say that NASA's rovers would be able to detect life on Mars, which wasn't anything like the truth. This was a war of words in which I was going to respond in kind

The chance came when I was standing up at a morning press event at Imperial College, scene of my previous misdemeanours with Princess Anne. There were about forty journalists present; the questions had a flavour of "why is Britain spending all this money on Beagle 2 when NASA is already doing it?" implying doing it better. The next questioner took it a little further adding "They have two rovers looking for life on Mars." I was already ****ed-off with claims that NASA had experiments on Athena to look for life and had expected this question was coming. I leaned a little forward on the lectern and said "Beagle 2 is doing science, the Athena rovers are going sight-seeing," referring to the fact that they only had cameras and a couple of chemical analysis spectrometers.

Boy, was that a quote to stop them dead. No scientist had ever said such a thing. A junior reporter from Radio 5 Live had recorded it. Somebody from the Today programme wanted his tape. He wasn't going to get it and only made matters worse by pompously saying "Today is the senior programme."

Predictably, Mr Credland was soon on the phone, his opening words "What have you done to me now? NASA has withdrawn from the review." NASA HQ had rung ESA and complained about me. Wait a minute, a man from NASA becomes a team which morphs into an official delegation. I could have said lots in reply to Mr Credland but confined myself to "If NASA has a gripe why don't they ring me?"

He wasn't as angry as he could have been. No doubt he was rubbing his hands with glee. I had antagonised NASA; I had given Beagle 2 the kiss of death; NASA would deliver the coup de grace. I soon learned that NASA had "relented" and the review would go ahead chaired by John Casani, a well known JPL 'Hit Man'.

Even with all the aggro during the summer of 2000 I was still able to do some fun things. Just to be different, Judith and I decided to go to Mars for our holidays. There are about ten villages called Mars in France; because we were looking for places to film for the documentary, we visited most of them. We didn't get off to a good start. As we orbited Paris on the Peripherique, a light drizzle was falling. On the Paris inner ring road one minute the traffic is hurtling along, the next it's stopped; you need to concentrate. Judith was concentrating when the vehicle in front suddenly stopped. The car load of West Africans behind us weren't and didn't. It was a bizarre sight, a crowd of men in flowing white national dress surrounding two British tourists. We joked about an impromptu inspection by the PP police. We spent the rest of the trip with a boot that wouldn't close.

We had another trip across Europe to Barcelona for me to give a keynote invited paper at the Triennial International Conference on Mass Spectrometry. We crossed out of Spain via Andorra, stopping off for a little while at the World's biggest supermarket dedicated entirely to the sale of duty free drink. We bought a few samples, making a mental note to visit before any Beagle 2 celebration party.

I also gave the invited lecture for an international meeting of veterinary scientists who carry out animal doping tests. The meeting was organised by the Horse Racing Forensic Laboratory where I had collaborated with the Deputy Director Ed Houghton on using stable isotopes to catch drug cheats, who use substances that occur naturally in an animal's (or human's) body to enhance performance. When we did the work it was pioneering. Now isotope mass spectrometers are commonly used for this bit of detective work. It's one of those space related spin-offs that nobody knows about. The public believe it's only Teflon frying pans, which is actually wrong; Teflon was invented in 1947.

There were a number of other filming opportunities for various TV companies. We, Judith and I, were asked several times to demonstrate the difference in scale between Beagle 2 and the Athena rovers, so off we went to the local golf course, borrowed a golf buggy to carry our model on my lap and proceeded to drive into a bunker. No sooner had we got there than it began to rain.

One of the requests for an interview contribution was for a documentary about a plan Britain once had to launch rockets out over the Wash from a place called Brancaster Sands. The site, not the interview, was still-born; prospecting for oil would have put paid to it anyway. Doing the interview gave us an idea for our own filming. We would have a day out on the Isle of Wight to visit the site where the British had tested rocket engines, when we were still interested in being a nation that launched its own spacecraft.

By now Circlevision were regularly joining us whenever we had something appropriate to film. For the Isle of Wight John Macnish insisted on hiring a helicopter for what he called a "value added" shot of me as he swooped down over the concrete emplacements built into the cliff. John liked action. Aware of the ESA machinations that were preoccupying me, he kept nagging for me to get him into to one of the 'blood on the walls' meetings. I told him "They'll never allow it," so he said "I could get an undercover camera and wire you for sound."

Before catching the ferry back from Newport, we made a diversion into a second-hand record shop where I bought a 1972 45rpm record of "Is there life on Mars" by David Bowie in its original sleeve. We were really getting in the mood now, anything was better than fighting with ESA, so that evening we decided to come home via Portsmouth, to drop into a pub there called The Mars. Seeing as how it was Portsmouth, it was Mars the warship not Mars the planet. It was in a not very salubrious area, but conscious of my avowed intention to tell anybody about Beagle 2, we went in. Before we had even bought a drink I committed a cardinal sin by sitting in a seat which, I was immediately told, wasn't mine to sit in. Some lady customer who came in the same time every night would expect it to be empty for her; presumably all the locals knew and had felt the lash of her tongue on previous occasions. Whilst the barman was pulling the pints I noticed a sign above the bar which read "The use or handling of prohibited substances will not be tolerated." We decided that some of the clientele wouldn't take kindly to being filmed. Discretion being the better part of valour we drank up and left whilst we still had the camera in one piece.

I didn't dare suggest getting a few seconds of the Casani review either, or a sound-bite from its Chairman. I would have dearly loved a full length interview. The review began with John Thatcher taking the Panel to dinner since their deliberations were going to centre on Astrium's site at Stevenage. They sent seven members from NASA, mostly JPL, plus an official from HQ and enough ESA engineers to paint the Forth Bridge. The cost of their travel and subsistence alone would have made Miles very happy had it been given to him. John thought he would take the opportunity to pour some oil on troubled waters by saying to Casani "Of course Colin's remarks about Beagle 2 and the Athena rovers were misquoted in the press." Casani looked him back in the eye and said "You're not going to tell me next that Pillinger is so naïve as to not realise what he was saying." John let the subject drop.

When the meeting started the following morning they had a huge list of items for discussion. We knew because ESA had faxed the list to Rudi and John had nicked it off the fax machine. Every possible system and sub-system you could think of was on that list. We told ESA "We aren't prepared to disclose some things, just as NASA wouldn't tell us." In fact NASA often won't tell you anything; there are a set of regulations called ITAR (International Trade in Arms Regulations) which are strictly enforced, so that no American will give you info about space systems for fear of imprisonment and a $50,000 fine. Nevertheless they expect us to be free with our information and in fact we told them most things about Beagle 2.

One surprise was they wanted to spend a whole day on an excursion to the OU to see and hear about the GAP. This they definitely didn't need to know, it was science not spacecraft. I humoured them, knowing full well that they wouldn't be able to copy it even if they tried, and besides it kept them out of everybody else's way for twenty-four hours. It worked; one of them commented "You have a nice experiment there." "We like to think so," I said, "we're offering a specialist mass spectrometer that nobody can match." It was true at the time and the situation hasn't changed since.

The other area of interest involving the OU, Judith and myself was PP. We knew we had this cracked when, after only a few minutes, Jack Barengoltz, NASA's main man, in a practical sense, for PP, said "It would be a delight to work with you guys, I spend my whole time at JPL watching what engineers are getting up to." All Judith had told him was "The GAP experiment is the whole reason we're sending Beagle 2. As far as it goes for PP, Colin is going to make sure nobody compromises him. If he has to stand up at a press conference to announce that we have discovered life on Mars, he'd better be right." Jack was very free with his advice.

They kept us at it all week from morning to night, when they went off for their dinner and presumably to talk about us. On Friday, the ESA people said "Casani's planning to have the report drafted by 1.00." By 3.00pm there was no sign of it. Maybe he was still on California time or had meant 1.00am because when John, Mark and I sat down with him it was past midnight, early on Saturday morning. Rudi and his new side-kick, an Irishman called Con McCarthy, dressed in the same kind of worsted suit favoured by Rudi's last henchman, were opposite Casani, smirking. I guessed this looks like they know already they have the outcome they want.

But they didn't. Casani's first sentence, looking at Rudi, was "Nobody is going to give a rat's arse, pronounced ass, about your orbiter, if you go to Mars without Beagle." We were prepared for a fight, we believed whatever we did in the review it was going to be a fix. Now here was this man, who everybody believed was a hired assassin, putting ESA in its place. If you saw the faces of the Bayern Munich players after they had snatched defeat from the jaws of victory against Man Utd in 1999, then you know just how the MEx Project Manager reacted.

Leaving him to reflect what might have been, Casani turned to face me and John and said "Your style of management is nuts but it seems to work!" Then back to Rudi "MEx risk management is a joke!" And what he meant by this he spelled out to Rudi and Con, "Give Beagle 2 some more mass, some relief on the schedule..." "Impossible," Con muttered. "And some funding" Casani went on, ignoring him. Now you know why I wish I had accepted John Macnish's undercover 'Glasses Cam', as he called it.

There were pages more of good engineering advice and an off-the-record reprimand to me: "Watch what you are saying to the press." I would, I had achieved what I wanted and didn't need to criticise NASA again; the US Space Agency had told ESA what was what in a way I could never hope to. Casani didn't say it but one of the other JPL men did: "Your Beagle 2 versus two Athenas outburst will keep us on our toes; good on you." Everett Gibson had already told me "When I read out the version of events regarding you and Athena, published on the BBC website, to everybody at the Lunar Receiving Laboratory's weekly meeting, I, that means you, got a round of applause." There's no love lost between the various NASA Centers.

Casani finished the debrief by offering John and I a copy of his draft which looked a bit like a war zone with crossings out and rewrites. Rudi, snatching it away, said "They can't have it; it belongs to ESA." Casani's parting words were to thank us for our openness and frankness with an intimidating bunch of outsiders. And about Beagle 2, he said "We have our arms around it," surprisingly sentimental for a hatchet man!

The following week I realised a lifetime ambition, I got to meet Charles Chilton, now a very sprightly 80-plus year old, and David Jacobs, to talk to the pair of them about 'Journey into Space'. I had tracked Charles down through a company he's involved with called 'London Walks', and through him David, probably better known for his chairmanship of TOTP's forerunner 'Juke Box Jury'. Charles and David's association began with wartime broadcasting in India. I've got two hours of priceless videotaped interview including David's longest speech in 'The Red Planet', Britain's fictional mission to Mars. As the Zombie Whitaker, he would monotonously intone "Orders must be obeyed without question at all times." I don't know why I remember it because it's a maxim I've never subscribed to.

Rudi and John Credland must have had to do some quick reappraising of what they were going to say to ESA's SPC which met ten days after Casani went back to Pasadena to review Athena! What happened, why and what their motives were at SPC, is a matter of opinion.

The first person to give their version was John Credland to Mike Rickett, who told John Thatcher, who told me early on the morning of Friday 13 October! Credland had begun by asking Mike the question: "Who is the person most likely to wreck Beagle 2?" He answered it himself, "Paul ****ing Murdin." He said "ESA presented a case for increased funds for Beagle 2. Everything was proceeding nicely until Paul Murdin popped up and said 'Britain has all the money it needs, it's only asking for a contingency.' It resulted in the SPC throwing the whole deal out. ESA has been working behind the scenes ever since to resurrect something. Now we are going to offer a loan of 20Meuros which you'll have to pay back." A smug Credland had reported to Mike, "Afterwards Paul said 'I don't know why I said that'."

I later got Credland's account direct. He told me "There was a lot of animosity at the meeting, not just to Beagle 2 but against you personally. The French actually named you." He told me, "It was unethical and unprecedented." In this conversation, Credland also said "Paul Murdin made that statement deliberately. He's too clever to make a mistake like that."

By 8.10am I was on the phone to Dave Hall who had also been at SPC. I said "I haven't heard anything about what happened yesterday. I was at a lecture last night and had my mobile off. Can you fill me in?" Dave obliged adding more detail. "ESA reported the outcome of the Casani review," he said. I thought to myself "I bet that was the expurgated version". "Credland and Rudi said they could work on the mass and schedule aspects, Agustin added

Beagle 2 science was excellent. But SPC have to approve helping with Beagle 2 finances," Dave continued.

In Dave's view, things weren't looking good for getting the necessary two-thirds majority in favour of supporting Beagle 2. "Only Germany looked a certainty for a 'Yes' vote, France and Belgium were dead against (Belgium always voted against us; it must have had something to do with MARESS and their Snow experiment that had 'melted' away), Italy and Spain were looking like joining the 'No' vote," Dave said, "so Paul pre-empted it by saying we've got the money, except any contingency. I think the use of the word contingency was unfortunate." The idea for the loan of 20Meuros had come up at the coffee break; he didn't say who suggested it but I knew it was a Dutch idea because Credland had already told me. Dave went on again "Now France became less antagonistic and it was decided that we should go away to come back on 8 November with our finances in order."

Why on Earth had we let ESA do this? SPC now had every excuse to cancel Beagle 2 on 8 November. I wanted to know where the additional money to repay a loan we hadn't asked for was coming from, DTI, OST or PPARC. And who was going to ask for it? Then there was the question of who was going to tell Lord Sainsbury "We told you we had saved Beagle 2 but now we want at least another £10m." Dave wasn't. I certainly wasn't. "Where is Paul?" I asked. "Gone to Chile for a week," was all I could get out of him. PPARC have a share of a telescope there. Again I said "I want BNSC to remember that I didn't start this fiasco. I never asked for the project to be given another £10m." Matthew Patten had clearly told 'Jim'll fix it', "Just stop dithering about approving Beagle 2 so that I can get on with looking for sponsorship." Instead ESA were getting in his way.

I certainly wasn't asking for £10m now. It was going to be bad enough having to tell Miles. I went to get it over with. When he heard the bit about Chile he said "Is it far enough? Is it long enough?" He was concerned we had agreed a deal on the basis of needing £29m: now ESA had scuttled it by saying we needed £39m including £10m we hadn't asked for; £10m that wasn't going to reimburse him for the Underwrite. "What's more they are going to claim they are the biggest contributor and try to call the shots," I said. I can't spell the noise he made but it's described as a 'raspberry'. I concluded he wasn't any happier than me but for different reasons.

Soon I had another version of what had happened, from Colin Hicks. It was clear they had gone along with Credland in a bid to get money out of ESA. Colin then left for Washington leaving Dave Hall and another David, Leadbeater, to sort out the mess. The new David, a tall dark-haired man, with horn-rimmed glasses and limping gait, replaced Paul in the action a few weeks later. He was our delegate to the Industrial Programme Committee. I had met him once before at a meeting of the Parliamentary Space Committee, where he had answered a question with a single sentence, easily several minutes long, without hesitation, deviation or repetition and with impeccable grammar: but without saying anything. The Chairman commented that it was "a perfect civil servant's answer". David's filibustering skills turned out to be valuable in situations which needed Committees to forget the difficult question somebody had asked before the end of the answer.

But back to Dave Hall; in a second call he had told me, "Some of the countries said they won't give money to make up the new shortfall ESA says exists, but they offered support in kind. The Canadians have phoned and asked if they can do the robotic arm." This explained a phone call I had from an Italian company; a voice had said "We've heard Beagle 2 is getting over 20Meuros from ESA, we want the job of making the sample handling system." There had been no hint that it was for free.

I was angry with Dave and told him "All these people had a chance at the beginning to be in Beagle 2, but didn't support us, now they get a whiff of some ESA money they are trying to get in to grab a share. Then everybody will want a seat on the Board for supplying a nut and bolt. Somebody, probably the French, will want to change the payload, then they'll want to have a joint PI. We'll end up with the same shambles as Rosetta. It'll be a disaster. We have to keep Beagle 2 as it is or we'll never meet the launch date or get the Underwriters' money back." My voice was getting louder. "We, that's we the people, who have put in all the effort so far to do what we need to do to get this spacecraft to Mars, will be squeezed out. The lander will be postponed until later, which means no lander. ESA will have got what they really want, an orbiter without a lander."

After this call I couldn't resist phoning Andre Brack. He would be in the know about what the French actually wanted to supply as part of the Beagle 2 package. He said "One French scientist believes you've changed the instruments on Beagle 2 without consultation." My answer to that was "If he wants to choose the instruments tell him to organise his own mission."

His countrymen's biggest beef was that they didn't want to be called 'adjunct scientists'. We had invented this term for the obligatory 'dining club' people who weren't providing any hardware but were supporters and would be given a chance to interpret any data we got. Andre had started to have meetings of a group of scientists, who we filled in with presentations about the science Beagle 2 might achieve. Andre had already reported most of this group were very happy just to be a small part. "But the French aren't," he said. "They want more." "But they haven't done anything to deserve it," I said. "Let them provide the Champagne!" It was his suggestion not mine; so much for French unity.

What was going on here was the old, old story. PPARC think we can have clever ideas (which cost nothing) and other people will pay for them. It's what I call the 'let's all go down the pub, I don't have any money but I'm such good company, you'll buy the drinks' syndrome. When will our funders ever learn we're not the life and soul of the party anymore and give us a proper space programme budget? Then we won't have all this grief.

I then got a lot of "But John Credland keeps telling SPC you'll fail without ESA help," from Dave. To which my answer was "If he was to stop slagging off Beagle 2, and ESA was to say unequivocally we were on Mars Express, Saatchis could sell the sponsorship, we'd have the money, be masters of our own destiny and could get on. He is undermining us and you know it, and some of the people supposed to be on our side are helping him."

I also talked to Alan Wells to see how his scheme for getting money out of the Millennium Commission for Beagle 2 was going. "Not well," he said "NSC has its own shortfall and need all we can get to complete its plans. Anyway Sainsbury doesn't want to see Beagle 2 being used as an argument for NSC funds," about summarises his much longer speech. I'd never believed the Millennium Commission idea would work and Miles was unhappy about negotiating through third parties. It was always going to be a chicken and egg situation; Alan had tried hard but, as my mother would have said "Don't count your chickens…" We commiserated with each other about the situation; I remember him specifically saying "If you sup with the devil, take a long spoon." This was certainly true; everybody at this particular dinner table had their own menu on the back of a tiny spacecraft that was carrying more than my experiment to look for life on Mars. I was going to have to be very careful not to let it get weighed down.

There was one more view of the SPC fiasco – PPARC's. I was told that various officials expressed every emotion from concern to being very angry. I'm not sure why, unless it was because their scheme had gone wrong.

Then surprise, surprise, I got Paul Murdin's own take on events. He had an hour whilst changing planes and decided to phone me. This was the 'How I saved Beagle 2 from cancellation' version. To paraphrase Paul "Credland painted a very bleak picture; I had to eat a lot of humble pie about various things which had delayed us. 'But' I said, 'we're out of the wood now'; despite this it was obvious we had two votes definitely against us getting the money

ESA were bidding for; it just needed one more and Beagle 2 was dead. So thinking on my feet I said 'We just need some contingency money.' When SPC postponed the decision it bought us time." I then got the bit about how ESA were genuinely concerned and were trying to help. I said "Crap, they are just trying to get their hands on Beagle 2."

But faced with the same alternatives as Paul I think I would have done something similar. Although more likely it would have involved two words one of which was "off" coupled with "keep your money." Nevertheless, I began to think Paul had 'gone native' in respect of Beagle 2, but John Credland had another interpretation about the effect Paul had had.

To complete the circle I left a message on John Thatcher's answer phone ending "If we ever get to Mars it'll be worth about sixteen Knighthoods for various officials and a plastic replica MBE for the team to share!"

Two weeks later, at a meeting held at BNSC, I found out that SPC had voted on Beagle 2. They had been asked for, and would give it 24.2Meuros. One third was to fix the telecomms. This was a problem we hadn't created, it was the Italians who let everybody down, but ESA were blaming us and hiding the extra costs (8Meuros) in our budget. Two thirds of the money was a loan to be repaid. Some of the two thirds was going to pay for ESA management (John Thatcher and I preferred to use the word interference) we didn't need or want. I later found out another cut went to Astrium Toulouse, who said they needed it to put a lander on MEx which they hadn't anticipated doing. This was being slightly 'economical with the truth'. I challenged Clochet about this excuse and wrung out of him the answer "We need it because ESA have asked us to change the schedule." Another economy with the truth; Mark still had his piece of paper from the dustbin.

In return for the money we didn't want, and weren't getting much of for work we had to do on Beagle 2 anyway, ESA wanted 'Europeanisation', responsibility for the release of data, for them to handle the PR, control of what the sponsors could do to publicise their involvement, two seats on the Board and joint chairmanship. This wasn't going to be good for Miles' blood pressure. Oh, and I forgot, a letter from Lord Sainsbury agreeing to the conditions. I asked the meeting "What's Lord Sainsbury's take on this?" The question was ignored; clearly nobody wanted to put it to the Minister. Even he might have used the word "stuffed" in the answer.

There was no way John Casani wanted any of this; I was there, I heard what he said and the way he said it. He wanted ESA to give us some more mass. The Credland version of Casani's report was what he hoped it would say. And I don't care what is written in the document. Casani couldn't have written what he said down, it was far too blunt, and what he did write down was designed to help us, not cause us more problems with ESA. Having heard ESA's wish list, I'm certain that I would have modified "stuffed" to something a little more robust and added "where the sun don't shine." I phoned Miles to brief him on the latest turn of events. He told me he was off to the USA. "Tell me when it's safe to come back," was his signoff from the call.

After this meeting, John Thatcher and I rushed to Kings Cross for a train to Stevenage. Fortunately we missed it; it crashed, killing four people. In my haste I had forgotten to turn the sound up on my mobile, Judith had heard about the crash and was frantically ringing until she got through to us, sitting on a slow, actually stationary train, cursing our luck.

We were still trying to fathom what it was that ESA actually wanted. Mark Sims asked Agustin about 'Europeanisation' and got the answer "We want to add some European instruments." When Mark said there wasn't room, Agustin had changed it to "Swap some of the instruments, what about the microscope? The Germans have three instruments." Mark said he told Nick Thomas, the ex-pat Brit working in Germany who was making the microscope for us, ESA's idea, using the words "for microscope read descope." He said to me "You should have seen Nick's face." Nevertheless Agustin told us ESA now wanted to review the instruments. Even Dave Hall agreed we had had enough reviews; He said "Casani looked at the instruments; they spent a whole day on GAP."

I tackled Con on the same subject at another Critical Design Review. He answered "It's standard practice to review the instruments at this stage, but it could be said to have been covered already by the thorough going-over Casani gave you," and went on "ESA will only give you additional mass for Beagle 2, as Casani recommended, if you show willing. Either that or you will have to descope the instruments." To which I said "We can only get any mass from the instruments by getting rid of the GAP, then there's no point in having Beagle 2." John Thatcher was there and challenged Con on the subject of giving more money to Astrium Toulouse. Con answered "It was all to do with late delivery of the flight model of MEx to the launch site of the Soyuz-Fregat in Kazakhstan because of Beagle 2."

Then he asked John a question: "If Beagle 2 is late how are you going to get it to Baikonur in time to be fitted?". John Thatcher simply replied "Colin will drive it." I would too if necessary. The model went into the back of our Discovery easily, so why not the real thing?

I asked Dave Hall if there was any precedent for being paid extra for a late delivery because it sounded to me as though they were being given more time to complete their work. He told me that there were plenty of occasions when late delivery had resulted in a cost penalty, i.e. the contractor had been paid less, but couldn't think of one where they'd been paid more. The CDR concluded that Beagle 2's mass was critical but they didn't give us any more.

One could be forgiven for believing two sister companies Astrium Stevenage and Astrium Toulouse could work together. Not these two; once when Alain Clochet was being particularly obtuse about the SUEM, the means of getting Beagle 2 off MEx which Toulouse claimed they had not budgeted for, John went out of the room. Five minutes later Clochet was called to the telephone for a call from Toulouse. Miraculously, when he returned the SUEM difficulty had gone away. "What did you do?" I asked John. All he would say was that "Somebody told Clochet he was making a career limiting move."

Whilst the CDR was going on, a Channel 4 TV crew arrived at Astrium to film for a documentary called 'Rough Guide to Mars'. During the shoot, I was casually talking to the producer whilst the cameraman set up. "We wanted to film you talking to Rudi Schmidt," she said, "but he told us he wasn't going to be upstaged by you!"

I heard about Giacomo Cavallo wanting directions to the OU to come and discuss Beagle 2 PR before 8 November from John Credland's secretary. I think I had more secretaries on my side than bosses. I guess Giacomo drew the short straw because they knew I liked him and might not give him a hard time. Wrong! Poor old Giacomo stepped right into the firing line with me and Miles doing a very nice line in the 'bad guy, good guy' routine. John Credland was supposed to be there but due to 'the weather' was unable to make it. The rain had been torrential, the worst storm since the hurricane of 1987. He was lucky. I was already angry; the storm had blown my greenhouse away.

But seriously, a couple of days earlier I had talked to Credland: "Giacomo is preparing a paper for the SPC meeting on 8 November" he said. I asked Giacomo for a draft. It began by saying ESA would appoint a European PI to share the responsibilities of running Beagle 2 and went on about European Co-Is everywhere, ESA running the PR, the sponsors and the whole works, even a requirement that the OU agreed not to do anything to harm ESA! I was incandescent. Giacomo said "Credland told me to write it, he gave me a draft." I was back to Credland on the phone in no time, he said "Agustin gave it to me, I didn't read it; Agustin said you agreed to the wording." Credland went on "Probably Agustin's boss wrote it." I tried to find Agustin; he'd probably gone into hiding, so back I went to Giacomo again. Now the story was "It's in response to a letter from Colin Hicks." I said "Well why haven't I seen a copy

191

of it?" Then I tried Dave Hall "Colin Hicks is in the United States, perhaps he sent it from there and hasn't had the chance to send you a copy yet." Again back to Giacomo, I asked for a copy of his copy of the Hicks letter. "Well it hasn't actually been received at ESA yet. It was a telephone call."

All this was like *Alice in Wonderland*, I would wake up soon; it was only a bad dream. Only ESA could get a man who I couldn't find to write an answer in response to a letter which didn't exist from a man who wasn't there either. It reminded me of the rhyme:

As I was going up the stair,
I saw a man who wasn't there.
He wasn't there again today,
I wish that man would go away.

I had one more try at Credland who asked "What's wrong with it?" I said "Everything, there's no way I'm agreeing to any of it." To my surprise he said "I've talked to Marcello, we agree it's unreasonable to expect you to. It's the Science Division's doing, not the Technology Division."

So I was waiting for Giacomo when he came to see us. Politely I introduced Miles as 'Mr Big' in Beagle 2. Then Giacomo and I had a real set to. ESA weren't getting anything to do with the PR or anything else for that matter. And as for statements about harming ESA they could sign one agreeing not to harm the OU. He offered to include a statement to that effect. "Good," I said "The OU is a bigger brand than ESA."

To emphasise we weren't harming ESA I produced a pile of statistics to show how many times we had credited them. I wanted to say "ESA only mentions us to slag us off," but I confined myself to "I have to get sponsorship to repay the underwriters and I can't whilst ESA are continuously saying Beagle 2 needs to be rescued; it's got to stop." Giacomo answered "I can't write that. The paper would be weaker than it was at the last meeting." He was practically pleading, "SPC won't agree to give Beagle 2 the money without concessions," he said.

The battle carried on for a while. Previously, we had conceded to ESA that we would refer to Beagle 2 as the British-led lander, now Giacomo wanted more "It has to be the European lander." That only had me repeating "We gave everybody a chance to join us at the beginning. They didn't want to. Anybody can be one of Andre's adjunct scientists, but he tells me the French don't like that." I then took the opportunity to give him an argument he couldn't disagree with, "ESA have reduced Beagle 2 from 108kg to 60kg, how can we possibly take other people's experiments now?" The French had tried to get me to drop Beagle 2 in favour of Netlander, with a sweetener about their next, now non-existent, mission. When I asked him "What's all this about joint PIs for

Beagle 2?" He said "Some members of SPC wanted you completely removed as PI and replaced." To this, I said "**** off."

By this time we were eyeball to eyeball. Nothing was said for thirty seconds; Miles hadn't opened his mouth for a full ten minutes. Suddenly Giacomo turned to him, "Mr Hedges, you appear to be a reasonable man; I won't deal with Professor Pillinger; I didn't come here for this. I came to be reasonable. What do you want?" I let Miles clean up. Giacomo reluctantly shook hands. Miles showed him out. "On the stairs," Miles said, "I told him you were under a lot of pressure from the OU." I felt sorry for Giacomo, I don't know why, after what ESA had tried to do to me. I think that day the genes from the bare-knuckle Harris ancestors had shown themselves.

It was Friday before John Credland rang. I was expecting it. In answer to my question "What is going to happen now we've strong-armed Giacomo?" He replied "He might have been angry with you, but not as angry as with me. He felt others in ESA had let him down." During our fight Giacomo had said to me "You signed the MEx PR agreement." I retorted "You'll have to show me." I hope he didn't spend too long looking for it. He wouldn't have found it; it's still in my filing cabinet.

What I wasn't expecting was John Credland to say "ESA still wants to be one of the Underwriters." I told him "That might be acceptable to Miles as long as the OU and Astrium get their money out first; I'll have to talk to Miles." Credland wanted to know if he could make small concessions to the various members of SPC to get their votes. "A bit of the XRF here, a pressure or a radiation sensor there," he said "but I'm not hopeful, a lot of people want revenge on you." I left him to it with "No deals on the GAP."

I had an inkling by now that ESA weren't about to kick Beagle 2 off, when before speaking to Credland I had had a phone call from Con who wanted to tell me "ESA are still interested in the EDLS, I might be able to broker a deal." He was almost whispering as though he might be overheard. "The deal will involve MBA working direct to ESA." Where had I heard this before? I spoke afterwards to Steve Lingard about it. It was obvious he had been primed. He jumped at it too eagerly. It was also apparent that somebody else was in the room, just as John Thatcher was sitting in silence at my end. John and I agreed that it was probably Mr Badman, and MBA had possibly been seduced by an offer which meant that most of any ESA money would go direct to them. We discussed whether it was designed to destabilise the Consortium. We weren't about to find out. I rang Con back; from his answers it was obvious it had been his own idea and he had been told "Con, no deals," by somebody higher up. He was apologetic and mumbled "It's no longer on the table."

193

As for Credland's revised paper and the terms of who would get what out of the sponsor's money, and in what order, or how they would share the profits after we recovered, if we recovered the outlay, they could argue about it all day and night with Miles if they liked as far as I was concerned. And they did. Paul Murdin was back from Chile and busy crossing sentences out and removing bullet points from Credland's presentation for SPC. Lord Sainsbury was saying he would only sign a letter if Miles agreed. MBA were feeling rejected, I was told; so what, that wasn't my fault, it was a situation of their own making. They wouldn't have got far with Miles; he wasn't in a good mood. He had come to a fund-raising dinner with me and Matthew, missed his train home, couldn't find a hotel and spent the night wandering the streets around Euston. I expect he found lots of young ladies willing to look after him. A wandering Miles would have looked a good bet to ladies of the night. Shuke Milledge and her assistant James Pillinger would have homed in on him two hundred years ago.

Meanwhile what were Judith and I doing? We had had other problems. We had to get the vet to come to the farm to shoot a wild bull. Miles was on the phone to me when he heard the shot and wanted to know what it was. "Just a gun," I said. It provided a little light relief.

With all this going on the extraordinary SPC meeting had slipped to 13 November. I was expecting a phone call from somebody to tell me what had happened. I got one from John Credland. It wasn't what I anticipated. It was a question: "The French want to know what Andre's role is and who appointed him.". "I did," I said in answer to the last bit. At 4.45pm I got five calls in five minutes from Credland, Colin Hicks, John Thatcher, Dave Hall and Miles; it's amazing how people want to be the first one to tell you good news; we were still in. I phoned Giacomo and thanked him.

SPC had wrangled about Beagle 2 for three hours; the vote went eleven for, four against. The decision was passed as long as I provided a 'Management Plan'. I didn't ask "What sort of Management Plan?"

To remind me of all this grief, John Thatcher gave me a cartoon by Richard Slade, a mechanical engineer who worked at Astrium. He drew them in his spare time (Richard, you didn't have any spare time) to cheer us up. This one showed a bunch of lifeboat men in life jackets and sou'westers bearing ESA logos; they were bailing out their boat whilst a fully rigged ship labelled Beagle 2 sailed serenely out of view. I usually showed his cartoons in my talks; I couldn't use this anywhere there was anybody from ESA.

Marcello was charged with getting the Management Plan out of me, presumably on the grounds he was the only person left at ESA that I wouldn't savage.

I agreed to meet him at ESTEC for dinner on 16 December.

Anticipating it might be politic to have some new members of the adjunct scientists group, Andre called another meeting. Dave Barnes, from the University of Aberystwyth, was the only person we didn't already know about who came. He is totally distinguishable in a crowd; he has a head of tight iron-grey curls even though he's still relatively young. I'm glad he came and that he became more than an adjunct scientist.

I was contemplating another showdown with Marcello; Judith and I combined the journey with a visit to Zurich for me to give a long-promised lecture to the Technical High School. On the way we went to another Mars village; it was the scene of a major battle between the French and the Germans over Alsace Lorraine as usual, not instruments on a space mission. Both armies lost thousands of men in the first encounter. The Germans had a Pyrrhic victory in the replay (without penalties) a few days later.

The Swiss gave us a marvellous reception; after all they were in Beagle 2. We were taken out in the evening and finished up looking down on Zurich, from a high vantage point, at the blinking Christmas lights below. It was as though the whole place seemed covered with snow. Down in the town we found everywhere was hung with crystal glass; by comparison Oxford Street is very tacky.

It was in a Christmas mood that I met with Marcello. At ESTEC he stays in a small family hotel, not one of the chains. Our dinner was candlelit, well subdued lighting. In the middle, his daughter rang. She was doing her home-work. "Dad," or what ever the Italians say, "I have to answer questions about 'A Christmas Carol' by Charles Dickens." I answered them all, even though what we had just been through reminded me of the Crones arguing over the drapes around Scrooge's bed during the visit of the ghost of Christmas Future. I hope my answers were all correct and she got top marks.

In return, Marcello agreed to help me write the Management Plan. In fact he said "I'll draft it." Finally somebody from ESA was helping.

Chapter 13

SORELY TRIED

There was lots of publicity for the ESA/Beagle 2 'accord'. A number of the accounts published in the media said ESA had saved Beagle 2. I didn't like them. Clearly the leopard hadn't changed its spots in respect of claiming we weren't capable of building Beagle 2 without their 'help'. If I was asked by journalists, I denied it. Credland didn't like me saying they hadn't saved us and complained to Dave Hall. I had a cartoonist modify a Regency cartoon by George Cruikshank which shows a ragged man, gagged and in chains. Its title is 'A free born Englishman'; Judith put it in the next *Bulletin* with me caricatured as the ragged man. The project newspaper carried our version of the 'rescue' story.

Miles was annoyed by the front page of the *Leicester Mercury* which said that things, which he thought Saatchis were selling, were being done by the National Space Centre. He told them they weren't getting them for free and should come up with some money. The *Daily Mirror* published a scathing article about what a scandal it was spending £30m on going to Mars when half the World was poverty stricken. Nobody liked that.

Even the *New Musical Express* (had they ever written about a space mission before?) got in on the act. They suggested Fat Les should change their name to Colin and the Mechanics to record a Fulham football song featuring me with Mr al Fayed. They of course knew Fat Les was Keith Allen who was friends with the Harrods' owner. How they knew I was in Fat Les is a mystery but now there were plenty of people prepared to believe the spacecraft would soon be featuring the logo of a store in Knightsbridge. I did nothing to dispel the rumour. It could be a useful stick to beat the Government with, if ever I needed it. Keith was now working with us on a Beagle 2 TV documentary, with him as narrator.

One of the high spots was having my picture take with Damien Hirst, Alex and Dave for the *Sunday Times* magazine. The photographer was Gerard Mankiewicz of Rolling Stones album cover fame. We were asked to lie on a red background whilst he shot us from above. An hour and more than five rolls of film later, he announced he was satisfied. Before we could get up Judith blotted her copybook by rushing in with her 'box brownie' for what she described as "the official picture". The shot chosen by the newspaper includes Damien's half-drunk cup of tea. We got permission to put Gerard's version in the *Bulletin*; Judith's remains unpublished.

For another arty photo shoot, somebody had the idea of photographing the model of Beagle 2 reflected in my eye; he thought caption writers would have a field day with it. I don't know if the picture ever saw the light of day. A less sexy photo shoot took place at the Shanks and McEwen land-fill site. It was to go with a story about the GAP looking for methane in the martian atmosphere as an indicator of an active microbiology. The martian atmosphere is very oxidising; methane shouldn't be there unless, like Earth, microorganisms continuously produce it.

I was not popular at the next MEx SWT. The French Principal Investigators for the orbiter instruments were angry. Rudi told them "The money for the Operations phase (when the spacecraft is circling Mars) will be tight." They immediately jumped to the conclusion that Beagle 2 had taken their budget. Despite his protestations that we had only been given a loan, at every opportunity they came back to the subject, especially when he said "The deep space network of radio telescopes, will be too busy to give twenty-four-hour Communications for MEx." The unsaid moan, no they actually said it, was "It's retaliation for Colin Pillinger upsetting NASA." The really annoying part about it was they didn't need twenty-four-hour Communications whereas Beagle 2 did, but they didn't care about that.

My very presence seemed to antagonise them; Rudi suggested that I should leave. That perhaps made them even more cross: there was nobody to blame. The moment I was gone they demanded to know who was representing Beagle 2. Poor Derek Pullan stuck his hand up and was grilled about who were the sponsors? To which he truthfully replied "Not my counter." The meeting eventually did some work, discussing delivery dates and Operations; it ignored the fact that there would be a lander on Mars needing communications, except in a resolution the seven orbiter PIs drafted, complaining about it.

In January 2001, we held the first meeting of the Beagle 2 Board with ESA represented. John Credland was the new member. Nothing could have been more amicable. It was agreed that John Thatcher would be Programme Manager. I, as Consortium Leader, would be present to represent the OU, at <u>all</u> meetings. Con McCarthy was seconded to Astrium to keep ESA informed.

Part of ESA helping us was going to be that they would sign an 'accord' with NASA to allow us access to US facilities for testing. It was to be an 'at no cost' deal. The facility we particularly wanted was a tower at a place called Plumbrook. It could be turned into a simulated martian environment with the appropriate atmospheric composition and pressure for us to conduct drop tests of our gas-bags. We needed to be sure they could withstand the impact on Mars. After the Board meeting, Credland went off to the States to see the NASA Administrator.

So the Board were happy but not necessarily everybody at the OU. Judith had given Matthew Patten a pound, but Saatchi's official bill was considerably more. Miles had told two of the Pro-Vice Chancellors to put it on their budget. With no sponsors signed up, they were agitating for an explanation of what had happened to the money I'd already had. I was hauled out of a meeting with the BBC, discussing a broadcast slot for the documentary we wanted them to show. I wasn't sorry to leave, the TV commissioners were being tedious, "There's no US angle" they said. "But it's Britain competing with NASA to look for life on Mars," I tried. "Can't sell that in America," a BBC man replied.

I was given the third degree by the VC's surrogates, Geoff Peters and Alan Bassindale. I felt like the little boy in the picture 'When did you last see your father?' Indeed, I said "If I'd known I was coming for this, I'd have worn my ruff." I can't resist making fun of foolishly serious situations. I gave them my take on what I thought, so far, had been an enormous success. "I introduced M&C Saatchi to the project, Matthew Patten convinced the Steering Committee to come up with the underwriting arrangement. That forced ESA to put its hand in its pocket," I said. "OK, the OU is still in hock for its share, but it should get it back. Meanwhile the project is £30m to the good in its accounts. Not bad business really, is it?" I asked. In response they enquired why did I want to be an OU Professor; "Have you ever considered a career selling from the back of a lorry?" were the words one of them used.

John Thatcher asked ESA to add a test of our Communications package with NASA's next orbiter to the list of things John Credland was negotiating for us. NASA's Odyssey mission was standing at Cape Canaveral waiting to be launched. Lester Waugh, Astrium's telecomms man, a New Zealander, flew to the Cape with his box of tricks. It was a wasted journey; he spent the whole time he was there sitting in a hotel, waiting, he thought, for ESA and NASA to agree terms. The JPL engineers working on Odyssey would have been willing to help without waiting for the official blessing, but Lester didn't have clearance to get onto the Canaveral site. JPL's Manager said "ESA and NASA working out an agreement is like the airlines negotiating trans-Atlantic routes before the Wright Brothers have flown the first aeroplane."

Dave Hall decided to phone NASA HQ. They were surprised to hear that somebody from ESA was supposed to be there discussing telecomms and gas-bag drop tests at Plumbrook. "Pity you didn't contact us direct last week," whoever he spoke to said, "we were getting our budget and the schedule for Plumbrook sorted out. We didn't know you wanted anything. Unfortunately it's too late now." I asked "Where the hell is Credland? What's he doing?" Dave didn't know.

It was a shame; the messages that we were getting back from the US were that John Casani had been telling people "I'm satisfied that Beagle 2 is on track. There are no show stoppers." Scott Hubbard, NASA's Mars Czar, told Everett Gibson "It must be alright, Casani's hard to please." Another clue I had that Casani was alive and well was that Matthew Golombek, the worst culprit when it came to saying that NASA missions were looking for life on Mars, was now carefully watching what he said. "No, NASA aren't doing life detection experiments yet, we are following the water to find the places to look for evidence of life," he was answering questions.

All of a sudden some people in Beagle 2 realised that sponsorship might cause them problems. John Thatcher was told by MBA "We didn't know the gas-bags would have logos on them; that will cost more." They didn't want to do it; they suggested we could photoshop logos on to the pictures taken on Mars. Another suggestion was that we could etch logos on to one of the filters used with the cameras. "Everything will then have logos," they said. Judith and I weren't having that, everything was going to be honest and as above board as possible. We thought having your actual logo on Mars was a big selling point and Miles didn't want to be sued.

We had been working on Beagle 2 for a couple of years but only seriously since the underwriting agreement in the summer of 2000. Before that it had been 'Marslighting', now we had two years three months to go to launch day. Credland had told me on the quiet: "The drop dead date for delivery is 26 March." The official schedule we had been given said we had to be at Astrium Toulouse by much earlier; John Credland wasn't all bad.

John Thatcher went to Bremen to see the big bosses of Astrium. Mr Armand Carlier, the major shareholder in Astrium, was said to be keen that company's involvement in Beagle 2 should be exploited so one of the people John saw was a chief accountant. John said "He was a little man with pretensions."

The Bremen boss, Mr Emslin, told John "I want to be kept informed personally." John called it "My golden bullet – if I have any more trouble with Alain Clochet..." He let the sentence tail off. The Frenchman's Christmas card had predictably arrived on the 9 January; John's sarcastic comment was "This must mean we can deliver on 10 April." Everybody laughed. After his next meeting in Toulouse, John returned with a mass reduction problem, unable to move further than ten yards from a toilet. I called it an attack of 'Clochet's revenge'. Clochet, however, was happy; Astrium Toulouse now had a clause in their contract which stated that if Beagle 2 delivered late, ESA had to pay more cash.

The bits of Beagle 2 which drove Clochet mad were called 'frangi-bolts'. These were bolts that expanded and fractured when heated. They were used wherever we needed to hold things in place so that they didn't move during the violent shaking things experience during a rocket launch, or as they would whilst Beagle 2 was bouncing around on Mars. When they had served their purpose frangi-bolts couldn't be undone, they had to be fractured by heating in situ. We had them everywhere. Richard Slade drew a cartoon of Clochet removing the Beagle 2 heat shield to reveal the only things inside were frangi-bolts.

Whilst Clochet didn't like them, they had television potential. We set up a test and invited Rachel Buchanan to film it for BBC News. Rachel is a flame-red-haired-lady, very appropriate for Mars, and one of our biggest TV fans. It was a real test; it drove ESA mad when we did these in full view of the media because it exposed the fact that space missions weren't infallible. I thought tests were to find out what went wrong and it was good to show the public the efforts we went to and the frustrations that went with the job.

This particular test was a good example. The BBC crew spent six hours filming the SUEM on a cradle from all angles and in between sitting on the grass outside while it was shaken on a giant vibrating table, to show the bolts would hold during take-off. When the time came to heat the bolts the heaters switched on and a count-down started; there was supposed to be a loud crack when the bolts broke. Thirty seconds passed; nothing; forty-five, sixty, two minutes, still nothing. The engineer in charge of the test said "OK, take it all apart," and later "Oh dear, somebody's left a washer out. Start again."

The second time round there were three resounding and satisfying bangs. The only trouble was the bolts fractured in an unexpected order. But the BBC were happy with two minutes of film for a day's effort and a good piece on

News. The cameraman said "If we hadn't been here, I'd have been sent to film something about the Queen Mum's funeral." The test manager wrote a note in the paperwork for the AIV (Assembly, Integration and Verification) technicians, "Don't forget the washers!" It was underlined. A note was made to check the order the bolts broke in when the time came to fire them in anger.

Clochet, and ESA for that matter, had some funny ideas about the SUEM. It was the one way they could be sure of ridding themselves of Beagle 2. "It has to work," Con told Steve Burnage, "otherwise it will be impossible to put MEx into orbit; it will be overweight." ESA came up with the idea that the SUEM had to be tested, after Beagle 2 was installed on MEx. They wanted the bolts fired and the spring, to push the lander away, released. John said "Fine, but then it will have to be rebuilt, then you'll want to fire it again; it'll have to be rebuilt and fired again and again and again... We'll never be able to leave for Mars, let alone get there." They told him he'd have to fire the SUEM fifty times successfully in succession during tests before Beagle 2 could be attached to MEx; it all took time.

A critical job, after all ESA's messing about, was to choose a landing site compatible with the EDLS. We settled on a place called Isidis Plantitia; it's the third biggest feature on Mars and can be seen by amateur astronomers with a half decent telescope. It was possibly a sedimentary basin and good for Outreach and PR, if the public could look at it after we landed.

I had heard NASA was also considering it as a landing site for their rovers. I was talking to Everett on the phone about NASA's deliberations when out of the blue he said "There's a meeting going on about where to land as we speak." Jokingly, I said "What we could do with is one of the rovers to come to Isidis. If they find some nice samples, bring them over and the GAP can analyse them. I think I'll send a fax suggesting they select Isidis as one of their landing sites." I continued to wind him up with "Since we're going to land first, I'll say come on over, we'll have the kettle on."

After I rang off, Everett dialled NASA Ames where the US landing site selection meeting was taking place, found a secretary, carefully dictated my message and asked her to pass it to the Chairman. She interrupted the Meeting to do it. I never heard the outcome, but they chose two other sites so a magnificent, if rather far-fetched PR opportunity was missed. What a shame, it would also have allowed them to greet us, in Stanley meets Livingstone fashion, with "Beagle 2, I presume."

We still needed to get on top of the Planetary Protection. Judith had been handling it up to now, but this had to change if she and I weren't to be accused of collusion. By international agreement, Beagle 2 couldn't be launched if it didn't meet PP regulations. We needed a facility where the lander could be assembled, free of microbes and clean, no dead organisms or carbon-containing contaminants to confuse the GAP. John and I tried visiting Glaxo-Wellcome, a mile from Astrium's factory; we thought they must have facilities where they packaged sterile drugs and stuff. They did, but the company was busy with a merger with Smith, Kline, Beecham. Nobody knew what was happening therefore they couldn't make commitments. John was disappointed; he wanted Beagle 2 built near Astrium. I wasn't, I wanted it near me, but a drug company might have provided a sponsorship deal; they have massive advertising budgets.

We turned to finding somebody who could be the PP officer or manager. Whoever it was going to be would spend a lot of time on the road going round the premises of the companies providing the hardware. None of the candidates we interviewed fitted the bill; we even tried an out-of-work man somebody from Astrium had met at a Christmas party, who had said, quoting 'Boys from the Black Stuff', "I could do that." We weren't so desperate that we needed a 'Josser Hughes'.

Then, as usual, Judith solved the problem. We had visited a company in Swindon a couple of times because they had a procedure, using gamma rays, for sterilising surgical instruments. We thought it could be useful with big items like the parachute that couldn't withstand the heating for over two days at around 130°C required for sterilisation. Judith was following up with a phone call to Andy Spry, who we had met. "I won't be here next time you call," he said, "I've been made redundant this morning." By lunchtime he had a new job a hundred miles away. You have to move fast with a space mission looming. We acquired a biochemist in a suit; he would get some respect from the engineers and hopefully ESA.

Our second lucky break with respect to PP came when I was walking back to my office through the BBC's part of the OU. I was with a man called Richard from OU's Estates Department who suddenly said "We can take a short cut through here." In a fraction of a second I was in Aladdin's cave, an enormous garage, obviously unused for some time, there were old-fashioned outside broadcast vehicles with flat tyres. Next door was a big store room full of long-forgotten television stage sets. All my prayers were answered; a place perfect for building a giant clean room in which we could aseptically assemble Beagle 2. Better still, it was at the OU where I could keep an eye on it.

As I knew the BBC were relocating out of the OU, in a trice I was off to the University Secretary, the senior administrator, to get my grubby paws on this unused building before anybody else beat me to it. When I got back, an hour later, all the tyres had been blown up; it was a transparent attempt to make believe the place was still a vital part of somebody's empire. It wasn't, and my need for the building gave the OU a stick with which to 'encourage' the BBC on its way. In retaliation they tried asking for £4.5m towards their relocation budget for vacating the garage early. "Ha, Ha!" was all they got from Miles.

The world by now had Mars fever. The Russians had a plan for bringing back samples from the Mars moon Phobos hopefully by 2007, more likely 2009. Japan had launched a Mars orbiter, called Nozomi. The French, still smarting from the US postponing a Mars sample return, were claiming the Netlanders would be launched in 2007. In Britain, Judith and I organised a workshop at the Royal Society to discuss returning a sample from Mars. As soon as Beagle 2 technology was proven, it would be feasible to have a 'grab and go' mission. The Japanese had something similar going to an asteroid. I told the audience "We did amazing things with two hundred milligrams from the cores of lunar material brought back by the Soviet robots in 1972. With techniques available in the 21st century we will be able to work with a fifty micron-sized grain. It will be like a boulder. There are two billion such grains in a 200mg sample; enough to keep everybody happy for years."

Paul Murdin, still working for PPARC, was in the audience and all for it. He thought a Mars sample mission might appeal to Lord Sainsbury and therefore be a way to up the space budget. The journalists allowed in wrote articles with headlines like 'Brits fetching pieces of Mars back next'.

The news went around the world. I had a call from Everett. "Somebody whose initials are G.W. will be contacting you," he said. I thought, this is Everett getting somebody to call me to get his own back for the NASA landing site wind-up. I killed the call and rang his office straight back in case he had found somebody to impersonate him from another phone. If it wasn't Everett, it could only be somebody Damien had put up to it. But it was Everett. He explained "This G.W. is George W. Abbey, Director of the Johnson Space Center and Head of the Space Shuttle program. People around here call him 'the Godfather'. He asked for your phone number." George came to Milton Keynes; he seemed also to be some kind of roving Ambassador for NASA. He was a large man with a grizzly grey crew-cut; he didn't look the sort of person you approached without being invited. He bought me lunch in 'The Old Swan', a local pub, with a very low ceiling, oak beams and a roaring open fire. He said "If the Brits are serious about MSR, perhaps the US could donate a Shuttle to pick it up from Earth orbit." Who says I wasn't flavour of the year in America?

Not long after, the Human Spaceflight Division of ESA called a Committee of Experts to consider future Mars activities; it was a legacy from the days of Paul Clancy. I was counted as an expert. We were told "When ESA's commitment to the International Space Station has been met we will be looking for a big idea leading to the exploration of Mars by humans." The experts agreed going straight to a manned mission was a step too far. There would need to be more robotic missions, including a sample return first. The programme became known as Aurora.

During one of the coffee breaks at the Experts meeting, I spoke to Roger Bonnet, saying "Isn't it great that MEx and Beagle 2 have stirred up all this interest?" He was disgruntled, I thought maybe because his territory was being invaded by the other Directorate. But it wasn't that, he replied "If I had had my way Beagle 2 would have been cancelled by now." "Thanks a bunch! And you know where you can put the Mars Ball!" I thought, moving away before I did or said anything more drastic.

But Bonnet was already yesterday's man; the new Director designate was David Southwood, the research student I had met during the BBC's coverage of Apollo. Our careers had progressed in parallel, with him climbing the administrative greasy pole. He is a Miles equivalent: he ought to be a headmaster; he perpetually wears a suit, has lots of grey hair and a moustache, and is not happy unless he's dominating a Committee meeting, usually with long-winded speeches.

I went to Southwood's lecture on the British leg of his 'Here is my Vision for ESA' tour. Here are some quotes that I wrote down; "We [Europe] are the richest group of Nations on the planet"; "Europe has a GNP bigger than the US"; "Not all the clever people are on the other side of the Atlantic"; "There is no copyright on good ideas whose time has come"; "We [Europe] should ask for a 5% a year increase in the space budget, 40% by 2010"; "We need to learn a lesson, we need to be better at PR!" This really caught my attention and others in the audience. During the questions somebody who remembered when the British Government wasn't interested in space referred to me and what he called "the Beagle effect". He said "The Beagle effect might help with getting a bigger budget." Southwood never demurred but didn't say "Yes" either. He obviously had his own plans. If Southwood wasn't thinking that MEx and Beagle 2 were the way forward he forgot to tell Agustin Chicarro. I went to another Conference in Berlin where Agustin was enthusiastically talking about a follow-up Mars mission that could be built by 2005; it could be an orbiter and lander based on the heritage of MEx and Beagle 2.

NASA wasn't doing too badly now; they had got their next Orbiter, Odyssey, off to Mars. We had a party at Astrium and watched pictures on NASA TV from the cameras on the rocket looking back to Earth. We had to do something equivalent to this for PR during MEx and Beagle 2.

About this time, Matthew rang from Saatchi's to say "I've met a man called Paul Leonard from BT who's sponsoring Leicester's NSC to the tune of £1m. He believes they're responsible for Beagle 2. I've told him sorry no; if you want to discuss sponsoring Beagle 2 talk to me."

It's a long way from Berlin to catch a ferry back to England. I got delayed, couldn't find a hotel and slept in the car on the dockside at the Hook of Holland. Next morning, back in England, before 9.00am, tired and cross, I got a call from John Thatcher with bad news. "MBA have sent a stop working notice to ILC Dover," he said. ILC was an American company manufacturing the gas-bags. To cut a long story short, Astrium were in a tizz; John had summoned Steve Lingard to Stevenage. I diverted there. Steve had already arrived before me. It was a sob story that he told: "We've run out of money, exceeded the limit of liability. One of the Martin brothers got worried. I wasn't there and Mr Badman acted unilaterally, pulled the plug!"

Mike Rickett was wheeled out and took Steve into his office. I found out later Mike offered Steve a job at Astrium in an effort to solve the problem. It didn't do any good. When Steve left, Mike, John and I put our heads together; we decided we should tell ESA that Astrium would take over the EDLS, so Credland and Rudi were summoned to come to Stevenage ASAP.

Now there was another meeting. Everybody realised there would have to be a price rise, however a price rise with a committed Astrium was better than one with an uncommitted MBA and Mr Badman. If we gave MBA more cash it could happen again. Predictably, Rudi was all for kicking the lander off MEx. "It will wreck the mission," he said. I was first to respond "Not an option." Then I got the surprise of my life, up popped Credland with "If you do that I'll lose my job, I'll have to retire early." "Blow me!" I thought, "now Credland's gone native." It's an ill wind... but I believed all of a sudden we had John Credland on our side.

Whilst Rudi was still carping on about Beagle 2 wrecking his mission the rest of us discussed finding the extra money we now needed. We all agreed that David Leadbeater had to be brought into the loop. Credland's last words to me as he left were "If we save it this time, at least it will put an end to all this PR and sponsorship nonsense." He might have changed his mind and had his own reasons for wanting to keep Beagle 2, but Judith and I were still going to have to make our lander unstoppable.

We already had our next stunt in hand. Steve Wilkinson had told us Greg

Dyke was newly installed as DG of the BBC. Just like Southwood, he was on a round of morale boosting visits; he was coming to the OU. "I'll button-hole him about a slot for the Beagle 2 documentary," I said. "Oh no you won't" said Steve's boss. Why do all these people insist of making a pantomime out of everything by telling me I can't do something? Judith found out the route Greg Dyke would be walking, it took him right past the door of my newly acquired garage. We set up the Beagle 2 model right in his path, I told John Macnish "We're going to film him, and we are going to have a second cameraman filming you filming him for a fly-on-the-wall documentary." I was going to doorstep Greg Dyke. If he refused to listen to me I would have it on video. At the last minute John Macnish's wife rang trying to persuade him not to do it. "You'll jeopardise the business," she pleaded. What was there to worry about; we had done it to Princess Anne. I doubted whether Greg Dyke would be accompanied by men with guns or even a pair of bouncers bigger than Mike Tyson to brush aside the fans.

An hour later, mission accomplished, BBC Execs at OU fawning around Greg were saying how important they thought Beagle 2 was. By the end of the day, they had had a phone call to say "Plans to screen a Beagle 2 documentary are in hand." Two weeks later we had a slot on BBC2 and Steve's boss was claiming it was all her idea.

Now I had to put one over on Southwood and I had something stored up for the right occasion. When his secretary asked me to call him on his mobile, I did. I could tell from the ringtone that he was somewhere in Britain. From the background noise he was on a train. "Where are you off to?" I began. "It's Empire day, something to do with Queen Victoria's birthday, I know because it's also my daughter's birthday, I'm meeting her," came the answer. I assumed he meant his daughter not Queen Victoria and said "I'm glad you're into to all that sort of thing, because you've got the Union Jack upside down outside ESA HQ and on the ESA promotional video for Mars Express." For good measure, I threw in "Not really a very auspicious start for the British Science Director; it's disrespectful. Besides that, it's a distress signal."

After that I had him on the back foot. "I want you to know I'll do every-thing in my power to support you," he told me, "John Credland will have to be aggressive though." "We can kick lumps off each other for all I care," I interrupted, "as long as we succeed and go down the pub afterwards for a beer. But tell him to lay off the PR; it's what keeps the OU at the table." He signed off with what would become his catch phrase when he ended a phone conversation with me "You can call me at any time."

Of course there had to be another Board meeting to discuss the crisis.

Everybody had stopped paying everybody else; OST weren't paying the OU, the OU weren't paying Astrium. Astrium certainly weren't paying MBA, who said they weren't able to pay ILC Dover. It was more like 'Mutiny on the Bounty' than the voyage of the Beagle.

There was another element to this: the OU didn't have a budget to fit out the Aseptic Assembly Facility, what would become known as the AAF. It believed it was making a big contribution in the form of the building. Now I had the space, I asked John Thatcher for the money to from the AIV budget. He said "I didn't include it in the estimates." I couldn't believe it, "You should have, you always knew Beagle 2 had to be built under PP rules and you've been saying you want to do it at Astrium," I said. Now there was even more money that had to be found. At the Board meeting, Credland came straight to the point: "How would it be if we all put in another £2m, for starters." Soon everybody, including him, was giving all the reasons why they couldn't contribute. They all had to go away to consult.

Whilst they did, I attended a lecture at the US Embassy. NASA was taking looking for life on Mars so seriously that America now had a 'virtual' Astrobiology Institute, a network of laboratories working together. They were hoping other countries would collaborate. The Head of the Institute was touring Europe giving lectures to drum up support. The Embassy chairman, introducing him, referred to Giordano Bruno, who was probably the first scientist, called Philosopher in those days, to espouse other worlds teeming with life. "He became a martyr to the cause, executed without a drop of his blood being spilt," were the words used. Dave Hall whispered to me "There are plenty of people who would like to see you burnt at the stake."

I got myself rapidly to Kings Cross station. As the train pulled in, I was talking to Circlevision on my mobile. I was saying "The Bruno story will make a good filming opportunity." Suddenly there was a bang and everybody started screaming. "What's happened, what's happened?" I could hear John shouting. "The lady standing next to me just fell under the train," I said and cut the line. Later he moaned "Nothing exciting like that ever happens when I'm with you." Then he cheered up "Did you see any CIA men, with crew cuts, hurrying away?" The lady survived, by the way.

Safely on the train I received a call from Miles. "I've had an email from the secretary of somebody called John Taylor demanding my presence at a meeting. Who the hell is John Taylor?" To make matters worse Mr Taylor or his secretary, whose email address was 'carless.wendy', thought Miles was the MD of Astrium. "I almost answered it **** off," he finished. "Just as well you didn't," I said, "he's the Chief of the Research Councils, controls OST/PPARC and a lot more budgets." "Oh," he said, "careless Wendy. Anyway I am not going, you can." I went to see him for a briefing when I got back.

More bad news: he had been to the Vice-Chancellor's Advisory Committee and floated the idea of another £2m; he'd got short shrift. He was feeling very exposed. Sir John Daniel was leaving in September and Miles would be carrying the can for his Beagle 2 investments without Sir John's support. So I tried to cheer him up with my solution to the current problems.

Because all the money connected with Beagle 2 was flowing through his accounts, the OU was going to be eligible for some cash from a new government source called the Strategic Research Investment Fund, SRIF. The amount would be proportional to the University's outside research income. I told him "I reckon it will be about £2.5m more than it would otherwise be, just due to the Beagle 2 money we're getting through the underwrite." I went on "If we give the SRIF money to Beagle 2, Credland will probably match it. He can give his money to us for turning the garage into an AAF, we'll have it as a asset for the future if some other Mars opportunities come off. There certainly won't be more missions to land on Mars soon if we don't do Beagle 2."

I was just warming up, "If we make the first move, we can call the shots. You could make it a condition that we get first cut of anything Matthew gets." At first he wasn't keen, then after some thought said "I like it." Having got him pointed in the right direction, I suggested "Mark Sims can carry out a review of the costs and when he comes up with a number Astrium can do their bit towards a solution by accepting a fixed-price contract. The DTI can help out by being the last people to get their money back." He was now listening intently so I pushed on. "Maybe the NSC can still get something out of the Millennium Commission to spread the risk even further." He couldn't see any flaws in the argument so he put my idea to the VC's helpers; again they said "No more money."

I didn't tell him my other solution: pull the essential people out of MBA to form a new company for Steve Lingard. Miles had instructed me not to get involved between Astrium and MBA; particularly not to speak to any lawyers. I didn't tell him about the one who called me representing Marco Pierre White during the spat with Damien who I'd told "****-off."

John Thatcher didn't like the AAF solution; he threw all his toys out of the pram, turned his phone off and refused to talk to me. Mike Rickett said "He's getting too emotionally involved." Judith thought it would be a good idea to put an announcement up on the Beagle 2 website: "June 2001: two years to launch, major contractor pulled out, financial crisis, Programme Manager not speaking to PI, Inquiry threatened, International incident likely, ESA to put dog down! Welcome to the mad house." I said "The bit about the dog should clinch it; there'll be a public outcry." When the Soviets launched Laika, the first space traveller, the Brits picketed their Embassy because the dog was going to die. Nobody gave a toss when they sent Gagarin.

As if we didn't have enough trouble, the BBC were being dense. Some silly lady scheduler asked "Wouldn't it be better if we waited until nearer launch, when the programme will have more impact?" The way things were going there wouldn't be any need for a programme. I had argued over and over again with her that a Beagle 2 TV documentary should be a 'will they, won't they' cliff-hanger series not a fait accompli.

Mark Sims went through the Beagle 2 costs. Astrium sent accountants to visit all the MBA sub-contractors, mostly in the USA, and found they were working on the basis of what is called 'costs plus', which meant they passed on their expenditure to the project and then added a profit margin. There wasn't much we could have done about it. The project hadn't been in a position to sign any contracts, it didn't have any money. Beagle 2 had to rely on the goodwill of everybody to keep working.

The new money to sort the EDLS and the AAF out was looking more and more like another £10m, plus a contingency for future problems. One piece of good news was that Mike Rickett had met David Southwood, when both were at a rained-off tennis tournament; I wasn't the only one getting invitations to things. Southwood had said to Mike "Mars Express would be nothing without Beagle 2!" Rudi on the other hand took every opportunity at the next MEx SWT to say "I'm worried about Beagle 2." Everybody was, but not in the same way as Rudi Schmidt.

As a follow-up to our Chelsea Flower Show adventure, one Friday afternoon I went to Hadlow College for their annual prize day. The winners were disabled gardeners and those with learning difficulties, all of whom were Beagle 2 fans. I forgot my wallet and had to do some fast talking to get through the Dartford Tunnel to be home in time to pick Judith up. We were going to the Gala opening at the NSC. On the Monday morning afterwards, I told Miles, who had ducked the party, "I think we can forget a contribution from the NSC, we had to buy our own drinks; some gala!" And they had cast a steel cordon around Patricia Hewitt, the Leicester MP, and the Industry Minister who had taken over from Mandelson. Presumably, just in case I tried to get money out of her or, more likely, they were worried I might spill the beans that Miles wouldn't let the Beagle PR opportunities go to the NSC without a cash contribution to the cost of building the spacecraft.

Colin Hicks briefed Mike Rickett and me about the John Taylor summons. He said "Taylor wants to be reassured" and dropping his voice conspiratorially, "He'll do what it takes." Then he was gone. We weren't any the wiser. I'd had a message from Southwood that he was coming to see Taylor, would I phone him beforehand? This time when I phoned, he was on his way to see his mother. I said to him "I'm worried about asking for so much so soon after the Underwriting agreement, but circumstances have been forced on us." The words I used were "Like Mr Bennett in *Pride and Prejudice*, I'll be damned if I do and damned if I don't. I don't have a choice." He replied "It's only money," but added "I will have to go to the SPC for any ESA contribution. If I do, I'll be accused of favouritism towards the Brits."

Miles joined the meeting with Taylor by telecon. Astrium started the proceedings by announcing "The amount we need to take over MBA's role, and sort the EDLS out, is about £7.9m." Everybody present, and Miles on the phone, said "Unfortunately we can't see our way clear..." but nobody threw us out. Colin Hicks said "Lord Sainsbury is going to have to phone Mr Carlier, the OU's VC, Martin Baker and..." As soon as I got outside, I rang the VC's office. "The VC is at a degree ceremony so Lord Sainsbury will be lucky," his secretary said.

Before I left there was a row. Credland and Southwood wanted <u>all</u>, not just any, new money given to ESA and then they would manage the project. Mike and I told them something along the lines of "In your dreams!" They then insisted "We have to have a single customer. It has to be the British Government, BNSC or PPARC, not the OU."

Rudi now started bitching about everything yet again. He wanted control of Beagle 2; he said "You're making engineering decisions on the basis of PR." I said "That's crap and you know it; they're entirely decoupled." He called Beagle 2 an experiment which always made John Thatcher angry. John told him "Beagle 2's a lander and, almost by definition, more difficult to build than your ****ing orbiter." Rudi tried again, "ESA can descope the instruments and fly a package with just a camera." That provoked me, I retaliated with "Where's the mass that Casani said you should give us?" He answered "If you want me to be able to announce you've arrived on Mars fifteen minutes after you've touched down, I need it all for MEx fuel." By the time we'd had this robust exchange of views there was no way I would have let Rudi take charge of Beagle 2; he'd have cancelled it before we reached the outside door.

In the absence of the VC, who was taking his holiday entitlement, I had a meeting with his deputy Geoff Peters and Miles. I opened up with "I've been

told Lord Sainsbury was cross; Astrium got the 'he was very angry' version."
"Good," said Geoff, "it doesn't sound like the OU is being blamed." I didn't
care who was being blamed, he got an earful about all the people who would
be devastated if Beagle 2 went down the drain: "Kids who offered me their
pocket money, disabled gardeners, all the Astronomy clubs I've lectured," I
said, "and the engineers working at Leicester. Mark is so convinced we've
come to the end of the road, he's told his team they can expect to be made
redundant by Friday."

"It won't look good in the Sunday papers, NSC opens one day, Beagle
2 cancelled the next and everyone is fired. It's pretty clear BNSC have told
Patrica Hewitt Beagle 2 is going to be run from Leicester because Mark's the
Mission Manager, and they've lined up the Duke of Edinburgh for the official
opening. It'll be headlines for days." Now I'd got going I wasn't stopping.
"And you can kiss the British space programme goodbye; that'll look good
too. NASA big-wig offers me a Space Shuttle worth $700m on the strength
of Beagle 2 and the Brits let it go down the tube. There won't be any point in
having my group here."

He took that to mean I was off, leaving the OU to go to NASA. "Yes. Top
OU scientist leaves for the US," he said, "we could appoint you on the OU-US
payroll; you wouldn't have to go, just threaten to." I didn't think I was hearing
this; this was the man who said "Had I thought of selling things off the back
of a lorry?" Now he was going to use me joining the brain drain to bluff the
Government. The meeting ended with him saying "I'll talk to Lord Sainsbury,"
adding "and ask the OU's Chancellor for ideas." We agreed we could give the
NSC permission to run the Beagle 2 Operations Centre, to appease Patricia
Hewitt and get Colin Hicks off the hook. But there was no way NSC was
getting the Media Centre; we were keeping that for ourselves.

And so to the 'Gunfight at the OK Corral', another meeting held prior to
going back to John Taylor's office. It was a Friday and the usual players were
present, except Steve Lingard who had tendered his resignation from the Board.
Paul Murdin was also absent, he'd broken his leg. Miles said "Send him our
good wishes." They were the last pleasant words spoken. John Thatcher told
us another £10m was needed plus £5m more as a contingency to complete the
project. He blamed Martin Baker first. "They're responsible for 30% of the
new costs." Then it was the OU's turn; it was our fault wanting the AAF for
Planetary Protection. John was only just getting started. ESA got both barrels
"They haven't done anything about the testing at Plumbrook and their oversight
of the Management means more paperwork, more unproductive time." Leicester
hadn't delivered with the Millennium Commission; "The NSC wants something

for nothing." He criticised PPARC for saying "It doesn't matter if a review of an Operations budget gets top marks, we don't have the money."

These were the thoughts going through everybody's heads, he just voiced them. I agreed with everything except the bit when he said he didn't know about having an AAF. If we had to save money it wasn't going to be on PP and I wasn't agreeing to a mission without life detection. I had to keep them going. David Leadbeater tried to be positive. "We have to have something to put in Lord Sainsbury's box for the weekend," he said. I hadn't heard that phrase since barbers used to ask men the question when I was a kid. I always wondered what it meant then as I did now.

Miles, several times, tried to end the meeting by saying "I want to go home," continuously looking at his watch. We continued from 2.00pm until 8.30pm. The only solution on the table was for the Government to take the burden; the only compensation being that they moved to the top of the payback queue. Lord Sainsbury didn't get anything he wanted in his box. I hope it didn't spoil his weekend; at least he didn't have to be told Beagle 2 was dead yet.

In my rallying call I forgot to mention George Abbey's Space Shuttle. I rang John Credland on his way home. He was driving; I swear I heard him brake hard when I told him. If the line had gone dead and they had to pull him out of a ditch I wouldn't have been surprised.

I talked to David Leadbeater again on Monday morning, he said "Lord Sainsbury wants a crumb of comfort; a gesture of solidarity." I had to have another go at Miles. "Aren't you supposed to be on holiday?" he greeted me. "Obviously not," I answered and began on a new version of an old theme. I went through the argument about the SRIF money again. I said "On the strength of Beagle 2 grants you got £2.5m from SRIF." He said "It was only £1.5m." I said "It doesn't matter you've already got back some of your investment, if you put it back in again you stay at the top of the recovery pecking order. If you don't, you go down the snake, the Government will want to go top and you won't get anything more or not until they've had at least £10m if we continue; that's bad odds."

I then threw him a carrot: "I've talked to the Dean of Science, Steve Swithenby, he's agreed to let me have half a million from Faculty reserves. It increases your £1.5m to £2.0m." The £0.5m from the Science Dean was money that was technically mine. It came in as overheads on my grants and went into a shared pot for future initiatives. I was by far the biggest earner in the Faculty; the Dean could argue it was fair to give me some back. Miles said "I have to think this through," and went off for his fourth go at VC's advisers.

He had been thrown out on his ear after the third attempt, despite Geoff Peter's cunning bad PR plan of virtually exporting me to the USA.

Miles was gone for over four hours. I went back to his office several times. When I found him at 5.30pm he was sitting with a balance sheet of figures. "I'll call you in fifteen minutes," was all I got by way of news. A half hour passed until he phoned. "I've got to go," he said. "I can spare just five minutes." I ran to his office, three minutes had already elapsed. He said nothing, but pointed to a draft letter on his desk, indicating that I should read it. It was to David Leadbeater and spelled out the OU's conditions for putting up £2.7m towards the shortfall. The sheet of paper was headed 'Basis for an Agreement'. "So you've decided to do it," I said realising he must have at last followed my logic and sold it to the University.

There was still wheeling and dealing to be done, so my next discussion with Miles took place at 6.15am the following morning. Later I had a long argument with Alan Wells, who blamed Saatchis for not getting the money. I told him "Our fly-on-the-wall documentary" (we'd provisionally named it 'Beagle 2 Mars') "is now Greg Dyke's favourite TV programme. He's sent a memo round the BBC saying publicise Beagle 2. That's worth millions." "But you arranged it, not Saatchis," Alan responded and went on to press his case for more Beagle 2 PR at the NSC. I decided not to say Matthew had come up with the idea of Operations being in some sponsoring company's foyer. When he suggested it to BT, Paul Leonard said "If I get the money you're asking for it, I'll want it in a plastic bubble in Trafalgar Square."

I phoned Colin Hicks to discuss Miles' Basis for an Agreement. He said "ESA won't buy it, they want Planetary Protection." I told him "Tough, they're not having it. They'll screw up my experiment." I anticipated all the arguments I'd get. ESA would say that Beagle 2 should be built at ESTEC or, even more unrealistic, assembled at Baikonur.

There was no doubt ESA wanted the AAF. Southwood came up with an even sillier suggestion than I imagined. In one of his phone calls to me he suggested "We should hire a big military helicopter to pick up a mobile PP facility and fly it to Kazakhstan." I poured scorn on the idea that we could transport something like this half way round the world and land it in the wilderness. I said "You can't be serious." But he was. He clearly needed a realty check before the men in white coats came for him. He'd answered "I'll phone Miles." I thought, I'll let Miles deal with him, and warned his secretary Miles could expect a call from Southwood. When she passed the message Miles' dragon lady would be told to say "Unfortunately Mr Hedges is unavailable." It means don't sit by your phone for the return call.

213

I guessed Southwood hadn't got through to Miles when John Thatcher told me "Southwood has sent an email around saying you have broken the Agreement." I couldn't fathom what Agreement he meant and still haven't. Needless to say Southwood never copied that email to me and I've never seen it.

Judith and I left them to it and went to Mars again, the villages in France that is. This time we visited one that is really only a shrine in a farmyard. It has a stained glass window depicting the hermit St Mars with his hand held out asking for money.

In the middle of the trip Steve Wilkinson rang to say the BBC had woken up; they'd decided to broadcast our documentary, now called 'Mission to Mars', on 23 July. They produced their own 'Basis for an Agreement'. It said they wanted two more programmes before the Beagle 2 launch and the possibility of a live event at landing or when the first picture came back.

I got a copy of the signed Basis for an Agreement, the Miles one, on 17 July. I wrote in my notebook a quote from James Dean: "I cannot change the wind but I can set my sails so that I always reach my destination." Robert FitzRoy's book *The Narrative of the Voyage of HMS Beagle* describes the day when the ship nearly capsized off Cape Horn. There's a painting of the moment; it's called 'Sorely Tried'. If HMS Beagle had gone down you wouldn't have heard of her, Darwin, Beagle 2 or me. Maybe this time we had sorted everything out for Beagle 2 but I'd been 'sorely tried' in the process.

Chapter14

EVERYBODY KNOWS AN OU STUDENT

Having solved one problem, or so we thought, Judith and I returned from Mars. At our last stop we met Eric the Martian in a tiny French village that boasted an even tinier bar. It was the Café Martien, proprietor Eric, and was in the front room of his house. Never mind, it was a hot day and lunchtime. "Deux bierres, s'il vous plait, monsieur," I tried with my schoolboy French. "No beer only coffee!" he replied. It turned out Eric had a cousin who worked in Toulouse, home of France's aerospace industry. Soon he was a Beagle 2 convert, owner of a series of *Bulletins* and postcards to decorate his walls already covered with all things martian. In return he gave us two iron-on transfers for the purpose of making Le Martien 'T' shirts.

We arrived home to another round of torrid negotiations with the BBC over their 'Basis for an Agreement'. They now wanted to follow Beagle 2 as a fly-on-the-wall documentary; in fact they were prepared to dedicate several programmes to it, but they wanted to own even more than ESA. Not just the spacecraft, my soul and copyright of all the film rushes had to belong to them, their document revealed. They wanted to be able to pick and choose what they filmed; to have editorial control, guaranteed access to the labs, the AAF, even my home! They would decide distribution and they must be first with any News. Originally they wrote "News must be exclusive to the BBC," but changed it to "Colin Pillinger to agree not to talk to anybody else until the BBC has broadcast the story." I was not to speak to any other media for more than three minutes. Last, but not least, Judith and I weren't to talk to anybody else whilst they were negotiating with us.

It went on and on and on. They looked quite hurt when we blew them a raspberry. We didn't bother to tell them that Miles' likely response would be:

"Fine, £30m please." Then the BBC tried to pull a fast one. It was another eleventh hour attempt at getting a signature on a piece of paper. At 5.29pm one Friday afternoon, they sent a contract to the OU Contracts Office, where as a BBC contract they thought it would be rubber stamped. When I told them what I thought of this underhand tactic, a contracts man replied "The BBC already has an agreement with the OU which covers you and Beagle 2, since you work for the OU." My response to that was "You wish."

Dealing with the BBC was good training for handling the next phase of the 'who is going to pay?' negotiations with BNSC and ESA. The OU and Astrium had to sort out the putting together of Beagle 2 in the AAF. John Thatcher and I had had several rows on this subject. I called him for another discussion but before I could say anything he opened up with "I suppose I'd better tell you before the rumour mill does." "Oh God, what's happened now?" I asked. "I'm out of the project," he said. My immediate thoughts were, surely he's not resigned over the AAF or the problems with MBA. But it wasn't anything of the sort. He said "I've been feeling run down, so I went for a medical check-up and have been told 'You are going to have to take it more carefully'. The Doc said I wouldn't recommend two more years of the stress of delivering a spacecraft."

I couldn't have been sorrier. We had been working together 24/7 for over two years; I wanted to get to Mars with the team intact. We'd had to replace Martin Baker, now I needed a new Programme Manager. I talked with Mike Rickett who said "If there's ever a good time to change the management of a space mission it's now, because it needs a different beast to build and deliver Beagle 2." Based on this advice, I changed the Project Manager for the GAP. It had been Ian Praine, who I had borrowed from Astrium for the design phase. To make sure the instrument was totally integrated with the spacecraft, I swapped to Mark Leese, who had joined us from Canterbury and had previously overseen delivery of instruments to the Cassini Huygens mission.

Before he went, John put the PP aspects of building Beagle 2 into the hands of John Standing. John Macnish took some what he called "good television" sequences of me telling John Standing what was going to be allowed if the Beagle 2 spacecraft was going to meet the PP regulations. I was fairly vocal when it came to informing people what was needed if GAP was going to be able to carry out the experiments we needed done without fear of being compromised. I told the new John in no uncertain terms. "The AAF will be small; there will be no superfluous equipment; you can't build it unsterile and sterilise it afterwards, dead bugs are as bad as live ones; you can't take notebooks and diagrams in to refer to"; and worst of all "John, we are going to limit the number of people in there to four."

I had seen spacecraft being built before, not just at Astrium. The technicians doing the assembly liked nothing better than to hold a mothers' meeting around whatever they were doing in order to make sure they got it right. People are the worst source of microbiology and contamination. When building Beagle 2, anybody actually working on it was going to have to get used to getting their advice from engineers sitting behind a glass wall. And there was going to be no playing catch-up by working three shifts, all day and all night; I would allow two shifts but the clean area had to have eight hours to be cleaned and recover every day.

There were going to be differences about this but first we had to get the Aseptic Assembly Facility built. The OU issued an 'invitation to tender' (ITT) and got five responses, one from a company whose submission read "We'll build the clean room for free if the OU transfers its contract for electricity supply to us!" We didn't accept their offer and instead chose a company called Bassaire whose rep Mike Foster had supplied us previously for meteorite and lunar sample work, so he knew our problems. Bassaire came with the reputation of being the oldest clean room suppliers in Britain.

Now the project was on a different footing. Contracts had to be exchanged. A meeting was fixed between the OU and BNSC as the main funds were going to flow from the Government to Miles. Everybody was supposed to come supported by their legal advisors. The OU turned up with its solicitors only to find that the Government's legal eagle couldn't make it because he had trodden on a screwdriver!

There had to be back-to-back contracts between the OU and Astrium, primarily because it was going to be a firm-fixed-price (FFP) contract. ESA's contribution for the AAF would be an Industrial procurement through Astrium but the money would pass straight to the OU to carry out the work which was on our campus. The OU and Astrium agreed a contract with what was called 'a mutual release of chains' clause. It was essentially a continuation of the Gentleman's Agreement because everybody would have to agree that Beagle 2 was impossible to complete before the project was abandoned, without any penalty. Before Miles signed he wanted the Government and ESA tied in under the same conditions. We were confident that the Government would play along but not about ESA.

We were right to be worried. Almost before the ink was dry on the Basis for an Agreement document, David Southwood began saying things like "As Director of Science at ESA, I am in the position of advising BNSC [about the viability of Beagle 2]." It was obvious he wanted the decision about whether the project should continue to be his alone. Rather stupidly the Government, who would now be 'the Customer' for Beagle 2, had accepted his offer of 'advice'.

The sort of advice the Customer didn't need was of the type implied by Southwood's next pronouncement: "If ESA doesn't have all the information it requires, my advice will be not to proceed." These were words of somebody who hadn't got what he wanted, i.e. control of Beagle 2, so now was going to make life difficult. Suddenly too, Southwood introduced a completely new dimension in an effort to get control; he said "ESA has the obligation to meet the Planetary Protection requirement [for Beagle 2]." This was not true, the COSPAR regulations state unequivocally: "If a particular country needs to conform to PP, then it is the responsibility of that country's COSPAR representative to ensure the regulations are met." Britain's representative to COSPAR was the Royal Society. PP was a British issue not a European one.

Another shoot-out was about to happen. It was rumoured that Rudi was reporting directly to Southwood so that he could do his own negotiating. Southwood came to the next Beagle 2 Board meeting with a man called Ton Linssen, who at every opportunity went outside for a smoke. That didn't endear him to anybody. The pair's opening gambit was about Beagle 2's schedule. Southwood said "ESA have reviewed it; it's supercritical." Linssen pressed the point "Building Beagle 2 to Professor Pillinger's PP requirements is damaging the schedule for everything." I hoped we weren't going to have another round of "Why don't we just send a camera?" Beagle 2 was being built to look for past or present life on Mars. You can't answer a question like that by hoping a little green man will come up and peer into the camera lens.

Southwood then launched into the most ridiculous speech I've ever heard. "My technical team are urging me to allow Beagle 2 to fly, but I alone am keeping a cool head and urging caution. Beagle 2 shouldn't fly unless there is a 100% chance of success." Who did he think he was kidding? Two thirds of all missions to Mars hadn't arrived safely. You don't answer big questions before anybody else without taking a risk. Either it was a fit of pique or he needed a courage booster.

The meeting split into two. Astrium, Mike Rickett had brought Colin Milburn, a big man who looked and sounded like he didn't take prisoners. They went into another room with Southwood and Linssen. They emerged from their session looking like there had been a major row. The two pairs sat as far apart as possible during lunch. David Leadbeater, probably thinking it might be better to steer clear of subjects involving Astrium, decided to open up the joint session after lunch by addressing Planetary Protection and the AAF. It was a mistake.

Linssen started it with the statement "ESA can't go to the Industrial Programme Committee to get a £2m contribution for the AAF before October." It was still only 1 August. It was touch and go who was going to jump on him first; Miles won. He glared at Linssen and Southwood and said "You are telling me that you are blaming us for delays to the schedule but then say you can't do something for two months. And you want us to take the risk of building the AAF to maintain the schedule when you don't have any money to give me." He was about to authorise contractors to start work because the job was going to take twenty weeks and the schedule required it finished by Christmas. Like everybody else he believed the ESA money was already on the table.

The unsaid bit of Miles' challenge was quite clear, "What's more you are threatening me that you will cancel the project leaving me with a Facility with nothing to do in it, and a massive bill." Linssen clearly got the message because he said something to the effect "See it as an investment; you will be able to use it for future projects." I don't think it was the right thing to have said. By this time Miles' opinion of ESA was along the lines "if I never meet anybody from ESA again, it will be too soon."

There followed all manner of excuses from Linssen. "ESA needs to be involved in writing the AAF specification; we want to see the bids, have the figures, be part of the selection process; we have to have this information in order to prepare the bid for IPC." We had done all these things as fast as possible to minimise delays to the AIV programme. Everything Linssen said he wanted was countered by Miles with "Show us your money."

By 3.15pm, Southwood decided he had another appointment elsewhere and left Linssen in the firing line. Linssen was given a good going over because Credland had told us that ESA's contribution would simply be added to the money that they were already giving to Astrium; no mention of having to bid for it. Linssen said "We have to bid for it because it's an increase of more than 10%." I pointed out "It's less than 10% of what you claim in the press you are giving to Beagle 2, but more than 10% of what we're actually getting. So which is correct?" Linssen changed the subject. He said he didn't agree with Astrium's development costs. This was what the row in the private session had been about; I think either Mike or Colin had told him to mind his own business. Then it was the turn of the SUEM and a completely new one: software.

It was pretty clear from that meeting ESA were going to raise as many obstacles to Beagle 2 as they could. Miles was angry; he came home and drafted a letter to Lord Sainsbury saying "As promised, the OU were prepared to go ahead but we aren't taking any more risk." The letter ended with something of an understatement: "The European Space Agency are being unhelpful and thereby jeopardising Beagle 2." He showed it to me the next morning and said "I'm now going to phone David Leadbeater." He did so whilst I was still present and immediately asked "How did ESA react after we left?" Leadbeater said "Reasonable but not good enough; it needs to be stronger. I've asked them to be more positive; they're reflecting on it." At that moment my phone went off, I wasn't supposed to be there so I scarpered to answer it. Leadbeater could think it was Miles' mobile and he'd killed it.

Outside the room I got a message to ring Southwood immediately. I did. It was about the report he had received from Linssen. "Oh you've reflected," I said sarcastically. "No." No mention of reflecting, instead he ranted "It was all a disaster yesterday, software, SUEM, safety aspects, no slack in the schedule, sub-contractors on costs plus, no contracts, you can't do it for the money and Planetary Protection issues..." I tried to stay calm saying "This is not what you said earlier," whilst thinking, "is this what you mean by you alone keeping a cool head? And what happened to the help you promised? I certainly didn't believe any of it was warranted."

Southwood is a very difficult man to interrupt on a telephone; he never seems to come to the end of a sentence. I just listened to more and more in the same vein. "I am going to get it in the neck from SPC; I will have to justify giving you money." I couldn't get in "Why don't you tell them it was for a failed take-over bid?" but only managed "Welcome to wonderland," over the top of whatever else he was going on about at that particular moment. The only time he paused was to ask "What are you going to do?" several times. This was a clear invitation to either throw myself on his mercy or say "Oh dear David, we'd better call it off." I did neither. I said "I'll discuss your comments with my Management and colleagues at Astrium."

When he asked the same question for the third or fourth time, thinking only a fool would reveal their next move to you, I repeated the phrase that had upset him the previous day, "None of your business what I do," which only provoked the response "I'm on holiday but I'm taking the time..." he didn't finish probably expecting me to say "What about our holidays?". He changed whatever it had been to "I'll be on the phone if you want me." I just managed to get in "Have you said all this to David Leadbeater?" before he went. "Yes," he answered, but he clearly hadn't or Leadbeater would have told Miles in response to his opening question about ESA's reaction. I'd heard enough so I said "Thanks, anyway." I can't think why, he hadn't made the call, I had. Obviously his signature on the 'Agreement' wasn't worth a light if it came to a mutual release of chains.

I went back in to Miles to compare notes. He greeted me with "Who was that?" I said "Southwood; he wants to kill Beagle 2 but isn't man enough to say so. Not taking responsibility were the words he used. He put the onus on me. He practically asked me three times to cancel it. I wouldn't give him an answer but I did ask him if he'd spoken to BNSC yet. He said 'yes' which must have been a lie, because you were talking to Leadbeater and he'd have told you if Southwood had already been on to him." Miles picked up the phone and dialled David Leadbeater's number. It was engaged. "That'll be him doing it now," he said.

I left and went straight to my office, dialled Lord Sainsbury's office and asked for a meeting with him: "URGENTLY!" Sandra went away for a while before coming back with the message "The Minister's working on his box. He'll get one of his civil servants to call you." She'd obviously managed to convey to him that the tone of my voice suggested this wasn't a social call. Normally she would have asked what it was about, but was keeping her head down. I imagined Sainsbury, at this very minute, shouting "Leadbeater, Hicks, why does Colin want me, URGENTLY?"

After lunch I put in a call to Geoff Peters. I replied to his "How's things?" with a resumé of everything that had happened the previous year and the subsequent call from Southwood. I ended by saying "I've called Sainsbury's office." After he'd listened to my description of the whole episode, he commented "As acting VC I'm not allowed to say such things but I hope you'll make it clear to him what will happen if they try to cancel Beagle 2!"

He knew very well he didn't have to wind me up. Judith and I had a list of all the nasty news stories that were suddenly going to break if necessary. Beagle 2 was public property; we were going to make it very uncomfortable for the Government if Southwood bucked up courage to recommend cancelling our lander, I certainly wasn't going to do it for him. And I didn't believe the Government would either; they could only refuse to pay for it. Just in case, I planned to ask Keith Allen to get me an appointment with Mr al Fayed and let it be known I was doing it. The Government wouldn't like that, or ESA. Then public opinion would come into the equation. The next story released was going to be 'Octavia's pocket money'. Who was Octavia? She was a seven year old who wrote to us several times saying she wanted to be an astronaut and offering her weekly pocket money to make sure Beagle 2 flew. We would have to see if we could out-Clifford Max Clifford and get Octavia all over the front page of the *Sun*: "Beagle 2 cancelled! Foreigners can't tell our kids how to spend their pocket money." We could just see it.

There was plenty more where that came from and there was a list of examples of how helpful ESA hadn't been. We were going to fan the flames until they singed some very high ranking bottoms. It was August; Tony Blair was on holiday; John Prescott was in charge; who knows what grief we could cause with a 'Beagle 2 is cancelled' crisis with no other news around?

I talked to Mike Rickett. He wanted to come with me to see Lord Sainsbury. Mike had told Southwood "It's my problem if the FFP isn't enough. It's no good throwing money at Beagle 2, I can't use it, I don't have any more engineers I can put on it." This conversation appeared to have been at a social event. Mike said "I also spoke to Mrs Southwood, who said "I've had enough; we're supposed to be on holiday." This only provoked an "It's not me who's spoiling her holiday" answer. I didn't say "What about everybody else's?"

Mike then told me "I've fixed for Mr Carlier to tell Lord Sainsbury the FFP is a FFP and I've asked the Chief Execs of all the companies who Southwood claims aren't delivering to write to BNSC reassuring Lord Sainsbury that they can meet the schedule and their obligations." Mike said "But we've still got the problem of the SUEM and the risk that it might jeopardise the MEx mission." I suggested "We could use a pyrotechnic device to blow Beagle 2 off if the worst came to the worst." "No good," I was told, "too close to the fuel tanks." Con had already told us, presumably under instruction from Rudi, "If Beagle 2 isn't ejected [from MEx] the camera won't be able to see past its heat shield." As a consequence of the complaints we reduced the size of Beagle 2's heat shield. It might have been a mistake.

Lord Sainsbury wanted to go on holiday too. It was clear his civil servants didn't want me near him before he did. There were ways round them; they couldn't prevent MPs getting to him. The OU briefed the local member, Brian White. I contacted other MPs I knew like Tony McWalter. Geoff Peters wrote to Lord Sainsbury at his home address to make sure the letter got through.

I don't doubt everyone was aware of the dire consequences of us, especially Judith and her PR ideas, being let off the leash. It was having an effect; on 9 August, we were told David Leadbeater was going to speak to Lord Sainsbury about a decision. He would phone me immediately after. I was waiting for the call when I got another one from David Southwood. "I am keeping you in touch as promised," he said. "ESA can't give Beagle 2 a clean bill of health. Astrium have not got their backs into it, not put their best men on the project. There's no proper management in Astrium." The *******, then he said "with all due respect to John Thatcher, he's not doing it!" That made me furious but I bit my tongue as he went on "Astrium has asked for help. There's clearly a problem within Astrium."

222

This was outrageous. I asked "Are you saying ESA are going to provide a Programme Manager, what do Astrium think of it?" The answer I got to that was "Let Astrium make their own decision; don't cause Astrium not to accept this." The double negative was his, not mine. He babbled on "Please allow this to go ahead. Let ESA help. Have my men keep an eye on Astrium." He said "I'm telling you all these things because I promised I would. I'm telling you off the record." You bet it was off the record, none of it was true. I told Mike Rickett "I've had had a call from Southwood which, to say the least, wasn't helpful; you don't want to know exactly what he said but it included derogative things about Atrium."

What kind of relationship would I have had with Mike at Astrium, who had stuck by me through thick and thin, if I went along with Southwood who, so far, had done nothing but attempt to take over Beagle 2? Or, when he didn't succeed in gaining control, had turned to sabotage and trying to stop us. I didn't trust him, in fact I had written in my notebook, after his last phone call, "The more this goes on, the less I am going to regret writing a book about it."

At 1.10pm I had a call from David Leadbeater; he was clearly pleased, the Minister had said "Yes, and tell Colin I'm prepared to make a supplementary offer to Beagle 2." Leadbeater added that "ESA will help with the AAF, but they will treat Beagle 2 as a customer supplied instrument which means they will set a date for delivery, if we don't meet it we will be off."

I drafted a letter for Geoff Peters to send to Lord Sainsbury thanking him for saving Beagle 2. The draft included the sentence "We still have some concerns about the motives of ESA in respect of Beagle 2 and how these might affect the OU's efforts to recover its and the DTI's investments."

I phoned Mark Sims to tell him and his people they still had jobs. We had thwarted ESA again, until the next time. The next time turned out to be less than a week away. A letter arrived at Astrium stating "When the AAF is finished ESA requires ownership." They believed they were purchasing property worth more than £5m on the OU's campus in perpetuity. This totally unrealistic demand got the expected response from Miles. Nevertheless it set in motion another three weeks of threats and counter-threats. ESA informed Astrium they wouldn't get paid unless... David Leadbeater, at one point, said "The Minister will withdraw his offer if the OU doesn't give in to ESA." That only made Miles angrier.

Remember the piece of paper in the chest in the church tower. I decided to read ESA's contract terms and conditions very carefully. I discovered a clause that made it clear that when the Agency paid for something it only owned 'capital equipment which could <u>easily be removed</u> for use somewhere else'. I showed Miles and said "Call their bluff." Quite out of the blue, I wonder why, I got a call from Miles' assistant, Debbie Bomyer, she said "There's been an enormous climb down, everybody has signed up. As a concession, Miles agreed that ESA can have first call on use of the AAF for five years, if the OU has no other project requiring it, and they must pay full economic costs."

Work started on the AAF. When Bassaire and their builders, Becks, turned up to start the job, the MD arrived in a very large Mercedes, with the workmen. He seemed very pleased with himself and announced "I don't usually come on site, but this is a prestige job." There were all sorts of hiccups, none insurmountable and nobody fell through the roof. The most unexpected dispute arose when the BBC, who still occupied the studios next door, insisted we stopped drilling and hammering for eleven days because they had a programme to make! They were told "You jest, we have a rocket to catch." All the building work was completed a couple of days before Christmas, thanks to the efforts of the Project Manager, David Young. Somebody suggested there should be a celebration. All the bosses this time came; I went to the site hut with some bottles of beer, 'Becks' of course, for the guys who put in all the effort.

When he put up his share of the cash, Geoff Peters asked "Can you and Judith get somebody prestigious for an opening? Maybe we could arrange a PR hit to help Saatchis recover some money?" He looked hopeful and said "Maybe Lord Sainsbury?" We took the hint. I wrote to Tony Blair's Office. The reply came back "Unfortunately the PM is too busy to open the Asceptic (sic) Assembly Facility." Was he that sceptical about Beagle 2 flying? We did eventually get a picture of the Beagle 2 model with Tony Blair in it as he was passing an exhibit Taff Morgan staged at the Welsh Assembly.

Now for a change of scene; we were still using the analogies between HMS Beagle and Beagle 2 in talks and Exhibitions. Judith and I began wondering about what happened to our illustrious predecessor. It seemed that nobody could be sure except that the Navy had turned it over to the Coast Guard service and it ended its life as a deterrent to smugglers somewhere in the Essex marshes. Judith found a book about Darwin which said the remains of one of Britain's most famous ships were to be found amongst the wrecks on and around Foulness Island. The problem with this was the area is now a Military Zone. Several phone calls got us to a lady who said "Write in with a request." I enquired "Do you have a fax?" Unhelpfully she answered "Don't know the number. Anyway we don't know who you are." I thought about saying "How will you know who I am any better if the letter comes by post?" Or "I know the Chief Scientific Advisor to the MOD," actually it was true, I did, his lab had been next door to mine at Cambridge. "Why don't you ring up and ask him if I'm a spy?"

Instead we found an army man who described himself as "Assistant Range Operations Officer," which on second thoughts he changed to "Acting Range Operations Officer, because they've never replaced the person who was above me." I asked "How can my wife and I get permission to come to Foulness Island? We've been led to believe it's top secret." He answered "The easiest way is to ring Fred, the Publican at the 'George and Dragon'. It's a pub inside the perimeter fence. Say you want to buy lunch; he'll fix it." So much for our front line defences. Even so, we had to pass through the British equivalent of Check Point Charlie to reach the pub.

Fred knew another man who said Beagle was over at Paglesham; "Other side of the river," he said, "nice pub called 'Plough and Sail' there." Why does everybody in Britain give directions with respect to the nearest pub? We went to Paglesham in the afternoon. Whilst trying to get to look at a bit of timber sticking out of the shallow water, predictably my mobile rang. The call was about ESA refusing to pay Astrium again; I lost my temper, my balance and the connection, by falling into the mud. I had to wear Judith's shorts for the drive home.

I also had a new money lead to follow up. John Horlock, the former OU VC, who had said "Yes" to my going to Milton Keynes, was now Royal Society Treasurer. He told me "I've made arrangements for you to talk to the Wellcome Trust." So off I went to visit the Director, Mike Dexter and some colleagues, including Ted Bianco, who was in charge of technology transfer, at their HQ, an imposing building on Euston Road.

Wellcome is the biggest Medical Charity in Britain. I imagined they might want me to say something about building spacecraft, particularly complicated electronics, in sterile environments; "Could it be useful in a clinical situation?" I asked them. It was as an afterthought I said "We're building a mass spectrometer which will have to survive the rigours of a space flight to Mars, land with a big bump, operate autonomously at temperatures of $-70°C$, after it's been heated for a few days at $128°C$ to sterilise it. It ought to have lots of other applications." Actually the statement mirrors the last paragraph of Frederick Aston's first ever paper on mass spectrometry. He says in it words to the effect "If I get this to work there may be some uses other than separating isotopes." Mike and Ted liked my ideas and sent me away to write a proposal to elaborate. "Since it's outside our normal sphere of interest," Ted said "we'll send it straight to the Council, after peer review."

As well as all the other things going on I had to try and keep abreast of what others were doing in the field, so I managed to fit in a visit to Rome for the Annual Meeting of the Meteoritical Society. I hadn't attended since Dublin. I gave them an update on Beagle 2 which was well received. But the main purpose for going was to float the concept we had come up with for collecting a two hundred gram sample of Mars. Marcello Coradini said "I'll come and buy beer and sandwiches for a working lunch." He's from Rome and it offered him a good reason for a trip home. It was also a good opportunity for Circlevision to get an interview with him in the can. We did a very cheesy piece with me throwing a coin over my left shoulder into the Trevi fountains and wishing for a rapid return to Mars for a sample after a Beagle 2 success. It's supposed to be wishing for a return to Rome but I'd already done that. Like everyone else I had thrown my coin in 1969 when I last stood there, anticipating receiving the Apollo lunar samples.

That finished, we sat down for a beer and then began to stroll back to the Conference, when as usual my phone rang. It was Judith and 9/11; terrorists had flown Jumbo jets into the World Trade Center and the Pentagon. Judith said "You'd better get out of Rome; they are closing airports everywhere so expect a rush to the trains. They may even cancel them." Pausing only to tell the organisers of the meeting what had happened, half the attendees were American, I hightailed it to the station and home.

At my next progress meeting with Matthew Patten, he was very down. The advertising business had gone into recession in the aftermath of 9/11. He had people he was talking to who were saying "We're interested but can't possibly make any decisions at present because of the financial climate." He was worried the fee Miles paid him was about to run out and anticipated that the Beagle Board wouldn't want it to be continued in the current climate. We decided to go into hibernation for a while.

Now was definitely not a very good time to be talking to airlines which was a shame because Matthew had been trying to link Beagle 2's voyage to Mars with the Airmiles scheme. He had also been talking to a company in the Defence business; they had said "We're preoccupied with training fighter pilots at the moment." He'd decided not to pursue that one either as a sponsorship opportunity.

Our best bet remained Paul Leonard at BT. I thought I might have blown it with Paul. After our first encounter I had invited him to the OU to look around. I said "Come and see for yourself what's going on with Beagle 2." He had come the day I had declined Southwood's invitation to cancel the lander for him. I had arrived back in my office white with anger. Paul had taken one look at my face and said "I don't think this is a good time to be here." I had apologised and said "You're right; I wouldn't do Beagle 2 justice right now." I liked Paul; he was easy-going, didn't wear a suit and spent lots of his time at sporting events. He had tactfully gone home and we were trying to rearrange a date.

Instead Matthew fixed another session in London. Far from being put off by our last encounter, Paul was full of ideas about how BT might exploit a relationship with Beagle 2. He wanted it to fit with their core business: information and messages from Beagle 2 about results and activities direct to customers using their land lines for the internet or their mobile service O_2. He liked the advertising campaign Judith and I had dreamed up: 'BT is calling you from Mars' – not the planet but the various places we had found which were called Mars. It would climax when Beagle 2 actually landed on Mars at Christmas 2003 and we made the ultimate call.

Paul was very laid back about the amount of money Beagle 2 was looking for. "We have twenty-eight million customers using our land lines alone," he said, "we could add a pound to every bill to pay for the mission. They can cross it off if they don't want to contribute." A deal this big however wouldn't be his decision; "It will have to go much higher. Now is not a good time," he warned.

We had, hopefully, put an end to the wrangling about who paid what and to whom and had to get on with the serious work of building a spacecraft for delivery in just a little more than a year. We were having what we called the 'Systems Team' meetings every two weeks, rotating them between the OU, Astrium and Leicester. At these we went through the progress, or lack of it, that had been made with every part of the project. A couple of new faces were introduced: Stuart Hurst, who was the electrical engineer from Astrium and Terry Ransome who took on the essential task of gathering or arranging for all the myriad, bits needed to put Beagle 2 together to be in the right place at the right time.

The new Programme Manager, Barrie Kirk, was completely different from John Thatcher; he was totally focused on the engineering task in hand. When I suggested a get-together for the team at Christmas, I said "I don't expect there will be time next year." Barrie answered "I don't socialise." When I had said "We ought to thank Bassaire and Becks for all the effort they have put in to get the AAF ready," he replied "They'll only charge us for the time [they spend at the party]." I tried him on "How do I contact you?" to which the response was "I don't have a mobile." His one concession to PR was to agree to tell me whenever there was going to be an engineering test so that I could bring a camera to record it for posterity, and hopefully TV, getting agreement with the

BBC permitting. Barrie however was what the project needed if it was going to meet the schedule, I didn't need to love him, he was doing a good job.

I went ahead with the party. Mark Sims and I did a photo shoot at Xcape, the artificial ski slope in Milton Keynes. It gave us a chance to show off multi-coloured sweaters and bobble hats as favoured by anoraks. The pictures were used for the 2001 Christmas postcard. Actually, Becky borrowed the sweater I wore from Norman, one of our technicians. I didn't give it back to him in time for him to go home on a really cold day.

For the party we put together a compilation from the video footage we had collected and played Gene Vincent's 'I want to get you on a rocket ship to Mars' in the background. I now had a video collection the like of which had never been seen before. For example, Denis Leigh had the GAP mass spectrometer on test in his back bedroom so he could keep tabs on it twenty-four hours a day. You never see pictures of high tech equipment in rooms lit by a single bare lightbulb dangling on a piece of flex on 'Horizon'. Nor are the instruments supported by a pile of paperback detective novels. Denis's wife gave an interview in which she declared "Denis loves mass spectrometers more than me."

The activities of the Systems Team gave Barrie lots to report at the next Board Meeting. An uneasy peace had broken out. ESA had taken their proposal for giving more money to Beagle 2 to the IPC. Dave Hall said the discussion got quite "vitriolic". So much so the Chairman suspended proceedings. When the meeting restarted it was put to the vote and six nations, including the usual suspects, France, Italy and Belgium, abstained. The Italians wanted an open competition with the AAF sited at an existing ESA site, presumably in Italy. A decision on the contract was deferred until February 2002. It didn't improve Miles' temper or his opinion of ESA.

Although they weren't prepared to vote for Beagle 2 getting the promised money, it didn't stop the French from demanding that Astrium give them all the information the project had on the gas-bags for the EDLS, so the Beagle 2 designs could be incorporated into their Netlander project. Astrium said "Get stuffed." So the French went to David Leadbeater who said "Get stuffed!" as well, except it took fifteen minutes in civil servant speak, by which time the French had probably forgotten what they'd asked for.

An area in which the testing was going to be very visual, I hoped, concerned the gas-bags. These were made out of Kevlar, the material used for bullet-proof vests, coated on the inside with a layer of polymer, like the bladder in a football. Three of the bags would be laced together with Beagle 2 inside. They had to be inflated with a gas generator during the landing process but to test them on the ground they were blown up with gas from a cylinder. Leaks were looked for, in the best tradition, by submersing the bag in a tank of water to see if there were any bubbles. Primitive, but it worked when I was finding punctures on my first bike and it worked now. Unfortunately they weren't gas-tight the first time round.

We had finally got access to the drop-test facility at Plumbrook. We had to fit in with the test programme being carried out for NASA's Exploration Rovers. NASA had dropped the name Athena; their landers were called the MERs 'Spirit' and 'Opportunity'. Fortunately the same company, ILC Dover, was making their bags and ours. There was a difference however. The rovers had twenty bags whereas we had only three; when put together MER's protective cocoon was the size of a double-decker bus, our three had a diameter the same as the height of one of the bus passengers.

After a lot of wrangling over ITAR, I sent John Macnish to film at Plumbrook. He took a copy of the documentary that had recently been shown by the BBC to play for the test crew. It went down well, especially Dave Roundtree's comment about the cost of NASA's screwdrivers. In fact US test team said "We'll club together to buy one to send Colin." It never arrived; it must have been too expensive.

More likely, they were preoccupied with the proper inflation test which failed spectacularly. A set of bags were suspended on a hoist in the test chamber and a count-down started until the device to puncture the gas canister was fired releasing all the gas instantaneously to inflate the bags. They were recording the activity with a camera taking pictures at intervals of a fraction of a second. John said "It was quite amazing. In one frame you could see the bags start to inflate. In the next there was just a collection of rags spinning on a hook." John wasn't filming the bags but the people watching. The expressions on their faces said it all, "Back to the drawing board."

I told Barrie "If ESA get to hear of this, they'll go into 'Oh dear we have to cancel Beagle 2' mode again." He agreed, and to my request to refer any questions about the test, if the media got to hear, to me. As far as I was concerned it was a test and we had found out the limit of the bags. If they hadn't gone bang, we wouldn't know what their limit was. The biggest problem was going to be getting more slots at Plumbrook to perform a repeat test. We also needed another set of bags; we weren't going to be able to recycle this lot.

I was getting plenty of opportunities to spread the word about Beagle 2 far and wide. I was asked to present prizes at the Beagle dog show; the invitation came from a man who said "I work for the Government," but refused to elaborate. Judith and I walked around cages of beagles and were told that these dogs were their own worst enemy. They practically will open the doors

229

of their boxes, get inside, and close the door behind them. But let them off the lead outdoors and you'd be lucky to see them again. I was pictured with the Champion dog: 'Jesson Musket'.

On a more conventional science front, I was invited to give a lecture to the Rothhamsted Experimental Agricultural Station, famous for the fields whose crops, rotations, cultivations and fertiliser applications have been recorded since 1843 on an estate whose history goes back to the 1600s. The lecture was in memory of Ronald Fisher, who was described to me as the genius who single-handedly created the science of statistical biology. They gave me a plaque to commemorate the occasion which demonstrated that Beagle 2 was definitely uniting all the disciplines of science.

Milton Keynes Astronomy Society also decided to invite me to give their named lecture: the Richard Lambert Lecture. I thought no need to rush; I can easily get there in time. Wrong! I couldn't find the Hall; the secretary had given me written instructions. Quite how I was supposed to read them whilst driving in the dark, I'll never know. I was late; as I pulled up outside a limousine was drawing away. It was the Mayor's car replete with Mayor in gold chains. I thought "Oh ****, they must have invited him to introduce me." Wrong again, the Mayor had come for another function and found the Astronomy Society in session. A row had ensued as to whose booking took precedence, I fortunately missed it, but it made me realise audiences were now fighting to hear talks about Beagle 2.

The gig I would have liked to have done, but it never happened, was 'Space Rocks'. Everett told me the President of the University of Houston had offered the use of the 60,000 seat football stadium for staging a rock concert to coincide with the International Space Congress being held in the city. A lady who worked for NASA was trying to pull it together and phoned me asking "Can you persuade Blur to appear?" The band was up for it, but she never pulled it off.

We were still very much in business with BT, so when the chance to endear myself to them by another route cropped up I jumped at it. The Science Club at their research laboratories at Martlesham, in Essex, invited me to lecture. Judith and I made a special effort; we took several editions of the *Bulletin* and postcards to give away. We decided we'd put the model on display at the front of the lecture theatre. We arrived at Martlesham to find it was high security. After parking the car, I joined the queue to get a pass. On reaching the front I asked "Can we drive onto the site?". "No, it's access on foot only," the lady behind the desk informed me. With my host standing waiting in the background, and expecting him to leap forward at any moment saying he had cleared access already with security, I said "But I've got my model outside in the car." Quick as a flash, back came the answer "She'll have to come in and get a pass like everybody else." The others in the queue tittered as I tried to explain the kind of model I had in tow.

It didn't stop there either. We eventually got to the place where the lecture was going to take place. As we waited in the foyer, a smartly dressed lady in a floral print dress, high heels and even a large hat, entered. One of the welcoming party, clearly not recognising her, and believing he could use my visit to do a bit of recruiting to the Club, tapped her on the shoulder and enquired politely "Excuse me, are you a member?" The 'lady' turned to face us; she was clearly not a lady at all, but sported a very obvious five o'clock shadow. I hope she hadn't gained access to the site by saying 'she' was my model. I never found out whether she joined.

Even though he had said "It's not a good time to try," Paul Leonard fixed a meeting with Angus Porter, a very senior man at BT. We would have to get him on-side if our quest for sponsorship was to progress. Although I started early enough for the meeting, I had a nightmare journey. It started behind a tractor so I missed the fast train from Royston to King's Cross. The slow train got slower until it was late. Then there was a delay on the Underground. Up to the surface I rushed and joined others trying to get a taxi. I arrived at BT breathless, with a few moments to spare and no time to talk to Paul or Matthew. Not that it was likely to be a problem. I prefer to be spontaneous rather than rehearsed.

After the usual pleasantries and a brief summary about what Beagle 2 was trying to achieve, Angus, very pointedly, asked "Can you guarantee that we'll see a BT logo on the outside of the spacecraft on Mars?" Now Matthew would have instantly answered "Yes" anticipating that if we said "No" that would be the end of the interview. But me, I explained patiently "We tried to put a camera on the gas-bags to get the shot you're talking about but it requires too much mass and a short range radio transmitter or a risky trailing wire. We dropped it. All I can promise is that the logo will be on the animations we use and on the gas-bags. I can't even promise they'll stay inflated long enough to take a picture. I just hope they will."

"It's OK, I was only checking," Angus said. "Our sponsorship deal with the boat for the round-the-world yacht race was a disaster. The only time our logo was seen was as it slipped beneath the waves, when it sank." Matthew would have categorised that as a sponsorship success. Some of the sponsors he handled for F1 motor racing bought space on the less successful cars because they were in shot when they got lapped. Better still if they went off the track,

Matthew called it "crash and burn". It was guaranteed to be on TV and in the papers.

Angus was much more interested in the educational opportunities presented by Beagle 2, particularly if they were able to inspire and motivate under-privileged kids to take up careers related to science and technology. I was beginning to like Angus. I'd heard Matthew on the subject of reaching kids; it involved merchandising fluffy, little green men toys. Angus was now saying "I wouldn't just want to plaster everything with logos, I want events, and a proportion of the budget would have to be for exploitation, not just to reim-burse the underwriters." I could buy into this and probably the Government and the OU could as well. Miles would certainly say that exploitation funds were non-commissionable for Matthew.

Then I got my biggest shock, I wondered afterwards whether Paul knew he was setting me up. He said "Give Angus some statistics about OU students and graduates." When Paul had told me BT had twenty-eight million customers I'd said "We're a good match, two million people have registered for an OU degree; we currently have 250,000 students on the books. Everyone knows an OU student." I now repeated it for Angus. "Yes, my mother's one," he said and proceeded to reel off a whole list of people he wanted me to see: "the Advertising Manager, the Director of PR, Director of Sponsorship, the Marketing Strategy Division, Head of Education and Social Responsibility..."

Chapter 15

"YES, MINISTER"

You can't keep all of the people happy all of the time. It wasn't long before they were complaining about our documentary 'Beagle 2, Mission to Mars'. SSSL were upset because Logica got a name check; Astrium felt it hadn't got enough mentions, likewise ESA. John Credland suggested ESA might pay for a BBC documentary about MEx. I told him "It doesn't work like that." Nevertheless we asked ESA's permission for Circlevision to film at the next MEx SWT. It was refused. Shame, we would have got plenty of footage of Rudi going on about Beagle 2; about what a terrible state it was in and how ESA wouldn't take it if it wasn't ready in time. Even Alain Clochet got fed up with it and said "I'm more worried about the Italian Radar instrument."

Rudi's favourite topic was how the gas-bag test had failed at Plumbrook. Somehow he'd found out. One of the Americans who attended the MEx meetings took me aside and told me "The MER gas-bags test also failed." He said "The MER team were very bullish; they already had the success of Pathfinder behind them. They dropped onto some trial rocks at a higher velocity than was necessary, so the seams burst. They were pleased. Now they know how far they can push the system."

It was exactly my take on our test. I didn't feel so bad after that until Judith rang me. "There is an article in *Nature* implying ESA has been forced to pump 36.6Meuros into Beagle 2, because of the failed drop test," she said. Like Rudi, *Nature* didn't love me; it wouldn't be difficult to guess, their informant. Rudi had mentioned in his catalogue of all that was wrong with Beagle 2 "A journalist may have gotten hold of the gas-bag failure story."

John Macnish, who had been frustrated at not being allowed into the SWT, suggested "Next time you have some information you don't want disclosed, I'll take my camera and ask ESA for a contribution to a current affairs programme I make, called 'Final Frontiers'. It'll be interesting to see what comments I get." I dissuaded him from this bit of entrapment, even though I would have liked to have known for certain who was doing their best to undermine Beagle 2. When John Credland was asked to explain how *Nature* got the story at a Board meeting his excuse was "It wasn't ESA but a malicious member of SPC who did it." It didn't matter who did it, it wasn't very responsible journalism to print such a story without contacting me or Barrie.

I didn't mind the public knowing about our problems, I wanted them to feel a part of Beagle 2. We were going to use our footage of the drop test in 'Beagle 2 Mission to Mars part 2', if I could ever stop the BBC going on about exclusivity. What I objected to was the failed test was being used by ESA as a stick to beat us. Having Rudi continually saying "Beagle 2 isn't going to be going to Mars because the drop test failed" wasn't helping Matthew in recovering the money for the Underwriters. Anyway, if our EDLS was so bad, why did the French want the design? And why did the SPC threaten to withdraw its money if we didn't give them the data when, as they well knew, we couldn't because of ITAR?

I spoke to Dave Hall, who agreed; he said "I'll write to *Nature* correcting them and giving our view of the test." I said "Don't count on getting a correction published." Colin Hicks told Southwood to write as well. I said "Good luck." I was wrong, Southwood did get his letter into print but again, it took so long to appear that people must have wondered what he was writing about. Miles said "If only it were true about the 36.6Meuros, I wouldn't care what ESA or *Nature* said about the test."

The team held an investigation into what had happened at Plumbrook and decided that the gas-bags had been over-inflated, because we were worried about the leakage. We checked our leak rate compared to Pathfinder, NASA's 1997 mission, and found we were better. Nevertheless, we decided to have a belt and braces approach. If we added a radar altimeter trigger, we called it the RAT, to Beagle 2 to measure the distance to the surface as we descended, we would be able to inflate the bags at exactly twelve seconds before touchdown instead of the two minutes we were guessing.

Two minutes had been chosen because we wanted to be sure there was enough time for the ammonia, used to fill the bags, to convert completely from liquid to gas. The test had revealed that we didn't have to worry; filling was practically instantaneous. Adding the RAT was going to allow us to reduce the pressure but the mass required for it had to come from somewhere; the GAP got fingered. To make the RAT, we recruited Jason Hall from Roke Manor

Research. His company was developing radar for the purpose of allowing cars to travel long distances on the motorway without driver intervention. The idea came originally from the military, from unmanned airborne vehicles: 'drones'.

One thing we had to remember if we used radar was to include a command in the EDLS software not to switch on the RAT until after the heat shield had been dropped. We didn't want Beagle 2 thinking it was near the surface and inflating the gas-bags prematurely. We certainly didn't want a repetition of Polar Lander on our hands. Judith and I thought the RAT story was a good illustration of space engineers thinking on their feet. We used it in the next *Bulletin* which upset Astrium, although it was a positive story rather than detrimental to the project.

There was another reason why the gas-bags might have failed. They had already been used for an earlier test and could have been weakened. More important, we found that the lacing eyelets at the 'south pole' of the sphere were wrongly positioned. We might never have discovered this if the test had succeeded. We were already sharing the Plumbrook facilities with the MERs and, with them needing more time, we were going to have even less priority. We decided to move our programme to the Johnson Space Center where they had a smaller tower but were keen to be involved with Beagle 2.

John Macnish wasn't the only person refused access to the MEx SWT. Everett had submitted a travel request to NASA to go; he was going to be appointed as an interdisciplinary scientist by ESA because I had told Marcello I wanted him. Besides, he was from JSC, and therefore would be a quid pro quo for their help with gas-bag testing. A NASA high-up told Everett "You can't go; I'm fed up with Pillinger's short plays." I think this was something to do with American football and meant the bureaucrat, named Lavery, thought I was too clever by half. He told Everett "I want to choose any American involved with Beagle 2." Everett replied "Tough! Colin calls the shots." I had already turned down a scientist from JPL they wanted to appoint as a Co-I. To me Everett said "Lavery is a prat. He has a web camera trained on his office desk; when he isn't there, he leaves a pink flamingo on his chair."

The affair that John Macnish missed, which I would have loved to have on film, was the argument about the Project Operations Science Centre, the POS, for MEx. Because it was going to be sited at RAL, the MEx PIs had been told the POS was something to do with Beagle 2; an excuse they swallowed hook, line and sinker. It fell to some poor sacrificial lamb from RAL to tell the orbiter PIs "It's the office to which you'll have to submit requests for your MEx activities, nothing to do with Beagle 2." Since SWT was a science meeting Agustin was in charge, Rudi had left. The PIs demanded he return to explain why their Operations were being directed from Britain. He didn't come back soon enough, so en masse the French delegation picked up their chairs, turned them round and sat with their backs to the meeting. It would have made, as John always said, "Great television!".

Rudi still didn't show up; the meeting was going to overrun and we had all been offered a Christmas drink. Lutz Richter and I left the French to it; I had been told Southwood wanted to see me, urgently, again! The drinks party was as good a place as any to find him. When I encountered him, glass in hand, the explanation for his urgent summons was, he said, "I can't come to the next Board Meeting: it's my mother's birthday." Miles was going to say "Good, can't we find him a few more relatives to visit?" On the way out of the party I encountered Ton Linssen, I wished him "Merry Christmas." He replied "See you next week." He thought he was attending the Board. I thought, over Miles' dead body.

At least we were getting closer to HMS Beagle. We had found that the oyster fishermen of the River Crouch had complained about our namesake, she had been given a name change to 'WV7', the WV standing for watch vessel. WV7, like Beagle 2, was getting in other people's way. The local fishermen persuaded the owner of the river bank, Lady Olivia Sparrow, to allow the veteran ship to be moored against the shore. Consequently, after 1851 her crew were listed in the census as they were again in 1861. But there was no mention of them in 1871. Judith tracked down the reason: the Customs service sold WV7 at a public auction, to Messers Murray and Trainer, for £500. The announcement, giving the name as HMS Beagle rather than WV7, was in the *Times*. I wondered how much Beagle 2 would be worth if a manned mission to Mars ever recovered it and returned it. Stephen Baxter, the science fiction writer and Beagle 2 fan, had recently written a short story about such an eventuality. We had also found that we had an ally in the search for Darwin's Beagle: Robert Prescott, a marine archaeologist, who looked a little bit like a salty old sea captain. It was obvious that we should join forces.

The OU and Leicester still had to raise more money, but not from selling anything. We submitted back-to-back proposals to PPARC, to pay for Operations when Beagle 2 was on the surface of Mars. Nobody could claim I hadn't warned them this was coming. In answer to the question "Who's going to pay for the Operations?" from Paul Murdin at the meeting I held with him in 1997 I had said "If I can get Beagle 2 to Mars, the least PPARC can do is pay for us to carry out the science." He probably hadn't thought it would come back to haunt PPARC. But now the chickens were coming home to roost.

Operations were going to be split between us: the Science team would reside in the offices vacated in the AAF at the OU; Leicester would play host to the engineers who would rehearse the arm moves needed to produce the computer commands required to collect samples.

Both teams would have access to the data coming from the environmental sensors package on the lander. These were being provided by John Zarnecki, a recent recruit to the OU from Canterbury. We needed to know temperatures, wind speeds, atmospheric pressure, dust levels, UV flux etc. to run the spacecraft and interpret science measurements. We called these parameters the 'house-keeping'.

With ESA and *Nature* spreading bad news, Judith and I decided the time was right for another big PR venture. Dave Rowntree had already turned the Beagle 2 music into ringtones for mobile phones. We thought now would be a good time to release them to give SSSL, who were working hard on the software for Operations, the name check they wanted. We planted the idea with the Today programme saying "You can make an announcement that the Beagle 2 call sign is available interactively via your website." Once Beagle 2 supporters had the call sign we anticipated it would add to the embarrassment if the Government or ESA tried to cancel the lander. The announcement was a huge success; Today, followed by the TV version 'Breakfast', generated lots of extra media interest. I was still doing interviews at 10.00pm after a 5.00am start.

Not all PR ideas were quite as spectacular. The ring tones story precipitated a call from a man who said "My band is going to revive Jeff Wayne's rock opera 'War of the Worlds'. Will you come along and introduce it?" This sounded good, and thinking it would be in the West End at least, I asked "Where's it playing?" Wrong! His answer was "A pub in Stoney Stratford, just up the road from MK." Later I interviewed Jeff Wayne for the *Times* Higher Education Supplement when he revived the musical extravaganza. Other suggestions the story generated included one from a lady who wanted us to send the red lipstick from her company's cosmetics range to Mars. Another man thought it would be a good idea to ask Jonathan Edwards to start a campaign for people to pray for Beagle 2. The lady didn't offer any money. I assumed you couldn't expect people to pay for prayers.

We had already used the analogies between Beagle 2 and HMS Beagle many times to good effect. Now we decided that we would try to up a gear and to mount an exhibition that compared the mission with the expedition, and show examples of the similarities of approach to exploration even if the circumstances were two hundred years apart. Where better to have such an exhibition than at the National Maritime Museum, the NMM, at Greenwich?

To get our plan underway Judith and I had to get to the NMM's Director, Admiral Roy Clare. When we did he certainly didn't look like an old sea dog, but he was on-side as long as we could do a fifty-fifty deal to share the costs. This meant raising half of another £100k. Since the NMM got something like 750,000 visitors every year, exposure was going to work out at about 20p/visitor. The OU decided it was a good investment to advertise its courses to potential students and we were in business.

The OU by now had a new VC, Professor Brenda Gourley, from South Africa. Miles had met her and said "She will call a spade a ******* spade." "That'll be alright then," I said, "let's introduce her to ESA." When I first met her, she clasped her hands together and bowed to me in supplication. It was something I was used to from Japanese post-docs who had worked for me in the labs over the years, but not from VCs.

I say that we were in business, but it wasn't quite that simple. The Museum's publications department wasn't as decisive as its Director. We wanted to produce a book to accompany the exhibition. The idea was to tell the history of the search for life on Mars, set against a timeline established by events involving the nine ships that had carried the name HMS Beagle since it was first used at the end of the eighteenth century. The idea for the format had first occurred to us when the Captain of the last holder of the name had shown us pictures of some of its forebears. We would also compare the science done by Darwin and Fitzroy's technology with Beagle 2's. It would give us the opportunity to catalogue all the parallels we had found between the 1830s expeditions and the 21st century mission. We had a good name for the exhibition and the book: 'Tales of two Beagles'. One of the first things we had come up with in respect to other HMS Beagles was that two of the ships got involved in debates in Parliament. Once because the Captain hanged a troublemaker from the yard arm, the last naval commander to put a man to death. This was giving me ideas for how to handle certain people from ESA. I'm sure Miles wouldn't have complained if I resurrected the practice. Another time Parliament discussed an HMS Beagle was when an Admiral was accused of cowardice. His name was Gambier; he was an ancestor of our animation maker Anthony Gambier-Parry.

'Tales of Two Beagles' was going to be another novel way of getting a new audience for science and engineering without them necessarily realising they were learning something about space exploration. After what seemed an endless round of committees and talking to various people at the Museum, who kept referring us elsewhere to do market research and the like, it became obvious that Beagle 2 would probably land on Mars before we got a decision about publishing the book. The exhibition would certainly have happened so we took a chance and did what we always do in such circumstances, decided to become publishers to produce and sell the book ourselves. Our family motto ought to be: 'If you want something doing urgently – do it yourself'; I think there are continents that drift faster than some committees make decisions.

Although the OU had kept to the schedule for the AAF, the only work going on there was changing and filtering the air fifty times every minute. It was getting cleaner and cleaner. Andy Spry's technician, Brian, was using equipment to count the particles present; sometimes it failed to find even a single one, especially if nobody had been in for a day or so. There was something we could do in the meantime, train the people who were going to work there. Judith and Andy explained the joys of microbiology to the engineers. This included showing them the colonies of microbes which would grow from a swab of their skin. Anybody who refused to have it done was banned from the AAF. Brian had shaved off the beard he'd had for forty years just to say "I was on the Beagle 2 mission." John Macnish filmed it.

I hammered into those who were going in that a dead bug was as bad as a live one, and just how easy it was to pick up extraneous carbon contamination. I told them "One finger print contains detectable amounts of amino acids." I once knew a geochemist who became affectionately known as 'Finger print Hamilton' because he tried, in vain, to identify the culprits who contaminated his experiments from the amino acid pattern of their finger prints. It wasn't just finger prints, everything contains some carbon and the GAP could pick it up, and it wasn't only the live microbes I was worried about but fragments of virtually anything solid. GAP could measure every atom of carbon in all its forms.

We still had had no feed-back from Angus via Paul Leonard. Matthew was worried about it, particularly as Saatchi's were now working on commission-only basis; they would get a share of anything he raised. Then one day I had a phone call from somebody at a PR agency who said "We have a client who is looking for a sponsorship deal; can we pitch them Beagle 2?" There was no way they were going to tell me who their client was so I said "I can't stop you; everybody knows Beagle 2 is looking for a sponsor. Phone me if you have a concrete offer to make."

A bit later I thought I had struck gold, actually and metaphorically. A voice with a South African accent at the end of a phone line asked "Do you use gold?" We sure did; gold has the property that it is a very good absorber of heat and a poor emitter. Gold-leaf is put on spacecraft to conserve any energy they absorb from the sun. There would be a gold layer all over Beagle 2 for this purpose. My mystery caller represented a gold mining company that wanted to break into the European market; "Would you use our gold for advertising purposes?" he asked. I replied "I'm more than willing to talk about it if you are coming over from South Africa."

We weren't the only ones with money troubles; we heard NASA had a new Administrator. "His eyes glaze over when anybody mentions the word planet," Everett told me. It was rumoured that he was prepared to cancel one of the MERs because they were over budget. Steve Squyres, who was in charge, must have loved me. Actually we are good friends despite the Science *vs* Sightseeing outburst. Now he probably only had to say "If those Brits, with their puny resources, get to Mars and we don't..." to have NASA pleading with him to accept more money. His overspend when he launched his two rovers turned out to be much bigger than our entire budget.

As I said, we planned to give Beagle 2 a gold coat. Jim Clemmet thought a good way of saving mass would be to vacuum deposit gold on the surface of the carbon fibre shell being made by McLaren. He found a company that was able to fit large items in its vacuum deposition chamber. He sent them a fibreglass model of the Beagle 2 lander base and followed it up with a visit to see how the work was going. When he got there he found the man's dog asleep in the circular model base. This was a kind of merchandising Matthew hadn't thought of: 'Beagle 2 dog beds, out of this world luxury for your pet!' Matthew just wasn't as imaginative as Judith.

The business of keeping control of the mass of Beagle 2 was our biggest headache. At every Systems Team meeting Jim went through a spreadsheet, updating it as we got the actual masses of prototype items of equipment that were being delivered and weighed. At the end of January 2002 we did yet another mass reduction exercise, finding a gram here and a gram there we didn't need. The packed clam shell now weighed in at 34.419kg but we thought it could be reduced to 33.8kg. When the lander was enclosed inside the entry descent and landing system its mass increased by just over a factor of 2, to 68.950kg. Again we estimated it could be got down to close to 67kg. There was another 5kg which Beagle 2 needed; it was required to push us off MEx. ESA had said MEx would have the capability of carrying a lander or landers, therefore Astrium Toulouse had budgeted for it in their bid. We weren't going to have that 5kg foisted onto us at any price.

At 67kg we were about 10% above the 60kg we'd been allocated; this was exceptionally good for any spacecraft approaching the near to final configuration. Most ESA projects would have been given a contingency margin of twice or even three times that when the first mass estimates were made. Of course we had been given zero, only Rudi's threat of expulsion hanging over us, like the 'Sword of Damocles', if we went a gram over. Jim submitted what is called a 'waiver' asking for our mass allocation to be changed to 65+1kg; We would have liked to ask for more, ILC Dover were telling us that we should put another protective layer on the gas-bags to make them comparable to those being used by the MERs.

There were still other unknowns that could affect the mass of the EDLS such as the angle we entered the martian atmosphere. Our smallest engineer, Arthur Smith, from the company Fluid Gravity Engineering, ran computer models for us to simulate what would happen at the atmospheric entry stage of Beagle 2's journey and to predict where it might land. Arthur originally wanted to enter the atmosphere at an angle of eighteen degrees but it was now down to fifteen and suggestions were being made to reduce it further. Arthur refused to make it a shallower angle to create a longer passage through the atmosphere to slow the spacecraft down because there would be a greater chance that Beagle 2 would bounce off, like a stone skimming across the surface of a pond.

Just as we were making good progress, we were told by ESA there had to be another Review; we didn't want to be distracted by having to put together another pile of paper. Dave Hall, speaking for BNSC, 'the customer', agreed. "A half a day in March will be soon enough," he said. We were regularly videoing the Systems Team meetings, so Dave Hall's words in front of Con McCarthy are recorded on the film. We weren't too worried by a half day; it was no different from our regular fortnightly get together to which Con was already privy. We just didn't need another round of ESA trying to cancel Beagle 2.

If they dared, I might have to mobilise some powerful new allies. I had just sat next to the 'Father of the House of Commons' and technophile, Tam Dalyell, at a dinner. He was enthusiastic about Beagle 2; grasping my chance to extract some words of wisdom, I asked him "Why do you think we should spend money on science?" "Because I want my grandchildren to eat," he replied immediately.

It came as a shock when Barrie Kirk rang me. Not that Barrie rang, although he seldom did, I usually had to find him. It was subject of the call. Con had turned up at Astrium on 19 February with a message from John Credland "There will be a three-and-half-day Review starting 18 March." Barrie said "Con says John wants a twelve man Panel and the following week he wants you and me to attend the meeting when the report is delivered to John Taylor and Southwood." Barrie was clearly angry "It's ridiculous, we never agreed to anything like this." "I hope you said *******s," I contributed.

When he was off the phone, I called Dave Hall and threatened to call the media; the Today programme owed me a favour. I would call it in by giving an interview to the effect that ESA were attempting to damage our efforts to meet the Beagle 2 delivery date by asking us to waste time, stopping work yet again, to convince them we were making progress. "For a Review like they want, we'll spend three weeks gathering together the documents," I told Dave. "Last time when they claimed they only wanted minimal paperwork, we gave them three lever arch files, three inches thick and they complained it wasn't enough." To emphasise the point, I told him "If we keep having progress reviews, we don't have time to make progress." And for good measure added "Con comes to all the Systems Team meetings, so he ought to be able to report back exactly where we are. If he can't then he shouldn't be there!"

Dave, who also came to Systems Team agreed with this last point and wrote to Miles saying he thought ESA's attendance at the Thursday Meetings was to give them visibility. At the next Systems Team, Con said "Credland says Mike Rickett agreed to five and a half days." Barrie naturally contradicted him with "No he didn't." Then Con said "Rudi says ESA wants Andre Debus to look at the PP." Debus was French, "No chance," said Barrie. It then transpired that Astrium still hadn't received any money for PP from ESA. A week later, Dave Hall rang me saying "Credland's told me Mike agreed to the longer review." I said "Preposterous prefixed with some swear words." I managed to track Mike down at an airport and he said "I did no such thing, I've allowed ESA into the factory to observe what's going on, I'm not having twelve people traipsing all over the place disrupting what everyone is trying to do."

Two weeks later, Con opened the Systems Team meeting with "You," pointing at me, "have annoyed NASA again." "How?" I asked. "You said in an interview that Odyssey hadn't found water on Mars." "Oh for god's sake," I replied, "all I did was correct the interviewer. The instrument he was talking about can't measure water. It measures hydrogen, even the PI describes his numbers as water equivalent hydrogen, and I was only being scientifically accurate. Surely they can't be that thin-skinned."

Now Southwood had to have his oar in. He rang me with a convoluted story about a request he had had for an interview from a German TV journalist. "I told him he needed to talk to the mad scientist," he said, quickly adding "I meant it as a compliment. I said I'm only a dull apparatchik." Whilst there's many a true word..., I assumed he was ringing about NASA being annoyed and said "Where's all this leading? If it's a slap on the wrist get on with it. I've got another meeting to go to." At this he thought I was talking about the *Nature* article and said "No, I dealt with them," meaning *Nature*, "I told them in a mission like MEx it was impossible to attribute everything to exactly any particular budget." I thought "So why did somebody say it was forced on ESA by Beagle 2, then?" I answered him by saying "Forced is not a word that gets used accidentally by reporters, it had to be a quote."

He then muttered something which I didn't entirely catch but sounded like "I'm fed up with having to keep responding to things you say." I surmised he was now coming to the latest NASA complaint. I didn't say it, but could have replied "No, especially when they are right." Instead, I said "You didn't ring me up just for that," meaning again get to the point. I then got a sob story. "It's not me that wants the Review, it's John Taylor." It went on and on. He said "I was glad you agreed to do it." That was news to me. "BNSC put me on a spot," he said, "they asked me to do it. Taylor wants a final go, no go decision. First BNSC said three and a half days, now they are trying to get me to change it." I chipped in "Barrie and I have agreed to hold the meeting, off site, at a hotel, strict time-tabling and Mark Sims and I will organise site visits at the OU and Leicester. There has to be minimum disruption at Astrium." I quickly ended with "Got to go now." He rang off with all the usual "Here to help you and call me any time" goodbyes. I went off to see the acting VC wondering if Southwood knew the meaning of the word truth. Next I heard was Credland phoned Dave Hall and threatened to cancel the Review. Dave said "I nearly said fine, get on with it." But he didn't, so we had to go through it all again, but on our terms.

As if I didn't have enough trouble, Matthew had found out Paul had some news. We went to visit BT again; Paul first told us "Some PR company came to see me claiming to represent Beagle 2." It was presumably the one with the mystery client. "They offered me a deal." He said, "I had a job to keep a straight face and then I nearly burst out laughing when the no-so-bright dolly bird with the guy said, I wonder who sponsored Beagle 1."

This was all pre-amble to bad news that I think Paul was embarrassed to tell us. The army of Managers and Directors we'd spoken to had told him "Seven million for title sponsorship is too much for us." Paul said "I interpreted this as if Angus wants it, Angus can pay for it from his budget." He went on "They've offered £1.5m, over the duration of the project, for the Media Centre and Blur and Damien and the TV documentary and the education package and…" I had to cut him off with "They don't want much do they?" His answer was "They said we don't mind sharing the deal with some other sponsors." That could have brought the answer "But what's left for the companies involved?" But before I could say it, he went on "But nobody is to be brought in above BT as title sponsor." It was a try-on; they wanted to claim title sponsorship rights without paying top whack. "Thanks, but no thanks, we'll keep your bid in mind," I said. I didn't turn them down flat, but they were going to have to do better.

During the exchange Matthew made the statements we employed him to make: "Too many rights, not enough cash." He explained "Some of the engineering companies in Beagle 2 already have more than £1.5m invested, without a sponsorship name check. There'd be a mutiny if we accepted an offer like yours." To cap it all Paul had also said "BT must have a female presenter at the Media Centre, together with stewardesses in uniforms." It didn't seem to bother Matthew; he described them as "top tottie". I still don't know what the hostess angle had to do with science and engineering, education or life on Mars. Off-line Matthew told me he'd said to Paul, when I wasn't there "Tell them not to think they have already bought the Beagle 2 project by sponsoring the NSC at Leicester. Colin's boss, Miles, will block it if they try to claim that's where it's all happening."

When I told Miles about BT's offer he spent most of the time pacing up and down his office. Clearly <u>some</u> money was money to him. I thought it would make us a laughing stock unless we had two or three other serious sponsors to go with it. We agreed, Matthew and I should go back to BT asking two-and-a half to three million for far less of our assets. When I next spoke to David Leadbeater he knew about BT, presumably because BT had already been discussing their Beagle 2 sponsorship offer with the NSC at Leicester. Colin Hicks would have found out about it because he was on the NSC Board.

As a sideshow to the main event, I was still wrangling with the BBC about future TV coverage. I was offering a real-time suspense; a 'will they, won't they get to Mars and find life' docudrama. What's more I had all the film taken so far. "That doesn't matter," one of the group I was discussing with said, "we'll start again and reshoot it." "But that won't be reality" I came back. "Television is an illusion," somebody else threw in "we'll put in a top producer and researchers!"

The previous evening, Judith and I had watched a BBC production about the Civil War as a docudrama. The Roundhead Army had consisted of two bored looking extras. Referring to it, I said "If that's an example of what you could do for Beagle 2, I don't think too much of it." "But that was history not science," I got as an answer, as if that explained everything. To which I replied "Should be consigned to history, you mean!"

Anyway researchers, who knew nothing, were just what I didn't need right now, ringing up all the time saying things like "We'll have that test done when we have the crew on Friday." I told this particular bunch of TV idiots in suits "I have to decide what and when something is filmed; none of the things we've done already are being repeated." I tried to persuade them with "I'm offering you behind-the-scenes material, shot in places you couldn't hope to get into." Somebody with a death wish said "Of course, your contribution will always be valued." He got the retort "If you're so ******* clever why don't you design the spacecraft, provide the science instruments, think up the PR, run the Planetary Protection and deal with ESA." We had Steve Wilkinson and Circlevision, who I could work with; I wasn't going to start all over again with a crowd like this. We ploughed on, shooting our own material.

One senior BBC producer I met even questioned whether there was enough "content" in Beagle 2. British scientists, whose work has been overlooked in BBC documentaries, know to interpret 'not enough content' as 'we don't have enough American accents or jollies to California in it'. I had told him "You'll get joy, laughter, tears and sorrow, suspense and drama," and just to rub it in "and it's British! What more do you want?" I don't remember his answer; probably just as well because it wouldn't have satisfied me.

Frustrated, I threatened to find another broadcaster. That started a whole new round of who owned the copyright. Eventually I got reprimanded by the OU for damaging the BBC-OU relationship. For God's sake, I was looking after the OU's interests; Judith and I were trying to make sure they recovered their money. We couldn't seem to please any of the people, any of the time, at that particular juncture, so we stopped trying and went to talk to Channel 4. We introduced somebody who worked for them to Circlevision. Within five minutes, he and John Macnish's wife were practically throwing things at each other, over who did what. TV documentary people won't use each other's film, let alone collaborate, and I thought scientists were temperamental. We abandoned that idea; Beagle 2 on television obviously brought out the worst in people.

The latest Review was going to go ahead. I thought I might as well try to find out what the view was behind the scenes so I phoned my best pal in ESA – Marcello. In the conversation he confirmed he was Beagle 2's best friend in ESA, but "I'm no longer in the decision making process," he went on, "it's down to the Director." Suddenly he went into conspirator mode, practically whispering to say "There's a plan in ESA to send another rocket to Mars in 2005. I promise you Beagle 2 will be on it if you don't make it onto MEx." And then "Don't breathe a word to anybody!" You never know with Marcello whether an instruction like that is code for "Ring up Reuters, CNN, the BBC and every journalist on the planet." I took it as another ESA attempt to buy off

Beagle 2. I never heard any further mention of a putative ESA Mars mission in 2005.

Strictly speaking we shouldn't have complained about Reviews. All space missions have them. Ours just seemed to be thrust upon us and made more threatening than normal. The latest one took place in a hotel dining room with individual round tables laid out for different aspects of the mission. There was a table that I spent most time at; it had PP on the menu. Pardon the pun but every aspect of Beagle 2 was given a thorough grilling.

The PP table had an away-day at the OU to see the AAF. The instructions from Barrie and Miles were "They don't get any documents until we get the money due to us." Summing up at the end of the Review, John Credland said "The AAF is over the top; pity they didn't provide pencils and paper to write things down." It was a reference to the fact that not only we hadn't given documents to them, we hadn't let them take their bags into areas we were trying to keep clean. They didn't seem to understand the last precaution was so they didn't compromise our experiments. They weren't trained so anyway they couldn't go into the inner sanctum.

Despite having been made aware and agreed they couldn't own the AAF, ESA were still claiming they had to. When I later told Miles they still disputed ownership, he said "Next time I meet ESA I'm taking a diction-ary to explain what agreed means." At the Review, ESA introduced a new red herring; the PP reviewers told me "Since an American scientist has an instrument on MEx, ESA has to do the PP so that NASA will accept it is being done properly!" I thought I must have heard them wrong. "How was what we were doing affecting an experiment on the MEx orbiter?" When I asked, they tried a different tack "The OU can't do PP because NASA won't clear a University for ITAR." Both these try-ons were ignored; Miles could use his dictionary to explain the word truth as well. We knew Jack Barengoltz's view of Beagle 2 PP; he would have liked our over-the-top facility if he'd been at this Review but by this time ESA didn't like Americans telling them that Beagle 2 was doing OK and their orbiter had as much charisma as a rodent's bottom.

Going into the Review on the first morning, Barrie gave me a nasty shock; he'd had news from the JSC of another gas-bag failure. It was not quite so catastrophic. By this time we had four sets of bags: the first lot ILC Dover tried to inflate was made of new, lighter, material. The bags failed in a minor way when the fabric dried out after dunking in the water tank to look for leaks. ILC had put a patch on the failed bag and modified the others. We still hadn't done any drop tests; JSC hadn't been authorised by NASA Headquarters, who were claiming they couldn't afford to help Beagle 2. "If there isn't enough

The team that built the GAP (from the left) Nick, Denis, Jen, Mark (back), Norman, Jen, Andrew, Taff, James, Dudley, Steve, Daz, me and Ian

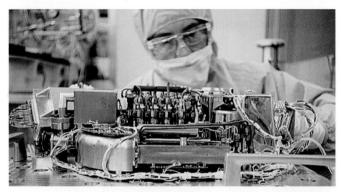

Simon Sheridan with the GAP

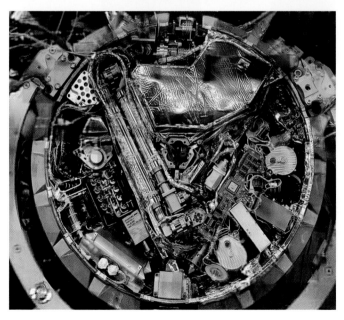

The packed Beagle 2 lander. The GAP is in the bottom left quadrant. The PAW in the bottom right quadrant

PLATE 17

The nearly good guys from the European Space Agency: Giacomo Cavallo, Marcello Coradini and Con McCarthy

The really bad guys from ESA: David "call me anytime" Southwood, Rudi "why don't you just fly a camera" Schmidt, John "we're here to help you" Credland and Roget "if I were Director, you would not fly" Bonnet

PLATE 18

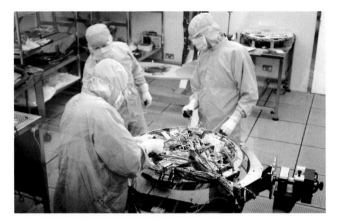

The AIV technicians in the Aseptic Assembly Facility putting the finishing touches to the Beagle 2 lander

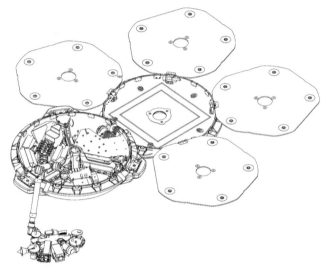

Computer Aided Design picture of the Beagle 2 lander

Richard Slade (left) and Cliff Ashcroft (right) watching the lander during the turnover test (2002)

Barrie Kirk, Programme Manager of the Beagle 2 project

PLATE 19

Dave Northey laying out the parachute canopy for the truck pull test at the airship hangar, Cardington, Beds (2002)

The truck pull, employing a lorry usually used for emptying cess pits (2002)

Stopping the parachute with a 4 × 4 after a drop from an aircraft over the desert in the western USA (2002)

Examining the parachute with Per Lindstrand after the balloon test at Oswestry, Staffs (2002)

PLATE 20

Nick Bown, with the Beagle 2 gas-filled bags inflated for a drop test at the Johnson Space Center, Houston, Texas (2002)

The lander falling out of the gas-bags after a successful drop and opening test at JSC (2002)

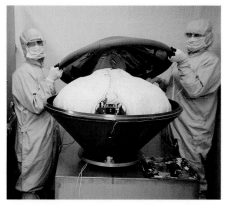

The lander wrapped like a 'plum pudding' in the gas-bags and loaded into the back cover of the Beagle 2 probe (2003)

PLATE 21

The Beagle 2 probe attached to Mars Express orbiter at Astrium Toulouse (March 2003)

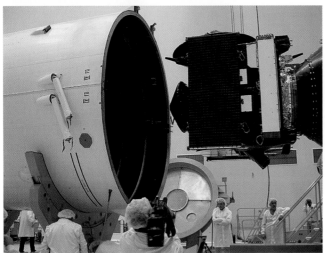

MEx being loaded into the faring of the Soyuz-Fregat rocket at Baikonur (May 2003)

The Soyuz-Fregat rocket being drawn out to the launch pad (June 2003)

PLATE 22

Launching Beagle 2 from a model of Mars Express

The Soyuz-Fregat with the tower removed
ready for launch (June 2003)

The 1668th successful launch of a Soyuz
rocket at 6.45pm (2 June 2003)

PLATE 23

The Beagle 2 launch party at British Telecom Newgate Street, London (2 June 2003)

Paul Leonard of BT, sponsor of the launch party

The ship that sailed to Mars used at PPARC's press conference preparing for the landing of Beagle 2 (just before Christmas 2003)

Lord Sainsbury with me and David Southwood. During this press conference Lord Sainsbury answered "[It wasn't Colin] it was all the other ******s who doubted" when a journalist asked "Did you doubt that Beagle 2 would get to Mars?" (November 2003)

PLATE 24

Celebrating successes with the family

My 60th birthday party in 'The Barley Mow' – my sister Doreen is standing next to me (2003)

Sitting with Shusy and Joe after launch of Beagle 2 (2003)

Shusy accompanying me to Buckingham Palace to collect a CBE (October 2003)

PLATE 25

The photo-shoot for a Christmas card at Xscape, Milton Keynes, me with Mark Sims complete with anoraks' woolly jumpers and bobble hats (2000)

The final Beagle 2 model in a shopping trolley used by 'Have I got News for You' (February 2003)

Filming for television on the SS Great Britain with an Isambard Kingdom Brunel hat (November 2003)

With Richard Hammond, filming for the 'Boffin burn', shown on Jeremy Clarkson's Top Gear (December 2003)

PLATE 26

Steve Burnage (Hunting Engineering) shows Prince Andrew, Duke of York, Beagle 2's Spin Up and Eject Mechanism at the 'Wish me luck as you wave me goodbye' party at the Royal Geographical Society (19 December 2003)

Barrie Kirk introduces members of the team to the Duke around a model of the Beagle 2 probe

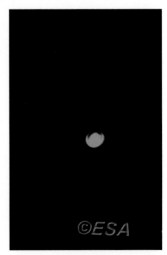

The Duke congratulates me after a successful ejection of the Beagle 2 probe from MEx (19 December 2003)

The probe disappears, spinning towards Mars

PLATE 27

Celebrating with the European Space Agency: with my presents at the Mars Express
Christmas party (held in September 2003)

John Credland presents me with a bottle of champagne after the 'Wish me luck' party

PLATE 28

With Pallab Ghosh, wearing his Beagle 2 hat, the only reporter to get an interview with Judith at 11.50pm (Christmas Eve, 2003)

With Damon Albarn, Ben Hillier and Alex James during the making of 'Beagle 2', the lander's call sign that was never heard from Mars

The press conference when I had to announce Mars Express had not picked up any signal (7 January 2004)

PLATE 29

Jean-Jacques "ESA won't be found responsible for the loss of Beagle 2" Dordain, Director-General, European Space Agency

With Agustin "ESA will stand by its fallen comrades" Chicarro

With Mark Sims, holding his Beagle 2 'Lessons Learned', freely available on the web

Q130 Chairman: Professor, thank you for all you have done to enthuse the British public about your work—we are very grateful—even though it has cost £42 million.

Public Accounts Committee Report

The Public Accounts Committee report in which the chairman thanked me for enthusing the Nation.

BEAGLE 2 MISSION TO MARS

'We've lost contact with the Inquiry's report'

MATT cartoon in the *Daily Telegraph* the day after ESA refused to publish its Inquiry report

PLATE 30

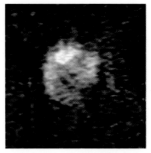

A picture of crater H20 seen as a negative – inside the crater is a dark clover-leaf form similar to the gas-bag lander during drop and opening tests (see plate 21)

Stuart Hurst, searcher for Beagle 2 on Mars

Stuart's so-called crater H – a 1 kilometre-sized crater in the middle of the Beagle 2 landing site

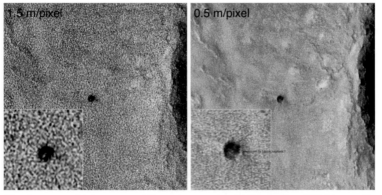

The features which attracted Stuart's attention in September 2005 in small crater H20, on the flank of crater H, seen in two pictures taken three months apart by Mike Malin, using a camera on NASA's Mars Global Surveyor

PLATE 31

Would Beagle 2 have found life on Mars? Anthony Gambier-Parry's representation from the Beagle 2 animation

PLATE 32

spare money in a yearly budget of $15b, what hope have we got?" I said to Judith. It was going to take at least until the end of April to sort out the drop test paperwork.

Beagle 2's engineers were able to show the ESA Committee lots of progress on the instruments and a working robotic arm. We took the opportunity to film it for a TV News item. It was never shown because the motors that drove the joints, necessarily, ran very, very slowly. On all space missions, the power to do things is often just a few watts, not enough for a light bulb. Watching the arm was like watching paint dry. It wasn't because the PAW attached at the end of the arm weighed 2.5kg. To simulate the arm/PAW on Mars we had reduced the test PAW's mass to a third because martian gravity is only a 38% of Earth's.

We couldn't test the mass spectrometer in the way we hoped to operate it on the Red Planet either. We did have a chamber in which we could simulate the martian environment, temperature cycle, atmospheric composition and pressure etc. We could run spectra, check if the pumps worked and so on, but if any adjustments were required the instrument's own vacuum system had to be opened up so it had temporary seals and gaskets. When we were satisfied it was working at its best we were going to weld it shut. If it didn't work after that it would have to be cut open and destroyed. We'd have to build another one; welding wasn't going to happen until we were sure everything was fixed.

The test that ESA wanted however was an impossible one. We didn't have what they called an end-to-end test, making the whole spacecraft perform all the operations in the correct complete sequence. We did as many linked tests as we could, but I always said "All tests are simulations; you can't simulate a landing on Mars. The only way to find out if you can do it is to go there and try. "

Just over a week after the Review, myself, Barrie, Mike Rickett, Alan Wells, Dave Hall, David Leadbeater, Colin Hicks, Southwood, Credland, Gavin and Gavin's boss, Oberfuhrer of OST, John Taylor, for whose benefit this was supposed to be, assembled in a grey Government building backing onto Bird Cage walk. Beagle 2 had just undergone its third CDR. John Credland opened the proceedings with a report. "There are no critical design issues" he said grudgingly. Mike Rickett responded "We're in much better shape than we were a year ago."

There were however plenty of criticisms, for example about the schedule. ESA didn't believe we could deliver before Christmas 2002 or New Year 2003. We knew there was slack in their schedule right up until March and Credland had admitted it. Southwood clearly didn't know we knew the real schedule and said "January 15th is hanging day." Presumably the out-and-out lie was designed to mislead John Taylor. If ESA held us to January, I was going to be hanged, no reprieve to be 'transported beyond the seas'. A couple of weeks earlier, Barrie had asked me to stay behind after the Systems Team saying "I want to talk to you." He wanted to say "I am still declaring December for delivery of Beagle 2 to Toulouse but it might even be March." He didn't need to tell me not to say anything. Barrie went up in my estimation; the Beagle 2 bug had got to him.

In Taylor's office, the discussion turned to mass. At the Review, Barrie had point blank asked Rudi "What's available in the mass contingency for Beagle 2?" Rudi had dodged the question but Credland, who was standing alongside him, had answered for him "MEx can handle any mass you throw at us." Now in Taylor's office he said "The mass of Beagle 2 is limited by the SUEM; it is only designed for a lander of 72kg." This was a ridiculous time to tell us. We could easily have changed the SUEM if we'd been told the true mass we had to play with for the lander. Another example of how helpful they were being to us to add to the long list.

Next ESA complained the Beagle 2 team hadn't done enough planning for Operations. "If Mark Sims is run over by a bus…" Credland let it hang. This was a PPARC issue, they had been supposed to provide funding by January 2002 and here it was the end of April and no money had appeared.

It wasn't the gas-bags test which caused the real argument but who was supposed to be negotiating with NASA. And it wasn't just the gas-bag drop tests either; it was the testing of the Communications link via NASA's Odyssey that we were going to have to rely on when MEx was 'unavailable'. Credland had been told, he said "NASA's budgetary constraints mean Beagle 2 can either test the gas-bags or the Communications." He probably didn't argue. "Which do you want?" he demanded. I said "For ****'s sake! You complain we don't do enough testing then give us an ultimatum like that."

Dave Hall said "It's ESA's job to negotiate collaboration with NASA," looking at Taylor. Credland responded "No, it's down to Dave Hall." Dave glared at Credland and said "I'll do it then." Now it was Credland's turn to try to regain the upper hand, he retorted, "No, we'll do it." You could almost hear the words going through Taylor's mind: "I don't care who ******* does it, just ******* do it." I could have said it but he couldn't.

There was another dispute of this ilk: whose responsibility was it to arrange Beagle 2's transport to Baikonur? Because of the radioactive source in the Mossbauer spectrometer being provided by a German, Göstar Klingelhöfe, Con had told us we had to have permission to overfly any country or go by ship or overland. ESA hadn't brought this problem up before, probably because they didn't expect us to be coming with MEx or it was just an example of lying by omission to create obstacles we could have avoided earlier. The source provided by a German colleague Göster Klingelhöfer was less radioactive than the smoke detector in your home.

We didn't get the "go, no go" answer there and then. The Executive half of the meeting went off to have their own little huddle in private. I'd have loved to have been a fly-on-the-wall but the Project Team were left to stew and ignore Credland. Colin Hicks and Southwood returned without John Taylor. They must have agreed to differ because Southwood gave us the news. "The results of the Review will go to Lord Sainsbury; the Minister will be asked to decide." Colin Hicks corrected him "You don't ask Ministers, you tell them. You don't let Ministers make unnecessary decisions." Sir Humphrey, of 'Yes, Minister' fame, would have been proud of the Director of BNSC.

John Macnish met me in a St James Park full of daffodils; it was a wonderful day. He filmed me apparently emerging from a Government looking building and phoning Mark to tell him the news. We were interrupted by a Nigerian tourist who wanted to photograph me with his mother.

Chapter 16

WHEN ELEPHANTS COLLIDE

First the good news, the Wellcome Trust invited me to speak to their Council about the GAP Mass Spectrometer. I had asked them for the funds to build the flight instrument and its spare for use in tests during Operations. After the mission I would employ the team to investigate possible applications of the technology in areas of more interest to the Trust. Rather than show them slides or give them a handout I decided to take actual Beagle 2 hardware.

I crossed the road from Euston Station to their building on the other side with a bag in one hand containing a large chunk of the Nakhla meteorite borrowed from the NHM, courtesy Monica Grady, and 5kg of kit including the mass spectrometer's magnet and mini-flight tube in a cardboard box under my other arm. Just as well it was a miniature mass spectrometer. My first surprise was the panel included a member who had been an undergraduate with me at Swansea.

I was supposed to take twenty minutes to give my presentation including questions. I started by passing my goodies around. Most of them had seen mass spectrometers that occupied a room, none of them had touched a piece of Mars. An hour and a half later I was still being quizzed. They eventually decided they had heard enough. Ted Bianco promised to phone me next day with the result.

The next day dragged on, I was expecting the worst until he came through: "Looking for life elsewhere in the solar system can loosely be seen as within the Trust's remit," he said, "the Council definitely were attracted by the idea of the 'blue skies' follow-on." I had given a long list of medical applications that I thought could benefit if we produced a miniature instrument. I had described it as the brick-sized mobile phone. "It can only get smaller," I said. The OU were suddenly about £2.5m to the good for staff and equipment.

I rushed across to Miles; I was going to remove the cost of the GAP electronics from a bill Astrium had demanded he pay. He was delighted. "If I kept champagne in the office," he said "we'd be drinking it now." Next I told Matthew, he wanted know "Can we announce it as sponsorship?". "No," I said, "it's a research grant, not advertising. You and Astrium aren't getting a share."

And a little bit more good news. I was determined that ESA was not going to use Planetary Protection to stop Beagle 2. PP was a Royal Society issue so I had approached its Physical Secretary, John Enderby, with my suggested way of having Beagle 2 confirmed as meeting COSPAR regulations. The project would disclose all the data gathered to demonstrate that the spacecraft was inside the proscribed PP limits to a Committee established by the Royal Society. I made suggestions for the make up of the panel: "Why not invite Geoff Eglinton to be Chairman," I said "he's an authority about life on Earth. Then there's Howard Dalton, a microbiologist and Chief Government Scientist at the Ministry of Agriculture. You can invite John Pickett, he's an analytical organic chemist specialising in mass spectrometry of microbial compounds." I went on "Colin Booth's another microbiologist, and CEO of Oxoid, the market leader supplying microbiological growth media. We'd need a space engineer. Ray Turner's a veteran of many space missions and Iwan Williams is a Planetary Astronomer, we can include him to keep the astronomers happy. So ESA don't feel left out, we can invite Gerhard Schwehm, Mission Scientist for Rosetta and Head of ESTEC's planetary missions section." The first three suggested members were all FRSs; Pickett's an unusual one who plays in a jazz band that performs at Royal Society events. The others all had undisputable credentials. I said to John "Nobody will suggest this is a whitewash or believe we can pull the wool over their eyes." I didn't add "Neither will a group of their calibre respond well to outside interference from ESA." But that was my thinking.

John was happy with the concept, the Royal Society's involvement and the make-up of the vetting team. I didn't expect to have all of them but all of them I got. To confirm his support he said he'd supply a secretary who would make sure he was kept informed. Regarding my fears concerning ESA possibly using PP as a stick to beat Beagle 2, he said "What did you do on Beagle 1?" Keeping a seriously straight face I said "I doubt if Captain FitzRoy and the Royal Navy bothered with it."

When Rudi rang up one day and said "ESA's lawyers have said I have to sign the documents which say Beagle 2 has met PP requirements," I had already out-flanked him. It didn't prevent Southwood writing to the Royal Society to make a similar claim. He didn't have the decency to send me a copy. Ruth, the secretary John Enderby appointed, told me about the letter and the reply which wasn't positive.

Now for the not-so-good news, John Taylor's office had rattled PPARC's cage. All of a sudden Mark and I were told we had to attend a meeting to consider our Operations costs. Clearly PPARC had found out about the Wellcome grant, although the Trust was not disclosing it until they had written a press release. PPARC had some crazy notion that the Wellcome money could be used to handle the data to come from Mars. I told their Committee otherwise. They also believed that when Beagle 2 was on the surface of Mars I was going to let Leicester take all the decisions necessary to run it; as a result the OU wouldn't need any money. To make matters even worse, neither would they recognise that Communications with Mars required twenty-four-hour working. They refused all pleas for doubling the staff in some areas. As primarily astronomers they just couldn't see why we couldn't dump data, like satellites built for telescopic observations, and look at it later, sometimes never. We had to interrogate the lander and respond immediately to its requests for instructions.

That review was so determined to limit our support I left without shaking hands and complained to Dave Hall that PPARC were dodging their obligations. When I had the opportunity I challenged PPARC's Chief Exec, Ian Halliday, who said "Take it as read, it's stunning science," but went on to plead poverty. At the same meeting he said publicly "I will take out to dinner anybody who gets *The Economist* to write an article about space." *The Economist* published several articles about Beagle 2 and a cartoon; I'm still waiting for the dinner. PPARC must really have been very strapped for cash; it couldn't even run to a curry for me and Judith.

There were people having greater troubles than ours. We heard from the launch site in Baikonur, where our Soyuz-Fregat rocket was being prepared, about a disaster that had killed eight people, when a roof collapsed. A lady journalist from the BBC approached me enquiring "Will the situation in Baikonur affect the progress of Beagle 2?" She was quite disappointed when there was no Beagle 2 doom and gloom angle, because the roof fall was in the part of the complex where the Russians kept their mothballed space shuttle 'Buran'. She obviously felt that a problem for Beagle 2 was bigger news than the death of eight Russians.

Now for our really bad news: whilst preparing for a drop test at JSC a gas-bag failed again. This time instead of video we had still pictures from

Everett, who was on the spot. Barrie didn't like it but I said "He works for JSC, you can't keep him out. Besides, in the event of problems he's available as an insider and instant negotiator to ensure we get better than commercial cooperation." At that moment it looked like his services might be required. ILC Dover was claiming "JSC must have done something wrong." MBA sent a letter to Astrium denying any responsibility.

Instead of having a panic attack, Jim Clemmet held a brain-storming session. It decided the proof-testing, in water, must be weakening the bags. We left out that step but it didn't solve the problem. Next we turned to the bag design; it must simply be unsuitable for inflation to the pressures needed to absorb the impact. ESA wouldn't give us the mass for the extra layer to make the bags stronger so we would have to reduce the gas pressure or find another way.

But if the pressure was reduced then so too must be the velocity at contact. We had to get the metaphorical slide rules out to calculate revised pressures and velocities. The question was how to slow the lander down more efficiently. We considered reinstating the retrorockets we had discarded to save mass five years earlier, but not for long. Even if we had had the necessary mass we hadn't done any work on retros, they simply didn't exist. Somebody threw out an idea of inflating a balloon. That didn't float far.

In the end we concluded we needed a bigger or better parachute. Bigger again might mean more mass, but maybe not as much as another layer on the bags. We needed some expert help so Astrium recruited Dave Northey, a silver haired, bespectacled man, to the team. Dave worked for a company called Analyticon, close to Astrium, but he had spent a lifetime in the parachute business and therefore knew who was developing what. More brain-storming produced two alternatives: either we could make a large parachute out of materials we were using already with a different kind of lighter gas-bags called 'deadbeat' or vented bags, or increase the size of the parachute using new lighter fabrics and reduce the pressure in the bags that way. It was a no-brainer: the first solution needed two developments, the second only one.

All this debate was a bit cloak and dagger and took place against a background of who should we tell about the problem? We needed more data: how much gas could we put safely into the existing bags? And then we would need to find out if they would survive impacts at reduced speeds, particularly when the impact took place onto rocks. Another concern was: would the pressure be high enough, after impact, to pop the bags apart to drop Beagle 2 and then roll away? Astrium's Commercial Management had to be brought into the discussions, because there were bound to be financial implications, likewise Miles. I said "He'll be sympathetic as long as I don't mention the word money." I was right, but I was glad to able to say "But we've made some progress towards a solution."

Like in every testing programme, we had failures. Some were engineering problems, others occurred because we hadn't designed the test properly. We found out how to measure the pressure in the bags accurately during inflation and realised when we tried the first drop onto rocks that it wasn't the rock that burst the bag but a sharp edge on the test platform.

The rig that was built to conduct all these trials consisted of a sloped platform with a hole. Through the hole there was an upside down elastic bungee cord. The speed of the impact was controlled by the tension put on the bungee; the slope could be changed to simulate what would happen because the bags wouldn't drop vertically but would be travelling horizontally as the package glided in to land. One of the test failures was because the inflated bags probably landed in the bungee hole which we should have padded to remove it from the equation.

We hadn't let ESA into the picture yet but on the 5 June 2002, nominally a year from launch, I had yet another message to phone David Southwood. He was in Rudi's office at ESTEC when I caught up with him. He said "There's going to be a very uncomplimentary article in the German newspaper *Die Zeit* tomorrow." He went on "It has the words 'disaster' and 'scandal' in it and is about money. ESA will deal with it. We will say most of the money we gave to Beagle 2 was a loan which has to be repaid and the rest was for 'Europeanisation' which has been achieved." I was baffled when he then said "I suspect a certain German PI is behind it." I replied "I thought the particular PI you have in mind was a friend of mine." I was surprised he didn't say anything about gas-bags.

Quite coincidentally, my daughter, Shusy, was working in Munich at the time so Judith had a copy of the article, complete with a very amusing cartoon, by breakfast the next day. Before most Germans had read it, she had a computer translating it and Lutz on the case. "It's a scandal," a photo researcher had said in an interview, "the [German] High Resolution Camera doesn't have enough money for Operations." The paper quoted Rudi saying "The Beagle 2 gas-bags have burst." The camera team member continued "ESA are wasting money on a hopelessly overloaded lander, it should only be carrying a tiny payload. Beagle 2 should only be trying to take a picture to show ESA has landed on Mars." Where had I heard that before? The article ended "Hopefully the [High Resolution] camera will not see Beagle 2 smashed." I immediately began wonder, why had Southwood alerted me to this when Rudi was so clearly implicated?

The reason became clear at the next MEx Science Working Team meeting a few days later. In his report to the Meeting, Rudi recounted a story about the piece in *Die Zeit*, making sure he quoted a line about 'Pillinger running off with all the money'. "A journalist friend tipped me off," he said, "and the article was on the Director's desk within five minutes."

I would be willing to bet Rudi expected a Beagle 2 bashing session to follow. Instead the Germans, the French and the Italians all turned on him. They were aggrieved because they had found out that ESA were only going to pay for one ground radio receiving station. Communication with MEx would be slow; it would take much longer to get their data from the spacecraft. Rudi tried to tell them "It was always planned to have only one station." He was shouted down with a chorus of "We'll be losing science." To which he answered "The Director has said two ground stations would mean you would be getting extra science. You're still going to get the same amount you were originally going to have. You're actually not losing anything." That made matters worse, especially when, in answer to a howl of "It's not extra data, it's what we were promised," he said "The Director is now very displeased and will not sanction any extra money for data or an extra ground station because of the article [in *Die Zeit*]." I think Southwood and Rudi knew there was a storm brewing over the Communications and had tried to divert attention onto Beagle 2 before it happened.

When, later in the meeting, Con had another go with "Beagle 2 is still having problems with the gas-bag tests," it passed almost without comment. The MEx PIs were still seething about their Operations. The orbiter PIs were soon up in arms again and not about Beagle 2. It was when Southwood's press officer made a gleeful statement saying "ESA has negotiated a deal with Ferrari to fly a capsule of their red paint on board MEx." This sounded to me awfully like the cosmetics lady's lipstick which I had immediately dismissed. Ferrari's paint made Jean-Pierre Bibring, a Frenchman with a very short fuse, hit the roof. "You should not waste one second or one euro on this," he shouted. He wasn't pacified by the answer "It [the capsule containing the paint] only weighs 250g." I was pretty angry too. Beagle 2 had sweated tears of blood trying to find enough mass for the RAT, nor could we get any for the extra layer on the gas-bags, yet ESA were prepared to waste mass on a copycat stunt. It was their version of Damien's spot painting but served absolutely no purpose.

I told Matthew about Ferrari the following week, he said "If I was doing McLaren's PR and found out Ferrari were sending a few drops of paint whilst McLaren was making Beagle 2, I would think all my birthdays had come at once." In trying to copy us, ESA might have made an amazing PR gaff with its own PIs, certainly with Jean-Pierre Bibring.

On the other hand our PR relationship with McLaren was growing. Judith and I had a meeting at their HQ in Woking. Ron Dennis had popped in, but no drivers. We came away with samples of the carbon fibre sandwich that Beagle 2 was being made from. McLaren agreed to let us have access to their factory, to film the processes being used in the spacecraft manufacture. We had to promise not to point our cameras at the £320k road car being manufactured right alongside. Whilst discussing with Damien production of his spot painting I told him about the occasion. He said "Anybody who can afford to get a McLaren ought to have a Damien Hirst original." I think it should have been the other way round, but we knew what he meant.

Whilst the MEx PIs were preoccupied with the ground station, ESA had discovered that Everett, who now came to SWT, had been at the gas-bag tests. He evaded all efforts to pump him for information with "Can't tell you anything," tapping his nose and confidentially whispering "ITAR." Everett told me after I had left for home he had gone out to dinner with some ESA people. "Somebody had the bright idea of putting extra wine on our table, hoping that it might oil my tongue," he said. Now I know Everett is teetotal, they obviously didn't. "Con's wife got a little bit the worse for wear," he confided.

With the problems we were having with the bags, BNSC had to be made aware. Miles wasn't keen but Mike Rickett thought he knew David Leadbeater well enough to believe he wouldn't be fazed. Mike had the added complication of a new German CEO, Evert Dudok, wanting to visit to find out for himself what was going on. At Astrium in Germany they were puzzled and angry about *Die Zeit*. "BNSC won't let it go now, they hate ESA more than we do," were Mike's actual words. After his visit to BNSC, he reported "David Leadbeater didn't fall off his chair. He said he'd see what he could do and added, meantime keep getting more technical info. He was keen that it didn't leak out but said it surely will."

As soon as I got back from the SWT, I went to see Jim Clemmet. There had been a fuller test: the bags were filled with gas to the new pressure we now wanted, dropped without the pressure rising excessively but they still had enough gas left to pop the bags apart and drop the dummy lander on the floor. The only damage to the bags had occurred when they hit the scaffolding of the test tower. At least there shouldn't be a scaffold on Mars unless ESA were planning a Norfolk Island welcome event involving hanging me.

Before I had gone to ESA, Judith and I had travelled to Norwood in the London suburbs to visit Robert Fitzroy's house, where one Sunday morning he had picked up his razor and cut his throat, making him the second Captain of the Beagle to commit suicide. I had no plans or indeed now no need to emulate Fitzroy and his predecessor Pringle Stokes. With the completely successful test, only using the gas generator which had already been tried, hadn't been included. It seemed like a good time to bring Miles up to speed again. "Oh Colin, I am pleased," he said, when I told him.

With Miles in this kind of mood, the following week I decided to readdress the question of more money. Hopefully it would be a less uncomfortable inter-view than other recent meetings which had largely consisted of Miles repeating the words "Fixed-price contract." He had already said he didn't think Astrium could be pushed any further. He had got his mother to buy a single share in BAe Systems which gave him access to Astrium's annual accounts. He knew they were a loss-making subsidiary.

I updated Miles on Matthew's assessment of the sponsorship-raising effort: "Paul Leonard says he's just looking for somebody to sign the cheque was the latest I've heard on the BT front." I went on "Matthew has reported Sony claims to be still interested and that there's a new game in town: a credit card company, he won't tell me who." I elaborated "A contact of Matthew's is waiting for a promotion which will see him as the sponsorship decision maker. If he gets it he's said he's likely in. According to Matthew the amount from them will depend on the contact's clout." Adding up Matthew's 'probables', I told Miles "I reckon it comes to about £3.8m." I left Miles thinking about it.

In one of my regular meetings with Matthew, about this time, he named another new contact: Tony Simpson. During the same conversation he said "There are going to be some changes at M&CS." Later he said "Tony's a merchandising specialist, done merchandising deals for the World Cup; he thinks Beagle 2 merchandise might be worth £1m." After that Judith and I met Tony. He was big, black and talked even bigger about the footballers he knew, but we were doubtful that he could deliver what we wanted. We were dubious about the items he was used to branding. We thought they were tacky. Moreover and worse, he wanted a retainer of £200k to look for deals. I couldn't see Miles parting company with that amount. If Tony was that confi-dent, I could just hear Miles saying, "Payment on results and tell Matthew to sub-contract him for a share of his commission."

Meanwhile we were working on a way to have a big PR hit and a means of offering moderately sized sponsors a way to contribute. We would have an 'away-day', a chartered plane trip to the Russian launch site at Baikonur. The land on which the Russian launch site is built is leased from Kazakhstan, a hangover from the old Soviet Empire. Our idea was to get the Kazakhs to invite us as guests to circumvent any objections ESA might raise.

But back to Miles, I asked him "Would you like to hear another one of my famous financial solutions?". "OK, go ahead, might as well," he was almost sighing. He had already intoned "I'm sympathetic with Mike but a fixed-price contract is a fixed-price contract." At the time I had said "But if Astrium withdraw now, then nobody gets any money back and we have no mission." He had muttered something about release of chains and lawyers.

Now I ploughed on again with my new solution. "Matthew is working on commission only, he must believe he can come up with the goods. If his figures are correct and we change the underwrite agreement again, promoting Astrium to the top of the queue, they would stand to receive £1.9m from the first share-out. If they don't continue to work on the parachute solution, under the terms of the funding arrangements, as it exists, they get nothing." It wasn't clear if he was following me but he was supposed to be the accountant, so I went on "If they do continue, they very likely get the cost of working on the parachute and maybe more if Matthew raises more." It was very simple logic and economics, Astrium had to spend a million or so to get back a bit more than their outlay. I had written it all down with the figures calculated regarding the OU's return. The interview ended with Miles saying "I'll take a photocopy of your piece of paper."

We had heard Mr Dudok, Mike Rickett's new German CEO, wanted to call an emergency Board meeting. David Leadbeater said "He can't, he's not a member. We'll call it an exchange of information between interested parties, in the presence of our technical advisors, ESA." So all the players in Beagle 2 except Leicester, Miles didn't regard them as financially involved, gathered round a table on 3 July, 2002.

Barrie, with Jim and his new parachute adviser, Dave, led everyone through the gas-bag saga starting with the RAT and ending with the series of successful tests, which he said "had gone from red light to amber to green." He then went through details and finally got to the point. "The project has identified a team that can design, test and manufacture a new bigger parachute over the next four months. It will be a sort of parachute called a 'ring-sail' that won't glide in the high speed martian winds," he said. Gaining confidence, he went on "The gas-bag test wasn't a disaster because we had a viable back-up solution. The new way of doing things even has advantages." Nobody had stopped listening so he continued again. "The team will be managed by Alan Haigh," introducing Alan who sat alongside him, "and it will be all British – no ITAR! They're all available to start but we need a decision by the Board." He wasn't talking to the Board but he might just as well have been.

Barrie then offered to show an ILC Dover video of the tests the project had carried out at JSC to demonstrate the gas-bags worked. What happened then was just gobsmacking. Southwood and his henchmen, Rudi and Ton, stood up and walked out, Southwood saying "We can't watch it because of ITAR." So much for BNSC's technical advisers; they needn't have bothered, the video didn't work; it was the wrong format for the British TV system. I later got it converted to VHS at the OU and added it to our collection.

With Southwood back in the room, the proposal to create a parachute 'tiger team' was batted around and questions asked: "Is the design new?" "No, it was used in NASA's Gemini programme to land Astronauts." "Is the lighter material new?" "No, it comes from the yachting industry." To Dave Northey, "Do you have experience working with it?" "We've recruited Per Lindstrand, the balloonist, whose company relies on the lightest of materials." "Is there an independent expert we could ask for an assessment?" "Yes, in Germany."

No stone was left unturned. The questions were played back with a straight bat. Finally, David Leadbeater directly challenged Southwood with "Do we have your support?". It prompted a diatribe about incredibly success-oriented schedule, Rudi being constrained by mass, threats to MEx etc. etc... Mr Misery-guts trotted out every excuse he could possibly think of for not giving anybody any credit for the effort that had gone into Barrie's presentation or any offer of help. At one point he even said "I'm responsible for the safety of people at the launch." I still don't know how a parachute to be used on Mars could endanger anybody in the Kazakhstan desert.

Barrie was clearly cross because he said "Delaying the schedule [one of Southwood's objections] was OK when Rudi asked us recently to change the Beagle 2 landing site." He then ticked off more of Southwood's arguments against "No supplier has said they can't do it, the mass and volume budgets are the same, there's no change to the MEx interface..." Miles interrupted "I have heard lots of technical information to suggest Astrium has a solution, they should be congratulated. I wonder why ESA is so pessimistic?" It was clearly a valid question rather than a statement.

At this Southwood looked straight at Miles and said "With all due respect, you are from a liberal arts background!" It was condescending and fatal, a "you don't understand, trust me I'm a scientist," remark. Miles is very proud that he's an accountant with a science degree and was following the technicalities of Beagle 2 very well. Rudi decided to support Southwood; he seemed to think it would be a good idea to try to bamboozle Miles with some more technical stuff. I leaned forward to interrupt him with an explanation of the Chairman's background. Miles, who guessed what I was about to say, put his arm across my chest and mouthed "Don't bother, he's lost it," "it" being the argument. Southwood had made an elementary error: he didn't know everything about Miles.

Mr Dudok had also heard enough, he made his excuses and departed, as did the ESA entourage. That was fine by me. I left Miles, Mike and BNSC's two Davids discussing money. I was appearing live on the TV programme Tomorrow's World in Birmingham with Olympic athlete turned presenter Roger Black. I jumped on a train. At the other end I was met on the platform by Becky. She had a taxi with the engine running. At the NEC, where we were filming, people opened doors for me, swept bystanders aside and generally shepherded me into makeup. Becky tore off my damp shirt and pressed it with a borrowed iron. They marched me onto the set for my interview. I went home thinking, so this is how it feels to be a celebrity.

On the way into the lab next day to see Miles I was accosted by a lady who asked for my autograph. When I duly obliged, she showed the page I had written on to her friend. "There," she said, "I told you it was him. I saw him on Tomorrow's World last night." Miles told me to send a video copy of the programme to David Leadbeater. He had privately told David my latest financial solution and said "It'll make him realise what assets we have."

After I had left the previous day, the responses to the new parachute idea had been all positive. There had been lots of motherhood statements such as "Can't stand around wondering whether to start", "Thinking about risks to MEx is not a good use of our time", and ultimately "If we don't make a decision it won't be necessary, anyway." Leadbeater had said to Mike Rickett "If we choose to ignore ESA's advice, it won't be the first time!". I suggested to Miles "We should get Matthew to make a presentation to Mr Dudok, ASAP." He agreed "Certainly before the next Board Meeting on 18 July," he said. My take on this was "Here we go again: it's July, it's the annual Beagle 2 crisis and Judith and I want some time off."

We managed to find a day everybody, that is Mr Dudok, Miles, Matthew and I, could make. Mr Dudok was available for just an hour so the meeting had to be in a room at Munich Airport and meant Judith and I driving from a holiday base in France. We didn't feel so bad on the journey there because it was lashing down with rain. That is until the passenger door window stuck down. Whilst getting it fixed in a garage, Matthew rang. "I couldn't do yesterday," he began, meaning make a meeting with Dudok, "because I was in Spain. I had to see the partners," presumably he meant Charles Saatchi and his brother Maurice. "You remember I told you there would be changes at M&C Saatchi, well I'm leaving!" I gulped. He went on "I'm guessing tomorrow's meeting is important, so how do you want me to play it?" I asked if technically he would still be employed by the Agency the next day. When he said "Yes," I told him "then plain and simple, do it as you would an Agency pitch. There's no need for anybody to know yet."

As soon as the window was mended, the sun started to shine. We made Munich in time to go out for a meal in a beer garden with our daughter. The following morning we visited Dachau, as if we needed some kind of morbid experience to put us in the right frame of mind for a showdown about fund raising that might go badly wrong if I had to tell Mr Dudok our fund raiser was on his way out. At least he hadn't said M&CS didn't want to continue.

Mr Dudok was much less difficult for Matthew to persuade with his spiel on the current sponsorship potential of Beagle 2 than I imagined. With Matthew gone, he said "I am extremely interested to find a solution." Miles grabbed his opportunity. "BNSC want to see Beagle 2 succeed," he began. "Civil servants don't like to say they are wrong. The last scenario they want is to have to tell the Minister he's spent his money for nothing." I hoped he wasn't over-playing his hand. He also told Mr Dudok "David Leadbeater always starts money discussions by saying he wants somebody to share the pain. The OU is prepared to change the debt repayment schedule, to help Astrium's cash flow." Time was up and the meeting was now obviously over. Miles demonstrated that his generosity didn't extend very far. When Mr Dudok made to pocket the Finance Director's fountain pen as he was leaving, Miles was quick to grab it and to point out "I don't give a free pen with every mission I support."

It had been a scorching hot day, the morning's depression lifted, that evening Judith and I enjoyed a celebratory meal on a hillside terrace overlooking a wooded valley. It started raining again the next morning at 6.00am; we never saw the sun again during the holiday.

When he arrived home Matthew rang me in a panic. "Did you pick up the manila file I put on the desk?" he asked. "No, Miles must have it; he was probably last to leave. I left him enjoying a joke with Mr Dudok," was my reply. "They were being very pally; I left them to it." "Oh ****!" came down the line "The file had a draft of my severance contract in it." "Then we'd better hope Mr Dudok didn't pick it up," I said, thinking of the pen.

The next problem was that Mark rang to say "ESA now want to spin Beagle 2 off MEx ten days before we get to Mars." "What?," I said, "that will make three weeks before we can communicate." "It's going to be another MEx-is-more-important argument," he replied, then "Jim told them Beagle 2's timer only has a seven day clock." He knew I knew it was a white lie.

We stopped off at an Aurora meeting in Paris on the way home. Franco

Ongaro, the guy putting together the draft future programme for ESA's Human Exploration Division, had been doing a good job. Things were looking rosy for Mars exploration. In the margins, I again spoke to Roger Bonnet, the Science Director Southwood had replaced. The conversation went something like this. Me: "How are you?" He: "Better than you." I looked quizzical, he added, "I am very worried about your hardware, if I were Director you would not fly." Me: "If we don't, this programme [Aurora] will be put back years." He, again: "If I were Director you would not fly." Me: "It's good then you're not." It was clear that there had been no attempt, by anybody in ESA, to say that we had been sorting out problems.

The 18 July Board Meeting, with twelve people in the room and Mr Dudok on a video conference line making thirteen, was begun by Miles asking "Anybody got any time constraints?" He then answered his own question "Good. Breakfast time tomorrow will do." Barrie ran through a Beagle 2 status report which had Linssen, representing Credland, worried about chromium plating on the SUEM. This was engineering and not relevant in the current situation or to the Board. When he was ignored, Linssen tried again. This time he wanted to discuss contamination by out-gassing from the parachute. I told him, "Don't worry; I'm more paranoid than you about contamination because of the GAP." These questions were just time-wasting.

We came to the real business of the day. David Leadbeater reported that the German independent expert had responded "The parachute is challenging, but can be done in the time." A German with a sense of humour, he'd added "This is a time when size matters!" Miles asked "Was there anything about a risk to MEx?". "No," David answered. It was time to discuss money. Astrium had been working to identify actual costs. "We can absorb £1.2m," Mike Rickett said, "that leaves a hole of £2.8m." Miles looked around the table and said "This has to be a private matter. Unless ESA wants to make a contribution?" this addressed straight to Southwood, "they can go." The ESA, and Leicester, contingents trooped out, not before Southwood threw in a final damp squib "Any dealings with NASA over Communications are down to you." It was superfluous; what we did about parachutes had nothing to do with telecommunication or indeed NASA but Mark answered anyway as he went out of the door "I'll take responsibility."

We discussed every topic you could think of: absolute minimum costs, deadlines for a decision, loans, suing somebody to recover the costs of the redesign and extra tests, future business opportunities, work on big projects such as Galileo (Europe's GPS) and Skynet communications satellites, Astrium's annual report, predicted losses (Miles was offered access to Astrium's books), how much it would cost if we went on or if we stopped, how much we might make, sponsorship, share and share alike schemes, bonus payments, incentives, whether MEx might fail at launch (or later), company year ends, the possibility that sponsorship deals would not be struck until December 2003 when companies found they had a surplus, etc., etc. There was absolutely no doubt that the nine people still present wanted Beagle 2 to go on. If there was a way, no matter how imaginative, risky or unlikely, it was explored.

We reached the inevitable conclusion: we had a technical solution and a dedicated team; it would be heart-breaking if we had to announce we couldn't go on at the Farnborough Air Show which was due to start the next week. Mr Dudok indicated that we were at an impasse by saying "There are bigger bosses than me at Astrium." It was agreed that these bigger bosses should meet with Lord Sainsbury at Farnborough the following Wednesday. Miles, or his bigger boss, was invited to be there. We split up with everyone giving everyone else mutual congratulations, thanks and farewell hugs, probably in the belief we wouldn't meet again.

At home, I got a phone call from Everett. He was incredibly miserable, not surprisingly. "I've been summoned back from Australia by NASA," he said, "Somebody broke into my office, and stole my martian meteorites. They didn't just take the samples; they took the whole bloody safe weighing five hundred pounds." It just went to show the lengths some people will go to for a little piece of the action in the search for life on Mars.

It wasn't until after the Board that I discovered Miles not only had Matthew's file, but he'd read it. "Why don't we just recruit him onto the payroll," I suggested, "short term contract, full time working for us on sponsorship." I left Miles to think about it whilst we filmed the first flight hardware to arrive for sterilisation in the AAF. Judith had fixed for a BBC Farnborough-related news story. We'd decided to keep Beagle 2 in the public eye; we'd take it right down to the wire.

Afterwards I went to see Phyllis Starkey, another Milton Keynes MP. She had connections to the Foreign Office. She agreed to initiate approaches to the Kazakhs. I came out of her office thinking we might as well get another Ministry involved who might be embarrassed if Sainsbury pulls the plug.

On Wednesday, 24 July, I guided Miles to Astrium's chalet at Farnborough. "Is it going to be black Wednesday?" I asked him, but got no answer. There we joined Astrium's biggest cheese, Antoine Bouvier, and Colin Paynter, the UK Managing Director, Mike Rickett and Mr Dudok. The latter greeted Miles with "Is he coming to the meeting?" pointing at me. Miles just stared him down and said "Yes." Not a good start!

The Minister arrived with David Leadbeater, the redoubtable Sandra clearing the way. They'd been stuck in the traffic and the Minister was desperate for a pee. That minor crisis dealt with, the Minister and Mr Bouvier were seated opposite each other. Leadbeater and Dudok sat, respectively and respectfully, by their sides. I, the man who wasn't wanted by Astrium, took a seat to one side where I had a good view of both the protagonists, especially the Minister.

Bouvier spoke first, it was a lot of flannel about how pleased Astrium were to have contracts for various projects from the British Government, "But, for Beagle 2, we need some more money. We've had time to think about it, the actual amount now is a bit less than we indicated at the Board Meeting..." he started to say. Lord Sainsbury stopped him "Are you telling me you are breaking a fixed-price contract? Am I hearing you correctly? Are you breaking a fixed-price contract?" The Minister clearly wasn't here to **** around, just to use the toilet facilities. Dudok tried to help his big boss out. "The job was more difficult than we anticipated..." he appealed to Miles who joined in with "Astrium have done a good job to keep the project alive..." Bouvier, feeling he had allies, rejoined with "We didn't have time to look at the job properly, we underestimated..." Lord Sainsbury wasn't impressed and interrupted again "That still does not change the fact that it is a fixed-price contract."

He and Mr Bouvier were staring at each other eyeballs out. Beagle 2 was right in between them and was going to be damaged if they decided to do battle. It was time to take sides and as it stood at the moment it was three against one. Turning in the direction of Lord Sainsbury, who was currently outnumbered, I asked "May I say something?" He indicated I should go ahead so I made my little speech: "I wouldn't have been here if it wasn't for you," I was looking at Sainsbury, "but you wouldn't have been here but for me." This said swinging in an arc around the others, coming to rest on Mr Bouvier. "But truly, none of us would be here if it wasn't for the Minister." I glanced towards Lord Sainsbury, immediately coming back to the Astrium man. "The Minister has stated his principles. We don't have a solution which satisfies the Minister's principles so we should let him go about his business whilst we find one between ourselves."

Lord Sainsbury looked relieved and got up, saying "I will go along with any solution you can negotiate which doesn't go against my principles." He was looking at me when he said it. His last words were "I support the OU's revised payment strategy."

With the Minister gone, Mr Dudok asked David Leadbeater "Do you think the meeting has gone well?" The answer he got was the shortest on record for David, a terse "No." Maybe the Germans like aggressive business meetings, for me it had been a very close call. Leadbeater now introduced a face-saving compromise. "Since the new parachute is a technological development, the DTI can share the costs with Astrium." His raised eyebrows and tone of voice to ask the question "50:50? I think the Minister will play ball."

He presumably had this up his sleeve all the time; he could go back to Lord Sainsbury and take the credit or now blame me for costing the Minister another £1.6m. The Minister would be happy that I got him out of the room with his principles intact. It was a win-win settlement. Later Judith told me "Lord Sainsbury must have come straight here. His first business of the day was to be photographed by the press, smiling, in front of Beagle 2."

We were still in business. A month later, on 27 August 2002, I was given a very distressing piece of information via Barrie Kirk: "You'd better know this, Mike Rickett is leaving." Mike has never told me whether he jumped or was pushed, but Beagle 2 had lost its best supporter at Astrium. A phrase which springs to mind is "When elephants collide, the grass gets damaged." I didn't know if I had any friends now amongst Astrium's senior management. If not, I could look forward to being trampled.

Chapter 17

"YES, PRIME MINISTER"

The new share out deal would give Astrium first call on any sponsorship money raised to recover their investment, not including the new money going into the parachute. The canny Miles however inserted "after the OU has claimed its expenses" into the small print. The OU would get half its investment out next, then share the final tranche of money raised with the Government.

To make sure, Judith and I were in control of all PR now; Debbie Bomyer, Miles assistant, was fighting with the NSC at Leicester over a contract dictating what it would be allowed to do; they weren't happy. Even within the OU there were PR conflicts of interest. Contact with the Foreign Office unearthed a can of worms involving a schools competition, nothing to do with Beagle 2, which the political office wanted me to promote and provide a prize for; I got a message saying "meeting Blur is the sort of thing we have in mind." I wasn't about to ask the band to do things like this.

We had a better political PR idea. We would commandeer the current HMS Beagle for a boat trip down the Thames from the House of Commons to the National Maritime Museum and exploit it as a money raising jolly for potential sponsors. The passengers would be delivered to the opening of the Tales of two Beagles exhibition.

We set out to find our friends on our current namesake. The Navy didn't want to tell us where they were; out catching pirates we surmised. Persevering, I obtained a phone number which turned out to be a rest home for retired mariners. Nice to know our enemies are being fed a smoke screen of confusing information by the Navy. More phone calls located a harbour master who had met a man who thought he'd heard she had been sold. I said to him "The last time HMS Beagle was sold it took a hundred and fifty years to find the paperwork." The joke was wasted on him. Eventually we located the man who had bought HMS Beagle to convert it into a floating 'Gin Palace'; he was gung ho for the idea as a way of promoting his business but HMS Beagle was now in bits so we were back to the drawing board.

We thought we might have difficulty with PR involving the US companies and NASA, because according to ESA "everybody in America hates you." It wasn't the reaction I was getting at the shop floor level; even JPL engineers had told Mark Sims "If we're not approved to provide telecomms for Beagle 2 we'll find a way of doing it surreptitiously anyway." Suggestions that I was persona non grata were definitely black propaganda.

When Dave Hall arrived back from a trip to the US having had talks with NASA he said "They've sent a document about cooperation with Beagle 2 to the Department of State for signature." He smiled "It was at no charge. I didn't have to agree to you being transported, commuted to a thousand lashes as long as you continue to behave." Speaking of lashes James Pillinger's father-in-law, also a prisoner on Norfolk Island, was given fifty lashes when he was aged seventy. For serious crimes in the Navy in Darwin and Fitzroy's day, some offenders were flogged round the fleet for five hundred or so lashes, assuming they lived long enough, that is. A few, where a few was about fifty, were delivered on every ship as an example to potential local miscreants. No doubt Mr Bouvier and ESA would have approved of the same treatment for me.

The proof of the pudding about US PR came when parachute tests began in the US courtesy of Irwin Aerospace. I had contacted them and they were delighted when I asked "Can we film you?" They were so pleased to have a chance to be in our film, they phoned to say "The tests are starting next week." The information given to me by Astrium was not for another two weeks – naughty Barrie! Consequently I was admonished when a camera-toting John Macnish turned up unannounced. By and large, the new funding arrangements produced a fantastic change in Barrie's attitude to PR. At every Systems Team meeting I got a list of potential opportunities to film tests. He just didn't want us at the chancy ones, which is exactly where we could make dramatic TV. I don't think Barrie realised by giving me his list he was revealing Astrium's schedule.

The parachute drop was carried out in the western US, not because it was a long way from me, but because it was supposed to have guaranteed good weather. The engineers at the site were extremely co-operative so we gathered fabulous footage, including shots inside the aircraft, when skydivers jumped out to follow the parachute down. Then the weather went pear-shaped; the final test was conducted with a gale blowing so we even demonstrated the parachute's performance in a high wind, akin to conditions on Mars. One of the best bits of Beagle 2 filming ever was a sequence of the parachute blowing across the desert but stopped by driving a 4 × 4 into its path.

We were still having Systems Team meetings every two weeks. Things were becoming clearer about what would be ready when, what its mass would be and whether it would survive the landing. Like lots of other things, a qualification model, QM, of the GAP had been shaken, dropped, heated, cooled and generally mistreated, but it still worked. Confidence was growing. Unfortunately the QM mass spectrometer had leaks; the electrical feeds, connectors that carried power to inside the instrument, weren't vacuum-tight. The tests hadn't caused the problem; we knew it was there before we started. It had to be solved before we delivered the flight version.

After one Systems Team meeting there was a farcical exchange about our mass budget. Jim Clemett had sent the latest details of Beagle 2's mass, calculated from weighing the individual bits, to Toulouse with a change notice asking for a new mass budget. The response came back from Alain Clochet "Request rejected." The grounds given were that we hadn't weighed the whole lander as a single item? I asked Con "Have you weighed MEx as a single item?" "No," he said. Before I could follow up with the next obvious question "Why not?" He volunteered "No point, its mass can only be obtained by adding up the weights of the individual bits." Having already shot Clochet in the back, he kept firing. "Weighing the whole thing would only be accurate at the 1–2% level. If Toulouse did it the error would be about the same size as the Beagle 2 lander." This was the sort of thing we were up against; Clochet was just inventing reasons for denying us. Some people went out of their way to obstruct Beagle 2. There were better things to do than argue with them; it wasted our time.

After the Arizona affair, Judith and I got better advanced warning. So we were there with the cameras when the RAT was tested at a World War 2 airfield in the New Forest, using a helicopter, carrying Jason Hall and Lester Waugh. The flight demonstrated the radar triggered at the correct height above the ground.

We hurried back from Hampshire to Henlow, Hertfordshire, and the Koi Carp farm to be precise. In the *Beagle Bulletin* we called such field trips 'Out and about with Beagle 2'. The 'fishing' trip was to film a test of the parachute being extracted from its bag. As usual as it was photogenic in an appropriate location for PR so we were going to share the experience with the TV public. The bag was placed on the ground with a cord attached over a pulley on a

30m high crane, like a giant fishing rod. A count-down to zero signalled it was time for the strike. A big lump of concrete tied to the other end of the cord was dropped to give a sharp pull. The parachute came streaming out of its packing like a fish out of the water. We abandoned all thought of other ways we had for extracting the parachute, for example dropping the concrete off the roof of a building or from a bridge.

Afterwards the film was slowed down so everybody could see what happened in minute detail. Filming like this had a value way beyond PR. It was a great way of demonstrating we were getting it right. For example, the shots we took in the US convinced people not at the test that the ring sail parachute indeed had minimal drift.

We were having more and more meetings with anybody who thought they might be able to sell sponsorship. We wouldn't sign any exclusive deals; our offer to PR companies/advertising agencies was "Come to us with a client willing to make an offer and you can take a commission." A friend of my daughter's worked at the Agency which handled the Budweiser advertising account; ESA wouldn't like it but I visited her anyway, opportunities for exposure were being missed. We had great tests taking place that could have been branded in front of a news-hungry media. The deadline for putting logos on actual space craft hardware was fast approaching.

A director of M&C Saatchi told me that with Matthew gone, she didn't have the staff to dedicate anybody to Beagle 2. I was glad I didn't know this before we went to meet with Mr Dudok. "But we'll want a cut if anything transpires with BT," she said. I told Miles "It will be a small cut now Judith and I are doing all the running around again."

Matthew reappeared with Tony Simpson, both of them Directors of a company called World Sports Solutions, WSS. He was prepared to go on working on a commission-only basis; Tony still wanted an up-front budget. In a meeting with the pair, Tony kept on about how he could make me a superstar, endorsing products, name on merchandise, personal appearances, and the like. Matthew kept trying to shut him up; his pitch might have worked with the latest over-priced footballer but it wasn't what we wanted to hear. I was trying to recover the Underwriters' money, not go on an ego trip.

Just in case anybody tried to claim they were representing me, I phoned Paul Leonard and said "From now on any sponsorship arrangements with BT can only be made directly through me." He said "I'm still on the case; Angus has put Beagle 2 to the BT Chairman, Pierre Danon."

Next Judith and I travelled to Per Lindstrand's factory at Oswestry to be shown a machine test the breaking strain of the materials and threads being used for the new parachute. I knew a trick taught to me by a veteran postman that allowed me to break multi-strand cord with my bare hands. It worked with everything I had ever tried, including the almost indestructible twine used for tying hay and straw bales. I tried it to no avail with the parachute cotton. It wasn't a standard engineering test but it satisfied me.

We met the lady who was going to sew the two hundred or so pocket handkerchief-sized pieces of fabric into the ring-sail. One of the sections was a piece that would rip out if the forces on the parachute were too great – this patch was called a 'diaper'. "After I complete the job," she said "I'm going to retire; there won't be anything more exciting to do."

Returning from Oswestry we thought we would drop in at the Darwin family home in Shrewsbury. Instead of being a museum, it was occupied by the District Valuer. We played the "We're from Beagle 2" card to get our film camera in and were shown around. The place was at the forgotten end of time, full of dusty cardboard boxes that could have dated from when the Darwins left. We filmed the minute box room where mother Darwin brought fifteen children into the world; it was small like Beagle 2 and gave a whole new meaning to the word 'confinement'.

I briefed Miles on all that had transpired since the stand-up fight at Farnborough. What shook him most was the departure of Mike Rickett. He couldn't believe another Beagle 2 too friendly Astrium man had now been purged. I also told him "ESA have carried out a PR stunt with Ferrari and two journalist friends have tipped me off about Rudi still bleating in the margins about Beagle 2 being over mass, over budget, late and may not fly on MEx." And they had informed me Mr Bouvier was on the platform at the press conference whilst he was doing it. I said to Miles "This is all in breach of the 'we won't do anything to damage each other' clause Giacomo insisted on. Miles just replied "And I have had an unhelpful letter from David Southwood. Even David Leadbeater says it's unhelpful."

He never showed me the letter but I think it must have been about the Royal Society President's response on the subject of Planetary Protection. The next bit of bad news was that now every time Astrium had the opportunity, they were sending Debbie bills. My comment on that was "We are paying people to run the AAF but Astrium haven't shown up yet." I warned Miles "If you get any protests about 'only the GAP is holding them up', you're being bull****ted." I left him and Debbie thinking about how to handle all these unhelpful diversions. Together with BNSC they prepared a press release refuting the negative stories.

The drafts went back and forward, whilst Judith and I carried on with maximising our PR as a carrot to sponsors. Phyllis Starkey had arranged for a Foreign Office civil servant to accompany me to see the Kazakh Ambassador. I was met by a man, who spoke English better than I did, at a splendid Embassy opposite the V & A Museum. He was delighted to have been asked to help. With a war in the Middle East impending, he wanted to foster relationships with the West. Since Kazakhstan had 40% of the world's natural gas reserves the Foreign Office were keen for me to put him in a good mood. The Ambassador said "My country will play host to a plane full of people involved in Beagle 2." I explained "There will be VIPs, politicians, sponsors, guests, journalists, celebrities, their families, friends, and so on." He looked hopeful when he asked "And Tony Blair?" "Don't know" I replied. He looked disappointed but nevertheless said "We will clear everything with the Russians, in return for you making a cultural visit to Almatai [the Kazakh capital] to give lectures." We had a deal.

On the way home Everett phoned; I asked him "Do you want to come to Baikonur?" "Sure," he said "and I've met a man who has made a lot of money in oil. He's called Marshall Cloyd. Can he come too?" "Absolutely," I told him. "He's just the sort of person we're looking for."

It was Systems Team time again. At this meeting, there was a lot of discussion about gas-bags. Could they be packed inside the probe? A trial had been successful but only with a great deal of huffing and puffing; it had gone on late into the night. There were lots of jokes about a very large technician being appointed to sit on it the heat shield to close it.

Judith was receiving piles of things from Astrium, what they called the MGSE (Mechanical Ground Support Equipment) that would have to be available in the AAF. She had them assayed for microbiological contamination, what is called 'bio-burden'. She found lots of vegetative cells but no spores. "There is life at Astrium," she said, "official". Brian, the now beardless technician, set about cleaning and sterilising them. At a meeting of our Royal Society PP Committee we were congratulated for providing answers that were more comprehensive than required by the questions they had asked at the previous meeting.

We held a review of the progress with the new parachute design. It was for BNSC's benefit; Dave Hall was the Chairman. ESA went into ostrich mode and refused to come. If they intended to go on criticising Beagle 2 it wouldn't do for them to know any true facts. Pity they didn't attend because the Analyticon people explained how they had got rid of Linssen's perceived out-gassing problem. "Instead of coating the material, to make it impervious, we 'calendered' it," Dave Northey told the meeting. This meant the fibres had been flattened and locked together by applying pressure.

I was fed up with worrying about what ESA were saying behind our backs. I asked Rachael Buchanan from BBC News, "Do you have any negative comments on tape?" She said "No, they evade point blank questions when the camera is running."

Nevertheless I got the information I wanted. The Royal Society thought it would be a good idea to have a public event, a panel talking about the future of space exploration: me, David Southwood and Dave Scott, the Apollo 15 astronaut, with Pallab Ghosh, BBC's science correspondent, in the chair. Pallab kicked off by bowling us each an easy delivery: "How did you get interested in space?" We all dutifully answered, Southwood ending with "I never believed a fascination with Sputnik would lead to me, an Englishman, launching MEx and Beagle 2."

Pallab hit him right between the eyes. "How do you explain the attacks you have made on Beagle 2 then?" His reply was "You can't just go around launching space probes anywhere you want; 2003 is the best opportunity for going to Mars for years. Beagle 2 can't be allowed to spoil MEx's attempt to go to Mars!" How patriotic of the Englishman proud to be launching Beagle 2. He followed it up with a lot of garbage about being responsible for making sure the people of Kazakhstan, or "Even the camels of Kazakhstan," he said, "weren't at risk from Beagle 2." Unfortunately the BBC's cameras weren't there, but John Macnish was and I have his film locked in a safe. And Richard Slade's cartoon of the camels in their tin helmets, wads of ESA manuals protecting their humps. And when I thanked Pallab, he gave me every impression he was put up to it but wouldn't say who by.

Southwood's 'help' was really getting on the Beagle 2 team's nerves. I had just sorted out a pile of emails from people whose opinion was entirely different from his. Here is a sample of just some of the hundreds we had. There was one from a student, who wrote "I'm proud the UK is undertaking this mission." "Ambition still lives in England," had come from a TV viewer; "I feel compelled to write. Nothing else yet has managed to fire me up" probably from a rebellious teenager. There were loads more like "I'm not rich but I would give you a fortune. If you need any picture framing done I'll do it for free." "If you need somebody to make the tea, I'd be honoured if you'd consider me." "I want to be a part, no matter how small a part," was another of several offers we had for the post of 'Tea lady'.

Astrium however wanted a positive news story to redress the balance with ESA. Their press lady said "Let's issue a press release to the BBC." I said "It's no good writing press releases, we have to provide some action to give them a story." Linstrand's were in the process of making the flight version of the parachute and its spare. They planned to test them by dropping the spare out of a balloon. Judith suggested they could do this over one our fields. Our farm was only twenty minutes from Astrium. I was fixing for the BBC to cover it when Christine McGourty told me somebody at ESA had given the BBC the information "Beagle 2 <u>couldn't</u> pack the gas-bags." Not "Beagle 2 <u>found it difficult</u> to pack the gas-bags during the first trial run." This could only have come from Con at our Systems Team meeting telling Rudi. I replied to Christine, "It's just spite, they go out of their way to make it sound like Beagle 2 is in serious difficulty," and she said in return "It's amazing, in all my experience, this is the first time I've ever known anybody briefing against their own spacecraft!"

I'd had enough of this. On 14 October, I told Miles "If you don't do something about ESA, you, the Government and Astrium can kiss goodbye to any chance of getting the sponsorship money back. Every time we get any good publicity for Beagle 2, it is getting countered with an 'ESA aren't sure Beagle 2 is going to be going to Mars' comment." I said "You should threaten them legally under the terms of the Agreement."

We managed to persuade Astrium to carry out the Lindstrand's parachute drop live in front of TV cameras. They rejected our field, so having stayed overnight in room thirteen at a motel, Judith and I joined a small gathering at dawn on another deserted airfield near Oswestry. We were going to shoot the drop from above and below, John Macnish was to be in the balloon basket, the BBC's cameraman on the ground. The balloon pilot warned the BBC's cameraman, "Don't get directly under the basket or I'll call off the drop." Balloons aren't that predictable so it flew straight over the cameraman, the producer and the sound technician. John got some really good shots of a group of people scattering when 20kg of scrap iron attached to the parachute was thrown out of the basket. The BBC crew were in so much of a hurry to get out of the way they dropped their camera; we never got the looking up sequence.

But we'd done a good test, there was a fault but in fact it helped to show what a good parachute canopy the project had designed. That afternoon we had three phones ringing nonstop as the media clamoured for our film, stills and comments. As I chatted casually to Per Lindstrand, as another interviewer set up his camera, the balloonist said "I might be able to persuade Richard Branson to provide an Airbus for the trip to Kazakhstan."

Despite the number thirteen cropping up everywhere, over the weekend we solved the mass spectrometer's leak problem. It was the problem that never was, only to Barrie who was haranguing me about the GAP "Throw more people at it. Work overnight. It's holding up Beagle 2," he would yell at me, in front of ESA to make matters worse. The pressure was ramping up and people's tempers were getting frayed; a new girl member of the GAP team, Jen, had already been in tears a number of times. Mark Sims, the peace-maker, told Barrie "Life in Universities isn't like in Industry." A few days later, Barrie phoned to say he was going on holiday. Mark gave the PAW group the weekend off, for a change, in celebration.

The GAP leak wasn't a real issue because the atmospheric pressure on Earth is one hundred and forty times greater than on Mars. The tiny leak we were detecting in Earth's atmosphere would be an extremely tiny leak on Mars; it wouldn't affect how the instrument worked. But we found it anyway. Dennis did it by holding his finger in a rubber glove over various spots on the mass spectrometer. Since we didn't have enough mass to send Dennis and his rubber glove to Mars, we fixed it with a spray of leak sealant, a high temperature rubber solution. We had been using this for years in the laboratory so why we didn't think of it before I don't know.

A 'value-added' outcome of this success was that we could get a brownie point from the University Estates Department by moving out of a temporary building with dodgy ladies toilet facilities. I had been telling Estates "We don't have time." In a last resort effort to evict us they offered to form a human chain to transfer our belongings to a new home.

The time was fast approaching when Damien would paint his picture; some of the materials had already been tested with the X-ray spectrometer at Leicester. Anticipating the PR that could go along with Britain's most famous and controversial artist delivering his work to the spacecraft, Judith and I went with him to see art dealer Jay Joplin, at a Regency mansion in London. We fixed with Jay that Damien's spot painting would go on display at the White Cube Gallery first.

Damien arrived with his brother Brad at the OU to paint on 4 November, I thought it would be one of his army of technicians but no, he insisted on doing everything himself. To prove the provenance of this particular work of art we have some unique footage of Damien in white lab coat, with pipette, putting drops of coloured pigment, suspended in space-qualified glue, into recesses machined into a titanium plate. It took two days because he wanted a copy to keep and we had to have a spare to compare with the data from Mars. And there was also a version where he got the paints in the wrong order. I expect Michelangelo made the odd mistake when he was painting the Sistine Chapel ceiling. In the middle of creating, Damien broke off to go to a firework party at Ottery St Mary, famous for men running through the streets with flaming barrels of tar. He was apologetic for not staying to finish. I said "I don't want it spoiled by hurrying, for want of a halfpennyworth of tar." It was another terrible pun. Yuk!

At last the NSC got some money from the Millennium Commission. It was spent to acquire a working Beagle 2 test bed called the Ground Test Model (GTM) from Astrium to put behind a window so the public could watch rehearsals of sample collection. The GAP lab model was to stay at the OU. NSC's CEO asked "Now do we get any part of a sponsorship money share-out?" It was Dave Hall's turn to say "Get stuffed." It did nothing to pay off the underwrite.

Once when I appeared on the 'Big Breakfast' with Johnny Vaughan he had wanted to run Beagle Mission Control from his shed on the set. Pity the programme was no longer on air, it would have been the ultimate outlet for us to encourage kids into science; we could have moved Johnny's shed into the NSC. Even if we couldn't now use Johnny, I was pursuing other possibilities with Channel 4. I had suggested to them that they might be an alternative to the BBC to show more of the fly-on-the-wall documentary material. When the BBC found out, they told the OU to tell me they were talking to the US about making a documentary of the MER rovers. I sent back a response saying "Make my day." The headline 'The Brits go to Mars, BBC shows film of US competition' would do wonders for Channel 4's viewing figures and for my ratings but not much for the BBC's.

We still didn't have a sponsor for the Beagle 2 Media Centre which I was determined to have in London. PPARC wanted to be involved and offered help in the form of loaning us their PR man, Peter Barrett, who in his smart suit and cuff links always looked out of place with a bunch of scruffy academics in jeans. Peter was great to work with and soon came up with the idea "We have to get Lord Sainsbury to come to the OU to see the finished Beagle 2 before you close it up." He was unaware we didn't have much more than the lander base at the AAF at the time and progress was very slow.

Barrie, who did know the state of play, wasn't helping with his continual "Mr Bouvier wants Beagle 2 finished before January; the GAP is holding us up." GAP wasn't the cause of the delay, so after another round of this I said "Tell Mr Bouvier to arrange the following words into a well known phrase or saying: 'stuffed' and 'get'." Barrie was not amused; he responded "My Management will call your Management." I replied "Won't do them any good." I told Miles "Get them off our backs. If they want Judith and me to be looking for sponsors, we will until there is no chance of selling the advertising rights, but we can't with Barrie going on as well as ESA." He said "I'll get Debbie to draft a letter to David Leadbeater, and by the way, because of mother's share, I know BAe Systems are trying to off-load Astrium."

We began making arrangements for a Ministerial visit. Everybody was running around in tiny circles trying to change diaries because the VC was going to Sweden the day Lord Sainsbury wanted. Because she wouldn't be there, there was a dispute over who would greet him. Was it to be someone from the Political office, a Pro-Vice-Chancellor or was the Dean of Science most appropriate? Before we could get an answer, Judith rang to say "Number 10 have been on the phone, Tony is doing something that day and doesn't want it upstaged." "Oh god, now we're a political football," I said, remembering Harold Urey's reasons for starting to study the Moon.

But it was nice to know Beagle 2 now had such a high profile, it could worry the Prime Minister. Reluctantly we said "Yes, Prime Minister" and cancelled the event.

Chapter 18

THE WORLD WILL BE WAITING

M r Bouvier's demands must have galvanised Astrium into action because the Beagle 2's electronics module, the ELM, the first item to go into the lander base, showed up at this point. It wasn't quite the end of October 2002. Andy Spry took it to Leeds to be sterilised at the General Hospital overnight. We were flat out; other things were to follow thick and fast. The same weekend Simon Sheridan began assembling the GAP flight model. He was working in our own private clean room so we didn't conflict with Astrium.

The argument about where we had to deliver Beagle 2, Baikonur or Toulouse, was raging between Jim and Con. During one exchange of views, Jim asked "What happened about my mass waiver?" Con replied "Good question," and added "I'm here to help you." If somebody from ESA said that one more time...

Southwood had written an even more threatening letter about PP to the President of the Royal Society, and for his pains he got back "This correspondence is at an end" as an answer. There was worse to come. One day, Barrie drew me aside and said, "This is for your ears only; Mr Bouvier had Beagle 2 as the first item on the Astrium Board's Agenda. He said if Beagle 2 isn't delivered by the 29 December, it's curtains for Astrium Stevenage." Our major industrial supplier was under pressure and they were now trying to blackmail me. This was Mr Bouvier's version of throwing the bucket of sea water over the flogged man – rubbing salt in the wounds.

Then just when Judith and I didn't need anything else to worry about, some stupid woman from the Ministry of Agriculture rang up and said "I have to see whether your cows have ear tags in them." I nearly said "Here's a list of their names, go to the gate in the field and call them." Cows are good at bringing you back to reality in times of crisis; usually one will lie down in the muck somewhere, in the middle of the night, to have a calf. It's good for taking your mind off things.

For a bit of light relief, we took Damien's spot painting to Jay Joplin's White Cube Gallery and watched the journalists, Science and Arts, fighting to get in. The coverage the story got chalked up as another success. Afterwards we gave the tiny titanium plate to Barrie, to be attached to Beagle 2, with a message: "Tell Mr Bouvier what might happen in the press if he upsets me."

The wrangle about GAP delaying the lander went on. Astrium insisted on putting one of their people into the GAP team 'to help'. He just got in the way, continually asking questions, then giving Barrie information he didn't understand. Barrie had a bigger problem than GAP anyway. The American companies involved in the EDLS, the final items in the build, had declared they wouldn't work over Christmas, from 20 December to 2 January.

Installing things in the lander base began in earnest on 20 November; it didn't last very long before the cursing started. The ELM didn't fit. A piece of the base had to be removed; it was more good reality television footage. I was now spending every possible minute in the AAF on the observation platform, not just because I wanted to make sure everything was recorded, but to watch out for anything which might compromise the PP and hence the GAP's results.

Because I was being uncooperative with the BBC, Steve Wikinson wasn't able to 'fiddle', I mean 'pay', all the filming costs. Most of the camera work was now being done by Dave Revell. Judith had found him languishing in the OU's Estates Dept as a porter and had been told he had hidden talents. We had recruited him as a technician and from then on he operated the cameras and pointed them wherever I directed. So now I was Director and Producer. We had one camera in the AAF making a time-lapse record at a speed of a frame every ten seconds.

There was one last test to perform on the parachute: 'the truck pull'. It sounds like something out of the 'World's Strongest Man'. We needed to measure the forces on the parachute's rigging when it was doing its job. To get the information, we were going to tow the parachute behind a lorry. Not just any lorry, this was a very powerful beast, its day job was emptying cess pits! In our case the ****cart was in front of the 'Lord Mayor's Show'. The venue for the lorry pull was inside one of the R101 airship hangars at Cardington, Bedfordshire. Anybody travelling around the outskirts of Bedford will have seen these massive corrugated iron buildings. The floor area inside each is three acres, the size of one of my fields.

Judith and I arrived with two sets of TV cameras and a something to take still photographs, to find Dave Northey already there with a helper who enjoyed the reputation of being the country's best parachute packer. They were laying out Beagle 2's canopy very carefully to avoid the lines tangling. After what seemed like hours, the truck revved up and charged down the thousand foot track, a beautifully inflated parachute trailing in its wake. Just before it ran out of space, the driver jammed on its brakes. With a scream of burning tyres it stopped; it wouldn't have done to go through the wall of a listed building. The last bit was totally unnecessary; with the parachute as a brake, the driver needed only to have taken his foot off the accelerator.

Meanwhile in the AAF progress on the lander was still slow, but at least the PAW had arrived from Leicester. Astrium's AIV technicians, Dave, Malcolm and 'Del Boy', were nowhere near ready for it, so Leicester's John Holt sat there all day waiting, then went home. Installing the ELM had, by this time, taken several weeks. Not that anybody was standing around idle, because the back cover was being modified to make sure the gas-bags went in without the specialist fat man to sit on the heat shield. Barrie, under orders from on high, had told ESA, "We can't deliver before 29 January and it's all Colin's instrument's fault." When he told me what he'd done, I said "Barrie, it's collective responsibility; if you start blaming people you will wreck morale and kill off any hope of anybody cooperating with anybody else."

There was no point in Astrium Management trying to rush us for contractual reasons; we had found out that MEx was also behind schedule and the earliest they would need Beagle 2 was going to be 15–17 February. We could deliver Beagle 2 at the end of January without causing anybody any difficulty or delay.

Con took the notification about the schedule slip very well, now MEx had somebody, i.e. me, to blame. Barrie obviously didn't relay my words of wisdom back to his Management because Mr Dudok wrote to Miles saying "Science is holding everything up." His letter practically screamed "Astrium will be seeking compensation." Miles replied with a letter which used the words "collective responsibility" and to me he said "ESA will blame us anyway; everything will be our fault, so what's changed? Ignore it. Anyway, it keeps Mr Dudok from fretting about sponsorship money."

Miles' response didn't stop everybody and his brother demanding meetings to discuss things; they'd have been more helpful letting us get on with the job. Calling meetings is just back-protecting, an excuse to pass the blame by saying

"We told him at such and such a meeting; here are the minutes." Everybody knew what they had to do and they were doing it eighteen hours a day.

I get up early, and I mean early; it's something I picked up from my father. Just before Christmas, at 6.00am OU Security rang me "There's been an attempt to break into the AAF, a door handle has been tried," somebody blurted out. At that time of the morning it would take me forty minutes to get there, so I got Taff, who lived nearest of the OU team, out of bed. By the time he arrived the panic was over. Taff phoned, as I was going over Brogborough Hill with another seven miles to go before I arrived, "It was one of their men; he tried the door to check that it was locked. Prat!"

There was indeed more work to do with the GAP. Part of the electronics which worked on Earth for testing could go bang with a big flash on Mars because of the different atmospheric composition. When we reached the planet the air would be very dry so the high voltage circuits had to be put inside a box filled with nitrogen and welded shut. There were lots of incompatible materials in the box and techniques we didn't have at the OU. Trips to the University of Birmingham, Culham, Portsmouth and all ports of call around the M25, in sequence, were required. I did the driving because I was expendable. All the team, particularly Nick, another of our specialist technicians, who had to connect three hundred and twenty wires in the right order, had already worked all night on several occasions to keep Barrie happy.

I knew things weren't going to go well when I had to wait until past midnight to receive the first bits from Birmingham. The next night, I didn't get the box for the third stage until 2.00am. It was delivered to home by Simon on a motorbike. It had to be in Portsmouth by 6.00am, so off I went. There weren't that many all-night garages open so I very nearly ran out of diesel. The company in Portsmouth did their bit quickly and I was back on the road again by 9.00am.

When I arrived at the next destination they were short of a component. "It'll come in the morning post," a man said. It didn't, so a courier on another motorbike brought it at lunchtime. But he hadn't been given the proper paperwork. Another man, who was in charge of doing the job, then said, "My MD says I can't do it without the paperwork," obviously a 'jobsworth' without a peaked cap. I gave his MD my advice on the subject of paperwork and customer relations.

Job done, I made the return trip to the OU for a bit more evening work. I had another early start on the third day to get to Woking. I arrived before 8.00am; the company there weren't open yet. The first man to arrive told me "Our machine's broken down. Anyway the diagram which shows which way up the feed-through goes is with somebody who won't be in until later." He got on the phone to another company who had a similar machine whilst I contacted Daz (Darren), our CAD man, to get another copy of the missing diagram faxed to me.

I set out for the substitute company, they fitted me in whilst their PR man, delighted to be part of Beagle 2, showed me jet turbine blades they had special-ist welded. I was now very late for my next appointment, indeed it was 7.00pm when I got there. Everybody had gone home except a man from the office who had stayed behind. He said "Leave it with me, come back first thing in the morning."

I got the box back early next day and took what I hoped was the finished box back to the OU for cleaning only to find Taff and Simon couldn't pump the air out so it could be filled with dry nitrogen. "We'll spray some sealant around to find where it leaks," said Taff, "then I'll take it apart." An hour later he called me and said "Come and look at this." When I got there he held the box up to the window. "Look," he said, "there's a hole in the weld so big you can see the daylight coming through." We got a new box manufactured (more cost) and I repeated the journeys all over again; after bribing a man to work some overtime at one factory at the end of the day, I mean week, it was fine.

Throughout this saga, Judith said "Turn your phone off and call me when it's safe." She issued all manner of threats, promising dire consequences for anybody trying to phone me whilst I was driving. She told everybody "You've got to communicate through me." She was pretty short with those wanting to discuss the schedule or to fix meetings. I'd lapped the M25 more times than a Grand Prix driver going round Silverstone. I was knackered; Denis Leigh's son, James, once asked me "Do you have trouble sleeping at night?" Worrying about the money, he meant. I said "No." He said "I do, it's the pumps next door to my bedroom!"

Whilst I had been circumnavigating the M25, ESA had been having another MEx SWT meeting. Agustin Chicarro had stood up and said "Beagle 2 is not represented. Professor Pillinger has been ordered not to come by his Government because there is a problem." Everett, who was there, said he couldn't believe it when Rudi announced "MEx has a problem too, Beagle 2 is not to be blamed. We're all in this together." I found out afterwards that Rudi was under orders from Southwood because journalists were demanding to know what was wrong with MEx. I suspected it was a double bluff intended to hint it was really Beagle 2's fault. Now I was getting paranoid.

There was still much to do but Judith and I still managed to get to the opening night of 'The Beagle Voyages' as the Exhibition at the NMM was now named.

Instead of a relaxing river cruise, we got stuck in the Blackwall Tunnel and missed the corporate speeches. At least we could be thankful for small mercies. When we arrived we found the place overpopulated with Darwin descendants, all claiming credit for something or other and saying "Don't listen to Uncle X or cousin Y." Con muscled his way in, delighted to meet Darwin's relations; I never thought there would be a time when I would be glad to see somebody from ESA. The only Fitzroy there didn't say once "HMS Beagle's success was really down to my ancestor, Captain Robert's, skills as a navigator."

Back at the OU, we were waiting for a last bit of the GAP. One of Astrium's guys out on the road just managed a pick-up at two minutes to 5.00pm one Friday evening somewhere in Surrey. Judith had to negotiate with a lady in OU security, who liked cats, to stay late to receive our missing component.

We had a similar series of adventures with the Sample Handling and Delivery System, SHADS, only it involved flights to Germany by Simeon Barber, another new member of the GAP team – I won't bore you with the details. And Barrie still thought we were dragging our feet.

Of course there had to be a Board meeting in the middle of it all. There it transpired Astrium had a problem with the Beagle 2 computer processor. There was a definite lull in the "it's all GAP's fault" nagging whilst Miles probed Astrium's problems. "Nothing like a bit of getting your own back," he whispered to me. Whilst he was saying "Run that past me again," for about the fifth time, the boys at the OU had time to put the GAP flight instrument in its transport container and set out for Astrium to be vibrated, simulating the conditions during launch. When the Board finally got round to asking about the GAP, Miles was able to say "It's at Astrium, has been all afternoon."

Deprived of the opportunity to jump on the GAP, the Board spent hours discussing various ways to get to Baikonur: air, sea, up the Volga River by boat (no boatman mentioned), rail or road (preferably not through the Blackwall Tunnel). All these possibilities were considered because of the radioactive source in the Mossbauer spectrometer. The Board meeting ended with Barrie saying "It's the most complicated thing we have ever done and everybody must be congratulated." Mr Dudok suddenly remembered sponsorship and demanded to know why I hadn't been working on it. If looks could kill, Miles would have been arrested. Dudok contented himself by saying "We shouldn't make any positive press announcements about Beagle 2, in case we build people's hopes up." "More likely worried about somebody asking why is Astrium going out of business," Miles said to me afterwards.

I spent the whole of the next day watching Astrium trying to shake GAP to pieces and worrying if anything breaks now... It was after midnight on Friday when I put it back into its transport box again. With Astrium's Cliff Ashcroft satisfied I delivered GAP back to the OU in the early hours of Saturday morning; Andrew Morse was going to work what was left of the night to make sure it was still performing as desired. "Yes, it's OK," he said, when I arrived back five hours later. He carried on collecting test data all that day and most of the next. Then, because it was ****ing down, we drove it the last few yards to the AAF for the GAP to be sterilised. It was 7.20pm, Sunday 15 December; nobody from Astrium was there to welcome us, certainly not Barrie.

"Sod Mr Dudok," Judith said. We had changed the date of our open day so as not to annoy Number 10 and gave the Press a last chance to see Beagle 2 before we closed its lid. The event was mobbed out. We put the GAP right in front of the observation window, everyone marvelled at it. All the celebs came, Alex, Dave, Keith, Damien with family and Patrick Moore, but no Minister, presumably put off by Mr Dudok's pessimism. Barrie said "My Management have banned the Astrium workforce from coming." Everybody, including Colin Milburn, their hard-nosed negotiator, was incensed. BAe had sold their shares; Astrium was no longer a British-owned company.

We had private viewing sessions for MP Tony McWalter, our original champion with Lord Sainsbury, and Paul Leonard. It was Christmas Eve; Judith suggested Paul might like to think about putting the BT name on the new block which was being built to house my group, if he couldn't get agreement about sponsoring Beagle 2.

On 27 December Astrium decided that they had to take the ELM out of the lander again to fix the computer problem. They had reached the conclusion it had been caused by a short circuit. "Just as well GAP wasn't in there," I told Barrie, "it would have made life even more difficult for you." To do the job, he ordered his people to work New Year's Eve until 11.00pm and again on 1 January. After he left, I found out he wasn't going to be in himself so I countermanded his order. I became a hero overnight with Astrium's workers, especially the ones already planning to call in sick next day.

During the first week of January lots of newspapers and magazines carried predictions that Beagle 2 was likely to be the story of 2003. I was glad they didn't know an Astrium test meter had discharged five hundred volts through an electronics board when they were removing it, with the ELM. Everybody on the test platform had gone white before the decision was taken to call in somebody from SEA, Systems Engineering Assessment, yet another Bristol company, who'd made the board. "*****" said Alan Senior, their engineer, when he was phoned, "I'm on my way."

I left them to it and went to lecture seven hundred science teachers in

283

Birmingham. The PA system went wrong and somebody else's lecture was relayed into the theatre where I was speaking. I pulled out every plug and wire I could see before it stopped. "This is definitely not the way to promote physics teaching as a career," I said to the organiser, looking at the mess somebody was going to have to clear up.

When I got back to the OU, I found Astrium holding a crisis meeting behind closed doors. Even Barrie's new boss was in it, but Mark Sims had been excluded. I marched in and said "Gentlemen, there are no private Beagle 2 meetings on OU premises. You have five minutes to conclude, then I want to be told what's going on." They were out in much less than five minutes. Barrie and I had a stand-up fight over whether I was allowed to be at private Astrium meetings. I said "There are no such things as private meetings. Read the Management plan I was made to agree to. The rules of the Consortium say that when anything that concerns the fate of Beagle 2 is discussed, I have to be there." Barrie's boss interceded with "We haven't got time to argue about who will or not be at meetings. Let's get on with fixing the problem."

The result was a decision to work only eighteen hour shifts from now on. It meant either I or Andy Spry would have to be in the AAF, probably both of us, at all times to make sure Planetary Protection rules were observed. During the fix, I made a nuisance of myself by reminding everybody working that they had to attach two wires to their wrists, with the other ends connected to earth, to avoid any more discharges of static electricity.

Judith and I were still trying to sell the Media Centre so I had to duck out for a few hours to go to meet with Sky TV. I offered them all the video footage we had collected over several years. I said "If you sponsor the Media Centre, because there can't be film from Mars, TV broadcasters reporting our results will want to use our simulations as background. Everything that's shown can carry a strapline saying courtesy of Sky." We had got the idea from seeing News bulletins covering Premier League football for which Sky owned the rights; they seemed interested in doing the same for Beagle 2.

I got back to some good news: the gas-bags, both flight and spare sets, had passed inflation, drop and opening tests and had been shipped air freight. "But," said Dave Moore, Astrium's chief technician in the AAF, "somehow, the flight set have ended up in Tel Aviv. The spare set is slightly closer, in Amsterdam; the ones used for qualification tests have arrived in Indianapolis via Delaware." "You're kidding, we want one set on Mars," was all I could think of to say.

By 10 January the ELM was fixed, all functions working correctly. We ran a test to show the computer could raise the robotic arm. Three days later, a little team of four lowered the GAP on a crane into the lander base; I dragged the VC, and a member of the OU Council she was entertaining, to witness it. It took two days to do up the fifty-two bolts; all of them matched the holes in the base perfectly. Even so there was absolutely no way I would have wanted to reverse the process and repeat it if we had already installed GAP prior to having the ELM problem. Astrium should have been thanking us for not arriving sooner.

Then it was the turn of the PAW. Before that could go ahead, John Holt was ordered to shave. Fortunately the OU's shop keeps razors and shaving foam. In order for Beagle 2 to take its first picture of the landing site on Mars, the PAW included a pop-up convex mirror. One of the cameras could look into the mirror to record a reflected picture without having to raise the arm. We tested this function and took a picture of masked engineers; you couldn't see John Holt's newly shaven face, anxiously peering over the lip of the lander like three 'Mr Sprods'.

Buoyed up by the success with the PAW, we started testing the GAP. It had been working on the bench after more than two days at 128°C, but now it was completely dead. The fault was a broken wire. "It must have been already broken when we installed it," said Mark Leese, the OU man in charge of AIV, meaning it wasn't the fault of my group of four. "We were just unlucky and dislodged it," he said. "No Mark," I replied, "we were lucky, it might have come off on the way to Mars."

We were approaching the last lap. We held what were called 'close out' meetings at which the Product Assurance, PA, man, John Ferguson, went through all the checks that had to be made to be sure the lander would do its stuff when we got to Mars. There were hundreds of actions which people around the table had to confirm as done and tested before John would declare each issue closed. His wife must love him going to the supermarket with a shopping list on Saturday mornings.

Another job left was the installation of the RAT. Con suggested it should be proved to be still able to detect the ground at two hundred metres by aiming it at the wall after it was installed. His idea was greeted with a chorus of "But Con, the wall's only six metres away." We hoped it would be higher above the surface of Mars when it was used in anger, but it was definitely working because it was put in fired, taken out, reset, put in, fired, taken out... ; Ian Wright was there watching for me. He said "It was like doing the Okey Cokey."

By this time work in the AAF started at 6.00am every day and ended at midnight. There was a snag with all this activity, we kept running out of the clean bunny suits; anybody going into the build area had to don fresh attire every time they entered. I arrived one morning asking "Where's Andy Spry?" They weren't supposed to work without one of us present. "Nobody's working," I was told, "he's gone to fetch more laundry on his way in." Andy lived in Swindon and the suits were cleaned in Sheffield. God alone knows what time he had started. An hour or two later he was on the phone to me, "I've skidded off the road; my car's in a ditch. I don't know how it happened," he said. "I do," Barrie said when I relayed to him the clean suits would be a while, "I told him he wasn't getting enough sleep." So Barrie had a heart after all.

In keeping with testing everything, we ran a simulation of the landing procedure using the lander's on-board computer, getting the signals back on the test bay as each step happened. It was only a theoretical simulation, we therefore decided we would do it for real using a replica test model at Astrium's factory. Several engineers, each responsible for different functions in the process, had to confirm to the PA man that an upside-down lander could turn itself over, fold out the solar panels and be ready to call home. This was something that had to be filmed; Dave Revell had to be there. Late one afternoon those in the AAF got the call from the factory that the test was ready for us.

As always, the Discovery was parked nearest the door of the AAF so I was first on my way. Everything was going well on the drive until I got as far as a roundabout at the edge of Ampthill. Seeing a car coming from the right, I stopped. The next thing I knew there was an enormous bang and I was pushed forward about ten yards. I got out to be greeted by an apologising lady saying "I'm sorry, I was looking the other way."

We exchanged names and addresses and I left her working out how to explain to her husband how come his Jaguar was a foot shorter than it used to be. Unlike the crash in Italy before Apollo, this one wasn't my fault. The Discovery has a rather substantial chassis, so I, with a dented bumper, continued merrily on my way to Astrium. The others coming to the test arrived more than an hour later complaining about "some woman crashing her Jaguar at a roundabout and holding them up."

The simulation of the entry descent and landing sequence went perfectly. The computer screen reported the test lander had dropped onto the surface ready for the real action to begin. A frangi-bolt was then supposed to fire but there was no bang. Suddenly there was a large group of people gathered round the computer. It couldn't be an error in the software because we'd already run that. Ten minutes passed before Stuart Hurst picked up a wire with a three pin plug dangling on the end. "Is this supposed to be plugged in?" he asked. It was the power supply; he was supposed to have inserted the plug and he's never going to be allowed to forget it.

After that false start everything worked. Dave Revell's shin was narrowly missed by the bolt. Richard Slade had to help the panels turn over because in Earth's gravity they were too heavy for the motors. But neither would be a problem on Mars.

We held a meeting where everyone was asked to agree it was now acceptable to close the lander lid. The answer was a unanimous "Yes." Barrie wanted to go ahead that night. I said "No, everybody should be here, anyway I want to take a series of high resolution photographs to make up a mosaic of the completed job." Looking at Beagle 2 from the observation platform, it seemed about as tightly packed as a pocket watch inside. I needed this giant picture for publicity. There was a row. Barrie said "I'll tell Mr Dudok you're obstructing me." I said "Go ahead, tell him." He said "Mr Dudok will phone Mr Hedges." I offered him Miles' home phone number saying "Do it now, Miles will be ever so pleased." It was approaching 10.00pm. It would have been near 11.00pm in Germany, hardly a time to get your boss's senior out of bed.

I didn't see the point of hurrying. Southwood had sidled up to Dave Hall at an ESA meeting and said "Beagle 2 can have another week to deliver." MEx wasn't ready for us. I told Barrie this; Barrie didn't want the extra week; it was costing his budget £15k/day.

The lid was closed at 2.15pm the following afternoon Tuesday, 28 January; we filmed it from above, the side and with a hand held camera and peeking under the descending lid. Everybody who could find a place was on the test platform, standing on the tables, chairs etc. Others who couldn't get in watched a television relay in the AAF's meeting room. I made a speech, ending "There are a lot of people watching today but when it opens the world will be waiting."

Chapter 19

ALL THIS AND BEAGLE 2

We still weren't finished putting the spacecraft together; we had to add the entry, descent and landing system to turn Beagle 2 into what we called the 'probe'. A team from ILC Dover, who had been hanging around waiting, swung into action. The gas-bags, now arrived from Tel Aviv, were taken into the AAF. Andy Spry rang me to say "There's a split in one of the bags." Before I could have a heart attack, he explained "I mean in the outer of the three layers of packing used for Planetary Protection."

ILC started on the Friday, the three days after closing the lander lid having been taken up by Brian Shaughnessy of RAL covering all the surfaces with gold foil. I didn't relish the involvement of the man who deposited gold using a vacuum plasma and his dog. There was also a major hiccup on Thursday at 4.30pm when it started to snow heavily. Most of the people working in the AAF had homes miles away. Some decided to leave immediately. Others risked staying a bit longer; they later regretted their decision. One guy took six hours to get home, a journey normally less than an hour. Many motorists, none from Beagle 2 thank goodness, spent the night trapped on the M11.

Judith and I were two hours reaching the farm. Next day the workforce in the AAF was severely depleted because people couldn't get through the drifts. We only got there by lunchtime because we had a Land Rover and towed a few obstacles out of the way in order to pass. That trip to Schloss Ringberg had been good practice.

Normality had returned by Saturday lunchtime. The canister containing ammonia to inflate the bags had been filled by Taff, in a fume cupboard, on Friday evening. The gas-bags were draped all around the lander and some heavy duty needlework and lacing was being done. Soon it looked like a giant

Christmas pudding. There hadn't been any hitches. I was on the observation platform Saturday lunchtime and suggested we all take a break before the next stage. No sooner had I got outside in the AAF compound, my mobile rang. We'd decreed that there would be no switched-on mobiles inside because the lander contained armed pyrotechnic charges. The call was from the BBC who wanted me to go to a studio immediately; the Space Shuttle had disintegrated whilst returning to Earth. I said "I'm tied up right now, try calling me at midnight," and rushed back in to tell the others about the disaster. We watched the news on a TV for a while and then returned to our task.

We had devised a way of compressing the bags, so that the plum pudding would go inside the probe. The parcel was put into a special plastic bag. Another bag made of the same material as the gas-bags themselves was put over and all the air trapped between the layers inside the bag pumped out, whilst compressing the parcel to the exact shape we wanted in a mould. The only thing left to do was extract the plastic bag, a procedure described by somebody as "Like taking a lady's vest off without removing her stays." A particularly ample lady, who worked for Astrium was mentioned as being appropriate to practise with.

On Sunday, we weighed everything just like Alain Clochet wanted. We had to hold a piece of board over the top of the scales because the down-draught of air in the AAF was making a significant contribution. The result of the process was within fifteen grams of Jim's prediction and quite a lot inside the 1 or 2% that Con thought was the best we'd achieve. Jim went home very happy.

Next day the plum pudding was carefully lowered into the probe's back cover. The cover already contained the main parachute in its bag and the pilot parachute in the mortar that would fire it into the martian atmosphere. Both had already been tested by MBA. Unlike the rehearsal, everything went in easily and the heat shield was bolted down without any swearing and cursing.

I called Miles across to see the results of over two months non-stop labour. He said "It doesn't look like I've got much for my money," as it disappeared to have its centre of gravity determined and to be spun and balanced. Miles stood talking to Barrie, who told him "Those men in there, who closed the spacecraft, have received emails this morning setting out redundancy terms." He elaborated "Astrium is now owned by the French and German company EADS, European Aerospace Defence Systems; they're shedding five hundred people at the British subsidiary."

Although we were ready to deliver, the French branch of Astrium in Toulouse was dreaming up all manner of reasons why they couldn't accept Beagle 2. The grape-vine was telling us that they wouldn't be ready for us until 22 February.

It was rumoured that the propulsion system of MEx had a leaking valve. Nevertheless Barrie wanted Beagle 2 gone and the cost of minding it taken off his budget. An Astrium directive from on high told both sides "not to wash dirty linen in public."

Despite Beagle 2 being ready, it still hadn't gone anywhere by the following Friday. But we'd made our minds up it was going that night, so I called the BBC News in and we began moving the probe in its stainless steel transport vessel out of the AAF onto the loading bay. Then one of the wheels jammed. We had to jack up the container but broke the jack spanner. A runner was despatched to Halfords for another. By now there were a lot of tired, angry, sweating and swearing people doing hard physical work. The container was still partly inside the clean area but the airlock door was closed and the probe safe inside the sealed vessel. I donned some clean room gear and joined in to take a turn at getting the wheel freed; eventually we were successful. I claimed "I knew I'd have to finish the bloody job myself."

Mob-handed, we pushed the sealed vessel up a slope into its shipping container; even Barrie took his coat off to help, but he was still fretting like a broody hen. It was getting late when Dave Moore said to me "Do something to get rid of him." I did, I asked him to go round everybody, make a list of what they wanted to eat then go to the fish and chip shop. The order was for seventeen cod and chips, two pie and chips and one vegetarian chips and chips. We sat eating in the meeting room, washing the food down with beer.

Finally the box was craned onto the back of the lorry, the scene lit by lamps borrowed from a building site across the street and with Del playing 'Auld Lang Syne' on his bagpipes. It was the signal for Andy Spry and Dave Moore to start spraying each other, and anybody in the way, with champagne.

The crowd dispersed at midnight but Beagle 2 couldn't leave; the lorry drivers were out of time. We bedded them down for the night in the AAF. Judith and I went home but were back with Dave Revell the following morning at 6.00am only to discover the biggest disaster yet had befallen Beagle 2: nobody had remembered to bring the Marmite for the drivers' breakfast. I bet it doesn't happen in NASA. Slightly less important, one of the drivers had left his lorry's lights on all night so his battery was flat. After another trip to Halfords, the tiny two-lorry convoy, Andy Spry riding shotgun, was waved on its way. I didn't know what to do with myself for the rest of the day.

It wasn't the last we saw of the probe. The plan was to stop on the way to Toulouse at the Atomic Weapons Research Establishment (AWRE) to carry out a vibration test to confirm everything to do with the probe was tight and could do no harm to MEx or itself on take-off. We had to go to AWRE because of the dreaded Mössbauer radioactive source. During a procedure designed to fill the probe with clean nitrogen whilst it was being tested, it was over pressured. As a result the seal between the heat shield and back cover blew out. We held a soul-searching session whilst continuing the test with a new seal. The vibration test gave all the expected results so our confidence levels rose; it was very unlikely that we had damaged anything inside the lander. To be sure we brought the probe back to the AAF and measured its shape very accurately with a reflected laser beam.

Whilst the measurements were being made the Systems Team, plus a few additional contributors, sat down to work out just how high the pressure might have been, how long it had lasted and if it could have affected various parts of the spacecraft. Taff Morgan carried out a simulation experiment to get some data on what the pressure rise might have been and its fluctuation with time. We had no numbers from the actual event because of the quick reactions of the technician who had been doing the gas filling at Aldermaston; he had instantly turned the gas cylinder off. After a couple of days of debate we concluded only the sensor to measure the atmospheric pressure on Mars might have been affected. The data that we hoped to get had been measured three times already by Viking and Pathfinder, so the fact that we might not have our own measurements would be annoying rather than catastrophic if we got to Mars and found our sensor wasn't working.

We were pretty sure we hadn't compromised Planetary Protection as the leak had been outwards and the seal was replaced with the probe in a 'Clean Air' tent. The tight parcel of gas-bags would have acted as a barrier against spores and other microbiological contamination. It would have to be a pretty virulent organism to have penetrated the plum pudding. The probe was likely to experience conditions much more threatening to PP sitting on top of the Soyuz-Fregat rocket at Baikonur.

So off went Beagle 2 again to Toulouse, still in plenty of time to arrive by their required delivery date of 22 February. Andy Spry took a video camera and obtained some footage that could never be screened of an irate Del saying rude things about the French when there was nobody at the Astrium factory waiting to receive the delivery. The security guards didn't seem to know it was coming or more likely couldn't understand Del's accent, even when the sentences were spoken very loud and slow. Unless they were keen football supporters they wouldn't have understood when he addressed them in terms usually reserved for blind referees.

There must have been somebody there who knew we were coming, and had arrived, because Everett phoned to say that JPL had inadvertently copied him in on an email saying "Beagle 2 is now at Toulouse." NASA had known before I did. How come? They must have had their own mole who believed it was important news. The technicians who went with Beagle 2 hung around for days in Toulouse, because the French didn't work weekends. Finally, after what we called the 'fit to fit' Review, the probe was attached to MEx, and then it was taken off again for the flight to Baikonur.

The next thing I knew was that David Southwood, plus a small army of advisers, was on a conference telephone line wanting to discuss PR. I believed at last Judith and I were about to get a pat on the back for the arrangements we'd made for the launch party event in Baikonur. "Courtesy of Richard Branson, I'm flying in a bunch of VIPs, potential sponsors, celebs, journalists, plus," I said, "some very heavy duty politicians if the Kazakh Ambassador has his way. This will raise the profile of MEx." Southwood wasn't at all pleased. "The French once tried a stunt like that," he complained. "The first I knew about it was when I got a call from Switzerland. It was the father of somebody on the trip angry because his son was freezing to death in Russia. I had to bail them out from a railway station in the middle of the night, at sub-zero temperatures." Oh dear," I thought, "put my foot in it again."

At the next Science Working Team it was announced that there would only be invitations for each PI plus one guest at the launch of MEx. "ESA will handle the press," said Rudi, adding casually, "by the way, there's a problem with MEx's power unit; it will take twelve days of three-shift working to fix at the launch site, and its main engine also needs to be realigned."

All space missions have problems. You have to overcome them; it's part of the routine. The public usually never hears about them and they wouldn't hear about these affecting MEx. The two that Rudi had just mentioned were reported to the MEx PIs as minor irritations. When Beagle 2 had problems, we dealt with them as they occurred. I've described many of the technical difficulties we overcame. But our problems were often magnified by others and used to our detriment; they were always reported as mega-calamities and news of them leaked to the press with some comment about Beagle 2 not going to Mars. We spent days trying to recover from the 'Beagle 2 isn't going to be on MEx' stories whenever we had even the smallest set-back. We had to dispel the ESA myths, if we were going to raise the Beagle 2 sponsorship money.

The main business at that SWT was devoted to Southwood being harangued about Communications and the fact that deployment of the radar booms might cause MEx to crash because the snap when they sprang out hadn't been tested. He didn't help matters by saying "The Beagle 2 lander and the radar are the two most important experiments on MEx."

I heard it with my own ears. Even though I was standing at the back of the meeting giving Rudi a hard time because he had just said to me "There isn't room on the flight to Baikonur for Andy Spry." "What if the Russians wreck PP by opening the Beagle 2 container?" I wanted to know. A compromise was struck: I guess they didn't really want Andy at all, but I insisted he flew on a second support plane. But only as long as I had an undertaking from Rudi that the first plane would have to wait for Andy to get there before anything was done involving Beagle 2. The flight from Toulouse to Baikonur was scheduled to stop at Moscow, and the Russians might prove difficult with a container they weren't allowed to see inside.

On 16 March, at 4.20 pm, I got a phone call from the OU's Reception. "There's a Mr Paul Leonard here wanting to see you," it announced. I would normally have sent somebody to collect a visitor but I scampered to the building near the gate. I greeted Paul with "Either you're bringing bad news or you've got a brown paper envelope!" I could see from his face it was the former. We drank coffee, not champagne, as he explained, "The commercial people who advise Angus say Beagle 2 only has a value of two hundred thousand pounds for advertising." He was clearly furious as he went on "I wouldn't expect to sponsor a junior six-a-side football tournament for that kind of money; I'm not going to insult you by offering £200k to Beagle 2."

That day wasn't a good one for anybody: the USA and Britain decided to go it alone and invade Iraq. The invasion contributed to the demise of the trip to the launch site in Kazakhstan. Nobody much wanted to fly into airspace which might become part of a war zone. Journalists began to say "My Editor says the budgets are stretched too far already by having everybody in the Middle East." The final nail in the coffin came when friends at BBC News told me "ESA say if we go with you, we won't be able to file our stories. We won't be granted access to the telecommunication links they control." ITN confirmed they had been given the same message.

I held a council of war with Miles. By my reckoning the OU weren't too much out of pocket. Because of the performance indicators arising from Beagle 2, the University had received two tranches of money from the Strategic Investment Fund, its Earth Sciences and PSSRI were rated five according to the University's Research Assessment Exercise, so the amounts received from the Government to pay staff were substantially better than they would have been if it wasn't for Beagle 2. Then there were the imponderables: how much was Beagle 2 worth in terms of student recruitment, retention and reputation?

I said to Miles "There are still opportunities that we can get on an ad hoc basis, and money I can save by getting others to pick up the tab. Our strategy from now on should be maximising the publicity so that when it comes down to it we might be able to sell individual events when we get to Mars." I told him "Paul Leonard is so mad at having the rug pulled from under him that he wants to show Angus's advisers they're wrong." I went on "He, Judith and I are going to arrange a launch party at BT's HQ in Newgate Street." I assumed he knew it was the site of London's best known prison; they'd kept debtors as well as robbers and thieves there. We'd decided if I couldn't take people to the launch, we'd bring the launch to them. Paul, who could pay for a launch party from his own budget, said "We'll show them what they're missing."

Beagle 2 arrived at Baikonur unscathed. At its Flight Readiness Review, John Credland asked "Hands up anyone who didn't think Beagle 2 would get this far?" He was the only person who put his hand up. The engineers at the launch site attached the Beagle 2 probe to MEx on 1 April; perhaps this was ESA's idea of a joke. The launch, which had been moving around on a day to day basis, was now going to be 6.45pm, 2 June, which meant arrival on Mars at 2.54 in the morning on Christmas Day. NASA's Odyssey would be available to relay a message just over two hours later at 5.28am. JPL would pass it to us as soon as it was processed having made the journey from the Red Planet in less than ten minutes at the speed of light. There was no discussion about a launch time that might have seen Beagle 2 arrive when communication would have been possible immediately.

There had to be an Underwriters meeting to break the news about BT. We also needed to tell them that Matthew found out that an airline in the Middle East he had been hopeful about were now out for obvious reasons. At the meeting David Leadbeater said "I understand the situation and am ready to go along with the OU's strategy of maximising the PR and the inspirational effect with young people by the Brits going to Mars." He encouraged me to concentrate on a deal I had been looking at with the *Times Educational Supplement*, *TES*, for a schools pack. This wasn't a money spinner; TES were looking for a sponsor themselves. David said "The Government might chip in," and looked at Miles, who shook his head.

Astrium were less than happy about everything we said. One of the representatives they sent to the meeting thought the idea of having a launch party wasn't 'rocket science'. He said "It's giving away our assets." I said "There has to be a launch event; I'm saving us, that is Miles and you, money since we would have had to pay for it." The new Astrium Management weren't like Mike Rickett, who had once said in response to the question "Why do you want to be in Beagle 2?" "Because I would like every kid in Britain to know

294

we're capable of doing it [going to Mars]." It was his version of JFK's 'not because it's easy' announcement, committing the USA to landing a man on the moon. The new Astrium hierarchy seemed to have read only the bits in the Underwriters' Agreement about getting back more than they put in and thought Beagle 2 was a commercial venture.

They began asking "Why aren't Saatchis sending us weekly written status reports?" "Who are the potential sponsors?" "Why aren't you ringing them on a daily basis?" The questions were directed to me. I said "It's not like that in the agency world. Anyway Matthew no longer works for Saatchis; he's now on a commission-only basis." They hit the roof. Miles hadn't passed this information on, probably because everybody was haranguing everybody else about getting the spacecraft delivered at the time.

I never got to saying "The Underwriters accepted Matthew's conditions when he took the job." He had said "Negotiating sponsorship is a delicate business, it's only part of what Saatchis do for its clients, therefore there is to be no interference, I'm not going to provide details of what is going on until I have a sponsor signed up or at the point of signing." In fact he had been very forthcoming to the OU and taken me with him every time he had an interested client. Miles had a big list of all the companies we had visited but rightly wasn't publicising it, particularly because of conflicts of interest with the NSC at Leicester, who were also seeking sponsors. There were lots of things Astrium's new Management wouldn't understand because they had not lived through the whole project like the rest of us.

They certainly didn't understand talking to the press. They turned to haranguing me because I wasn't giving them enough name checks. I said "The journalists only edit them out." That wasn't good enough either. "An Astrium spokesperson must be alongside you every time you speak to the media," I was told. The number of times I've heard this demand from people who have no idea about what was involved in publicising Beagle 2. Right then we were again enduring another media frenzy, speaking to places as far apart as China, Panama, Chile, Brazil and Colombia; we had suddenly become big in South America. I was also being interviewed for an editorial by Cassandra, 'the man they can't gag' for the *Daily Mirror*, and booked for 'Hard Talk' a probing interview on 'News 24'. Just to fill in I was doing back-to-back interviews for the American public service broadcasting network; my day for the media started at 6.00am and ended at midnight. I told Astrium "It'll mean somebody living with us." Judith, who was there, said, with unbridled enthusiasm, "They can do all the chores: the washing, the cleaning, the washing up, make the beds; all the jobs I haven't time to get round to. Then there's mucking out the horse and…" I'm not sure they realised she was being serious, anyway we heard nothing more about it.

Only a couple of days passed before Matthew rang me. "A man who informed me 'I'm the fourth most senior person at EADS-Astrium' phoned me," he said, continuing "he asked if I would like to work for them raising sponsorship for Beagle 2. He was offering to pay!" I told Matthew "If you accept their money you'll be admitting you aren't trying hard enough already." I thought he had realised what he might be getting into when he said "You can't raise sponsorship for a company; an individual, a University – yes, the Government maybe, but one company giving sponsorship money to another, especially an ailing one, is a non-starter." I hoped we'd nipped this blatant bit of interference in the bud.

My PA Michele, who fielded media requests from people who didn't have my mobile number, interrupted the call with Matthew, "There's a man from *Nature* on the line insisting he talks to you; he says he has a deadline and has to have a quote from you. He won't go away." I was feeling pretty annoyed and still hadn't forgiven *Nature* for lots of things; I said "Tell him if he must have a quote, to watch 'Gone with the Wind'." The last line of the film is 'Frankly, my dear, I don't give a damn'. His article described me as 'cantankerous'.

And all wasn't sweetness and light at the OU either. At long last the BBC had agreed to show two more fifty-minute programmes about Beagle 2. On one of the many occasions I had asked them when they were going to make a decision about a date for screening more of the Beagle 2 documentary, I got back the answer "We're very busy." I thought "Tell me about it." Circlevision were putting together a first cut and Steve Wilkinson and I were deciding what should and shouldn't be in.

The BBC was still claiming that, since I worked for the OU, I couldn't use the material with any other broadcaster. I had received numerous offers for Beagle 2 programmes, so I wasn't granting BBC a monopoly; they'd been given the chance to do a real time 'fly-on-the-wall' documentary and passed it up. Whether they liked it or not, I was supplying footage to any TV company making a programme, to maximise Beagle 2 exposure. I knew I had David Leadbeater's support, and thought I'd explained it to Miles who understood I believed somebody, like Sky, could become a sponsor for a Media Centre, but not if the BBC claimed they owned the copyright for the rushes and had exclusive access to me. I had taken my own legal advice and been told "You, who arranged all the filming, are the producer, therefore it's your copyright; it's all in your contract of employment." I was retaining the copyright for the benefit of the Underwriters but still getting grief for 'damaging' the OU's relationship with the BBC. I couldn't believe it.

I was even more annoyed by the end of the week. Miles forwarded me a letter he had received from EADS-Astrium; it implied that Judith and I weren't interested in recovering their money now Beagle 2 was attached to MEx and paid for. It accused us of giving up the search for sponsorship. Now this is just the sort of letter I wouldn't write if I wanted somebody to work harder. Judith said "Let's go home." I usually reserve the job of castrating bull calves for such occasions; it's very therapeutic. I've been properly trained to do it surgically; it substitutes for sticking pins in dolls. I hoped somebody was feeling the pinch.

That weekend was my 60th birthday. Shusy arranged to take us to any pub of my choice for Saturday lunch. I chose 'The Barley Mow', a low ceilinged riverside inn which featured in one of my favourite books, 'Three men in a boat'. I walked into the gloomy interior and immediately saw a face I thought I knew. What a coincidence I thought, fancy him being here. In fact everybody in the pub was somebody I knew; Shusy had rounded up a posse of friends and family, people I'd not seen for years to celebrate my birthday and Beagle 2 being at the launch tower. The next night Judith took me to see another favourite: 'Never on a Sunday', to remind me thirty years earlier she hadn't acted out the words of the title song.

To make Beagle 2 happen, we'd been given a licence to be awkward, and encouraged to kick doors off hinges. Now the end was in sight, lots of people didn't like the way we had brought them to where we were. Some, who had kept their heads well below the parapet, even believed they could have done it better. The following week I told Miles "We still have a mission to run. If these ********s want any money they'd better not write any more letters." He agreed to write a "robust" response to EADS-Astrium. In open defiance of the BBC, I went filming with Alex James for an Indie TV company making a series called 'Alex in Wonderland', for Discovery Channel.

Another Board meeting to discuss sponsorship was called. Again we were in trouble about media activities. We had done a 'Beagle 2 has been delivered to the launch site' story with BBC News. To emphasise the smallness of the lander, I had pushed our model in a supermarket trolley. Rachael Buchan loved it, so did 'Have I got News for You', who used it for a question. Matthew thought it was counter-productive. Rubbish! It was only that Judith was better at PR than the supposed professionals. It made an audience of millions sit up and take notice. Everybody I've ever met saw me on HIGNFY.

The not so imaginative people wanted a conventional pre-launch press conference. A lot of pompous executives turned up and sat on the stage whilst the media twiddled their thumbs during the corporate statements. When I got up to speak, I used slides taken from a 1920s fairy story, The Ship that Sailed to Mars, about an old man who dreamed of going to the Red Planet. Judith had seen somebody with the book on the 'Antiques Road Show' and put it on my birthday list. It was another example of if you want the media to cover a story again give them a new angle.

This was the press conference where somebody asked the question "Was there ever any doubt that Beagle 2 would get to the launch?" I answered "I never doubted." Lord Sainsbury chipped in "It was all the other…" He stumbled over his words. I have watched the video tape over and over again and am sure he was going to say "It was all the other buggers who doubted…" but thought better of it.

Matthew came to the Board meeting with Tony Simpson; they didn't work for WSS, which no longer existed. They were now called SPA, Simpson and Patten Active. Matthew must have agreed to work directly to EADS-Astrium, an admission that he wasn't trying hard enough. By implication, neither were Judith and I. Astrium suggested that if Judith and I didn't raise their money for Beagle 2, we should carry on raising cash for other things until their money was repaid! They must have been main-lining on something illegal. I thought "In your hallucinations, not just dreams!"

SPA had submitted a proposal to EADS-Astrium to raise money on their behalf from merchandising. It was the same document asking for more money to pay Tony to prepare a brief in support of his ideas. They hadn't even changed the text, just word processed the address. Miles had already rejected it on the grounds that Matthew had had two and a half years working for Beagle 2; he ought to be able to write Tony's brief, at no cost.

Then came the bombshell; SPA had a new idea, the 'stalking horse' sponsor. The project would make an announcement that Beagle 2 had signed its first major sponsor. I would have to do it. They said "Others will clamour to sign up as sponsors." "And who is the mystery sponsor going to be?" I asked. The answer I got was "EADS-Astrium." I said "*******s! No way; I'm not doing it. Throughout Beagle 2, I have never misled anyone." They tried to persuade me, perhaps coerce would be a better word. Then Matthew had an even better idea "I could get a seven figure sum for Colin's story," he said. You can guess who was in favour of that. I walked out.

Afterwards I told Matthew "Unlike you and Astrium, I'm not motivated to do this by money. Raising sponsorship is your job, do it but don't try to sell me." My searching for sponsors was over, especially now it was simply as a financial return for EADS-Astrium who'd accused Judith and I of not trying, and I certainly wasn't getting involved with any dubious stalking horses. At the Board meeting in 2000, the Underwriters had decreed it was Matthew's job. They had relieved us of it in order to use professionals. We were supposed to give Matthew the opportunity to sell sponsorship by raising the PR profile of Beagle 2; we had done our bit beyond all expectations.

I told him "Henceforth, Judith and I are going to use our PR skills solely to bring the excitement of Britain going to Mars to look for life, to encourage everybody from kids to pensioners to take an interest in science and engineering." The message was straightforward: "If you and Tony are now working for EADS-Astrium, earn your money!" The next interview I gave, I used a phrase that I would, afterwards, use over and over again: "The only thing I know that increases in value, if you share it, is knowledge." Miles and David Leadbeater had given us a free hand to promote Beagle 2 for altruistic purposes, not for money; we were to get what we could in the way of in-kind support. We began talking to Peter Barratt, about PPARC financing and running the Beagle 2 Media Centre which would release all the news.

All of a sudden, MEx and ESA wanted to become Beagle 2's best friends. Agustin Chicarro called a meeting to broker collaborations between Beagle 2 and the orbiter PIs. Agreements with the High Resolution and the Infra Red camera teams were arranged to obtain the Ground Truth they wanted. They would use our data to help them in interpreting theirs. They wanted Beagle 2 and their instruments to make simultaneous measurements. The HRSC group, in return, agreed to use their super resolution channel, an ability to see things on the surface of Mars less than half a metre in size, to look for Beagle 2, if the need ever arose. The German PI and I said to each other, "I hope this return favour never has to be called in."

Every day I was getting messages, relayed from the launch site at Baikonur by Terry Ransome: "MEx with Beagle 2 has been mounted on the rocket; it's being drawn out to the launch pad; it's upright; the fuel's going onboard today," and so on. The celebration launch event at BT went ahead at 6.45pm, 2 June with a massive audience of team members, their families, my sister, distinguished guests, rock stars, DJs, authors and media, indeed anybody who could lay claim to having helped was there, collectively holding their breath.

ESA gave me a contingency plan document briefing me about what to say if the launch went wrong. I stuffed it in my pocket without reading it. I'd cross that bridge if and when I came to it. I found it still there months later. There was one heart-stopping moment when the rocket was completely enveloped in steam and disappeared from view. Becky burst into tears, and had to be consoled by Keith Allen, until the 1668th successful Soyuz soared into the

Kazakh night sky, the tell-tale six pointed star of its engines disappearing into the distance.

The audience left the auditorium for the drinks and to wait the one and a half hours for the news that the next stages had been completed. MEx still had to get into Earth orbit where it would discard the rocket's nose cone, called the shroud, then restart the engine to boost the speed to escape Earth's gravity and go to Mars. For me it was mayhem, hugs and kisses all round; hordes of jealous students when Myleene Klass, a new Beagle 2 fan, wrapped herself around me. More sedate senior guests queued for a chance to shake hands with Charles Chilton, Patrick Moore and Sir Bernard Lovell. The Kazakh Ambassador was receiving everybody's thanks letting us use his country for the fireworks. Only those from the music world could know what it was like to have a crowd wanting to say they'd been there and actually touched you.

I noticed Everett Gibson and Marshall Cloyd giving Lord Sainsbury the NASA/US view of Beagle 2. Everett told me "The Minister made notes about what instruments we had but NASA didn't." Marshall turned his attention to acquiring a T-shirt from one of the serving girls, as a souvenir. Since I didn't see any topless waitresses, she must have given it to him later.

There were some who weren't there. EADS-Astrium had said "There are people we don't want to be exposed to questions from journalists," whatever that meant. Per Lindstrand was supposed to bring Richard Branson; we presume the intrepid balloonists lost their way and went to the BT Tower. Miles too was absent. In fact he was the 'invisible man'; he never came to any Beagle 2 PR event.

At the appointed time everybody trouped back into the auditorium to hear announcements from ESA. When they came it was obvious to me that the Agency had known for several minutes that they had a mission. If they didn't they would have expected me to read from their prepared script. Now they had put some poor guy sitting at a control monitor in front of a camera on ESA TV. He'd obviously never seen a live TV camera before. He was like a startled rabbit in the headlights. Somebody out of shot cued him to say "We have acquisition of signal." Then his mobile phone went off, which gave him the opportunity to display his juggling skills. It was probably his mother calling to say she'd seen him on TV. TV interviewers tell me it happens all the time.

I called a halt to the formal proceedings with a sound bite pinched from Coronation Day, 2 June, 1953 "All this and Beagle 2." Back then it had been "All this and Everest too." It was an apt quote, we had scaled a mountain to get this far.

Chapter 20

WE'VE GONE THE EXTRA MILE

On the way home Judith and I were stopped everywhere we went to be congratulated. Next day Tony, Paul's assistant at BT, said "The celebrating crowd drank us out of house and home after you left." A few days later Paul reported that the organisation realised they had undervalued the project. We'd made our point. However there was a sting in the tail, "Angus is leaving; he's been head-hunted by Abbey Life." Abbey Life was another company that wasn't doing too well. We couldn't hope for much help from Angus there. Paul was still going to be at BT, "But", he said, "I can't face going through it all again."

The BBC had chickened out of showing the two TV programmes we'd made until after launch. We had produced two cliff hangers of the 'will they, won't they make it' genre and they didn't put them on until the news came through that we were safely on our way. What a missed opportunity. And the title sequence, which Steve Wilkinson and I hadn't seen, had the Union Jack upside down! There seemed little point in going on with them. Because I'd been naughty, nobody was giving Steve the budget we'd need. I decided, with the help of Dave Revell, we would continue to collect our own film.

We weren't actually that safely on our way. Mark Sims at ESOC reported the star tracker camera needed for MEx to navigate couldn't find its star. But our frangi-bolts, holding down the SUEM, had fired and in the same wrong sequence as in the final test.

The most significant outcome of a hugely successful night was a meeting I had with David Southwood. We sat face to face on two chairs in the City of London rooms at the Royal Society because the private Fellows' Room was occupied. He was in an expansive mood. ESA had hired the company that handled TV for a recent U2 world-wide concert but it couldn't cope with the pressure of people trying to get pictures of the MEx launch. His pile of press cuttings was inches thick. I chipped in with Beagle 2's contribution: "So far the girls in my office have documented over seven hundred and sixty media reports referring to Beagle 2."

We turned our attention to how much coverage we might get when the spacecraft arrived at Mars. His first statement was "MEx is carrying more fuel than we expected. We may be able to get into orbit to relay Beagle 2's first signals." This was the usual bull****, you don't suddenly find you're getting more miles to the gallon than the manufacturer's published performance figures on a spacecraft. Still I wasn't surprised, I said "I couldn't believe you'd let NASA do it." It was clear he wanted ESA to receive the plaudits when Beagle 2 landed but he made no offer to turn MEx's antenna in Beagle 2's direction on Christmas morning even though Rudi had suggested ESA was making us save mass so that they would have enough fuel to make the move. Instead he began to voice his concerns over the Media Centre being commercially branded. I explained that this was probably no longer the case. "Since we don't seem to be able to get a responsible sponsor, I'm going to make sure it's used as a means of getting people interested in science. We're not going to have a sponsor just for the sake of it. The trouble is, I've got to pay the Underwriters back."

He was incredulous. "You're joking! Surely the Government isn't demanding its money," he interrupted me. "No," I said, "but EADS-Astrium is." He asked how much. I told him and said "By my reckoning, it's the profit margin on the amount they've had to run the project." He knew as well as I did what this was likely to be, because ESA contractors have to declare their margins. He cryptically hinted he could handle EADS-Astrium by saying "I'm their biggest customer and they will want work on ..." He reeled of a catalogue of forthcoming missions. He added "There are people at ESA who would pay to watch Ton Linssen negotiate contracts; I'll send him to see Mr Dudok." Linssen had been no match for Miles and Debbie; I wasn't convinced.

He turned to what the OU might do in the future. He brought up the subject of "a Beagle 3 or whatever you want to call it?" They were the actual words he used. Remembering the interest from George Abbey to the Mars sample return meeting we'd held in 2002, I said "The way forward after Beagle 2 is MSR." He began to criticise the plans of ESA's other Directorate, the Aurora programme and its ambitions to put a man on Mars. He had been discussing the plan with NASA. "NASA laugh at the people running ESA's human mission studies," he said. Then he really floored me by adding "They complain about

302

you, but they don't laugh; they take you deadly seriously." It was nice to know that somebody was convincing Southwood of the merits of Beagle 2.

I had to attend a 'Congratulations' meeting with the OU's VC; all the University's hierarchy came to claim any rewards going. We went over all the benefits Beagle 2 had brought, notwithstanding the missing sponsorship deals. She was impressed with the media coverage but wanted to be reassured Beagle 2 would dominate the Web when the time came to land and tell the world the results. I recognised there was the possibility of getting some additional people working for the group, so I suggested "The Beagle 2 should recruit a Webmaster and we could get Mark Sims and Jim Clemmet"; the latter was taking Astrium's redundancy package. "If we want to do more missions," I said, reporting that I had met a delighted Southwood, "Mark's the best Mission Manager around," adding, "we could upset Leicester though." "I don't go to bed every night with Bob Burgess [her Leicester counterpart]," the VC replied, "I shan't lose any sleep."

Talk turned to the potential teaching spin-off from going to Mars. "Of course there'll be a course based on Beagle 2," the VC said; it was a statement not a question. Everybody, except me, chorused "Yes." Ian Wright and I had suggested this idea two, if not three, years earlier. Nobody had done anything about it; even the OU's teaching staff hadn't believed Beagle 2 would be on its way to Mars at the end of June 2003.

I came out of the meeting with even more work. Fortunately Judith and I had already had the idea that we would produce the 'Complete Guide to Beagle 2', a book that we would distribute to the media as a resource for their coverage of Operations on the martian surface. It could double as a course text. Mark and Jim could help us and endear themselves to the VC.

My pleas for a Beagle 2 Webmaster fell on stony ground. The Beagle 2 website was going to have to be handled by my daughter, Shusy, who was trying to negotiate time off from her employers, IBM, for the purpose. It was part of our new policy of support in kind. Since the heaviest traffic would be over the Christmas period Peter Barrett had commandeered use of 'JANET', the complete British University computer network. It could deliver 1 gigabit/second and we would have their whole capacity over the holidays, another major cost saving. Joe, who had also finished his University course, had already come back home as the animal-sitter because I was away so much and getting back at all hours.

The night after my meeting with the VC it became apparent we no longer controlled the advertising potential of Beagle 2. Judith and I were watching a Saturday late-night movie when up popped an advert with somebody receiving

TV news footage on a 3G Nokia mobile phone; it was showing pictures of our launch, complete with sound track, saying "MEx and Beagle 2 are on their way to Mars." And there was nothing we could do about it. Our predictions had come true; the project was now public property. What was most annoying was that we had approached the phone company for a sponsorship deal.

On 4 July Mark and some of our team of engineers began a check-out of Beagle 2 on MEx. ESA, who had found their star, gave us the graveyard shift starting at 10.30pm. I stayed awake back at home; I would only be in the way and we couldn't afford to take Dave and his camera. At 1.47am my trusty mobile, on the bedside table, kicked into life. How did people run space missions before the advent of mobiles?

"This is the phone call you didn't want to get and I didn't want to make." It was Mark from ESOC. Judith said a four letter word and went to another bedroom. "We were doing OK, reading spacecraft temperatures, all as we wanted. When we tried to interrogate the timer, data stopped coming through. Nothing! No idea what happened." I anxiously demanded more information. They couldn't find out what happened because there was no data to consider. "We're debating what to do," was all Mark would say.

I spoke to him again at 4.00am, "No change," he said. Then, at a few minutes to six, he was back, excitedly saying "We're still in business." At 7.40am he was on again, "The tracking station is now off the air, we're going to bed and will go through everything in the morning." I said "Mark, it is the morning!"

As a result of the near disaster, we got another night communicating with Beagle 2 via MEx. On Sunday, I was given a fuller run-down of everything that had happened. "ESA almost put out a 'M'aidez' to get NASA's DSN on the air," Jim Clemmet said and went on, "all the other times we've run tests with the spacecraft there have been no problems. We've come to the conclusion that Beagle 2's memory overloaded, perhaps overheated, and simply decided 'my head hurts'."

He continued "When we sent a message, after a long debate about what to do next, the lander responded with the equivalent of 'I've been here all the time, where have you been?' If it's overheating it means that Beagle 2's computer has to be switched off periodically. Another possibility is there might be a fault with the umbilical which connects Beagle 2 to MEx." Optimistically, he ended "Of course the umbilical won't be there when we leave MEx to land."

I sighed; it wouldn't have been July if there wasn't some kind of crisis with Beagle 2. Next time I talked to Mark he was really angry, "EADS have sent an email saying they'll issue a stop work notice on Monday. They've spent all the money they had to support the Beagle 2 Operations; they want more," he moaned. I told Miles, who shrugged "Not from me. Give me a copy. I think I'll send them 'Colin has issued a notice saying he's stopped work on sponsorship' in response." That would be true anyway. As far as EADS-Astrium were concerned, Judith and I were on holiday.

Whilst we were away, Miles went to the next Board meeting on sponsorship without me. He agreed to re-engage Matthew, as SPActive, for another three months. He telephoned me to give me an update, starting "Matthew has done nothing about the event." Before I walked out at the previous meeting, I had said to Matthew and Tony "Organise an event, like the one we had at the Mansion House. It has to be at a location everybody wants to get in. If you do it, Judith and I will come. I'll make a presentation, circulate for drinks and you can take it from there." I could tell Miles hadn't been impressed by SPA's progress when his next comments were, "Matthew said he was talking to Royal Mail – they don't have any money; he will be seeing MasterCard, [this was the mystery friend from way back who was up for promotion] next week – it's always next week; and there was something about an Arab Prince, at that point I stopped listening." The temperature in London had been 33°C; Miles always wears a banker's suit and tie and EADS-Astrium had arrived very late, no wonder he was grumpy.

Talking to Michele in my office I learned they were pursuing the stalking horse idea and draft contracts were being bandied about for EADS-Astrium to become the mystery sponsor. They had got the message that I wasn't going to announce it; EADS had decided to hold a press conference at the end of July instead. SPA had had lots more brilliant ideas. The contract stated "There will be a competition in conjunction with 'John Craven's Newsround'; the winner will become a junior reporter behind the scenes at Mission Control. Tony will sell space for people to have names on Beagle 2 at ten pounds a time". He also wanted the right to peddle merchandise to two million OU students. I suppose whoever was paying for this had been told "Colin and Judith were hopeless at raising money, we'll soon make it now they're out of the way."

Michele carried on relaying what was in the contract. "Events, Exhibitions, the Media Centre etc. will be branded EADS-Astrium. They will have the right to veto any other sponsors they don't like." She told me that I was going to have to name-check Astrium every time I opened my mouth, give a week's notice of any press involvements, including everything to do with scientific results, and be available as a 'guest' at their events until 2006. They must have recruited somebody from the BBC to write this wish list.

I rang Miles and asked "Are they writing off their contribution to the underwrite in return for all these things they want?" His answer was "No; the value is to be set at £1.1m." He then disclosed it would be a paper transaction to boot; the OU would have to pretend the money was owed for additional work during the time we were putting Beagle 2 together. I said "Tell them to come down from cloud cuckoo land. Presumably they'll blame the delay on the GAP. The idea is preposterous. I'm having nothing to do with it. Neither should you. It's admitting liability." I went to see him.

I listed some of the things that were wrong: "It will be transparent to the media; the end of July is the silly season for news; junior reporters behind the scenes means parents, brothers and sisters; Newsround will bring cameramen, sound engineers, researchers and producers; the genuine media will have a collective fit and demand equal treatment; NASA has put names on their two missions for free. They'll want to brand the OU Beagle 2 course next; you can't release the names and addresses of our students to Tony. And as for all the things they want me to do...". I blew a raspberry, to which Miles, looking hopeful said "We could charge them top whack for your time – £1600/day." The look I gave him said it all. I knew the real way to get through to Miles – mention money so I said "Mission control doesn't exist except in the minds of the NSC, they'll want a share of your non-existent money." Somehow the NSC found out about the stalking horse and claimed they were the first sponsor.

Miles must have relayed some or all of my objections to EADS-Astrium because back came the message "Colin should heed Matthew's professional advice." I ignored the message and the advice. A notice appeared on the EADS website saying they had designed everything to do with Beagle 2, including the GAP. I told Miles "Threaten legal action if they don't take it down." In reply he said "I'm thinking of terminating SPA." Then it was his turn to go on holiday. Unlike me, he said "I won't have my mobile on."

MEx and Beagle 2 were leaving Earth at about 1.5 million miles/day but Mars was getting closer to Earth. It was going to be the closest it had been for 60,000 years. There would be lots of PR opportunities and with them the chance to explain science to the public. We decided to have a party for the group at the exact time Mars was closest and invite some media. As pure PR I was photographed with Alex James by super model, turned photographer, Helena Christensen. It was a strange picture, it only had half my face in it, but it sold at a charity auction. The event was sponsored by the jeans manufacturers Levis; I was supposed to receive a free pair of denims to wear – "36 waist, 30 inside leg" I said. They never arrived. Just as well, I would have had to give some Astrium suit-wearer a leg.

The group searching for HMS Beagle made an announcement that we were trying to obtain any information from anybody who could tell us about Messrs

Murray and Trainer. We needed information about the pair who had bought the remains of Fitzroy's and Darwin's ship for scrap. It got Robert Prescott and me seven minutes on the Today programme, mostly about Beagle 2, which was now upstaging its illustrious predecessor, and a phone call saying "Darwin's ship is a coal barge in Japan, it says so in *Nature*." I told the caller "You can't believe everything you read in *Nature*."

My stance on EADS-Astrium being a stalking horse, and my attitude to being their peepshow, didn't win me any friends; I had several arguments with the OU's new VC. In a conversation with ESA's new MEx mission PR man I mentioned Astrium's demands. He said "ESA don't want contractors name checked; they've been paid!" He had worked in Formula 1 and told me "The teams spend all their time protecting the drivers from the demands of sponsors. Their job is to win races not shake hands. You need to be left alone to do the science."

There was another aspect to this that I didn't like. Judith had stood down from the Planetary Protection role because we didn't want to be accused of anything underhand. The last thing I wanted now was to be accused of making announcements, which could be misinterpreted as hyping the PR connected with searching for life, for money. Sticking logos on spacecraft was one thing, sponsoring me to stand in front of an EADS-Astrium-banner, saying their name every other sentence, in announcements about life on Mars, was another. BT had once offered to back me personally instead of the Beagle 2 project. I had turned them down. Now I was turning down a company that accused me and Judith of not trying hard enough.

Merchandising was also causing big problems and I was upsetting the BBC again. I was told "The OU's Secretary is now involved – he's a hard man." When I stared disdainfully back, the person speaking realised he had just said the wrong thing. I don't suppose the OU's Secretary had ever met any really hard men nor had ancestors who fought bare knuckles. At the meeting I had with him, he was just a pussycat as I knew he would be. I'd saved the OU a peeping-Tom scandal for him when a man, presumably had cut a hole in the ceiling of the dodgy lady's toilet in our temporary building. A lady TV interviewer had looked up and seen an eye looking down. An angry Becky had screamed nasty things at whoever was up there. All the University Secretary said when he was supposed to be reprimanding me was "I don't think it would be appropriate to be sponsored from anybody with connections in the Middle East at this time." It was a reference to Matthew's rich Arab.

For merchandising to make big money, it has to be sourced from sweatshops. I had raised this at an early Underwriters meeting and everybody agreed each of the Underwriters could sell, or give away, their own merchandise. Judith had talked to the OU's merchandise outlet, the Student Association, OUSA, who told her there was virtually no profit in it; "Certainly none if you want quality and to be ethical," said the lady she spoke to. She also said "You have to treat it as providing things that make people believe they belong, not have them thinking they've been ripped-off. What little we make goes to disadvantaged students."

Acting on Judith's instructions, OUSA sourced us some items to sell to the project, the OU's staff etc. EADS-Astrium insisted on Tony pursuing his plan, "His mugs will be cheaper than yours and make more" they said. Miles, afraid of being sued, overruled Judith with a message from his holiday. It contained the words 'exceeded her authority'. She threatened to resign. Her contact at OUSA said "Come what may, there's no way we'll give out the names on our mailing list." And that was that.

After my advice that NASA had already done it for free, SPA's idea for people paying to put their names on the lander took on a different guise. "People will pay to have their names uploaded to Beagle 2 when it's on Mars..." Miles started to tell me what they'd said. I hadn't let him finish "But, I bet they also said we'll need some more money to advertise we're offering people this unrepeatable offer." My response to the whole idea was "They should be selling whatever they're smoking." There was no way Astrium would get away with using strictly limited telecomms time for fund raising. And I wasn't going to be the one who asked. I was thinking of all the rows there'd been at SWT, over the MEx believing Beagle 2 was restricting their access to orbiter data. I could just see what would happen if Jean-Pierre Bibring heard about Tony's 'good' idea. Instead I just said "The MEx PIs will go spare; they'll lynch me." The words "want more money" had caused Miles' eyes to glaze over; he hadn't listened to the rest. I waited for the obvious next ploy, "We could just pretend to upload names." Tony didn't risk incurring my wrath by suggesting it.

I told Miles and David Leadbeater "I've had enough of this," adding "EADS-Astrium are a defence contractor, they don't have quite the same image as the old Astrium, a telecomms and Earth observation satellite company." I also reminded them that when M&C Saatchi were appointed the agreement left the decision regarding who was an appropriate ethical sponsor with me. I threw in "If the OU agree to pay them for additional work done last Christmas it will nullify the fixed-price contract and upset the Minister!" This was the clincher. Having got that out of the way, I said "This is as far as I'll go. I'll say: the Underwriters have agreed that I can announce our aim is to use the

Beagle 2 mission to promote science and engineering to young people. We'll credit EADS-Astrium as the prime engineering contractor and put their brand on the animation." And about SPA's PR expertise, I said "Trust Judith about PR. EADS will get more from being seen to be magnanimous than making demands I can't and won't meet. Especially if they don't agree to wipe off the entire debt".

My conversation with David Leadbeater took place late one Friday night when he too was trying to go on holiday. I began by saying "I think there are people in this project now who believe it would be better off without me." Amongst the things he said to me were "Miles shouldn't do anything with which you are uncomfortable," and "Why didn't he say immediately to EADS-Astrium, when they took over, you are not the company we did the deal with. I don't know what on Earth he was thinking of." He could have added "He should have told them all the deals we made with Astrium were non-transferable." It was clear to me the Minister wasn't overly concerned with what I was or wasn't doing and wouldn't be pressing me for the Government's share of the money.

Judith and I thought about holding future press events with ESA. At one, when Southwood was present, he told me "EADS-Astrium asked me to sponsor them, what do they think I am?" Despite improved relations with ESA, the stumbling block for joint PR was always the same: we wanted events to be live, ESA wanted to do whatever it was first and announce it afterwards. They even thought we should delay the announcement of the landing. "Why don't we hold it over until New Year's Eve to hit the papers on 1 January 2004?" their PR guy suggested.

The schedule was coming together well. There would be a check-out, and a SUEM firing rehearsal on 17 December, a go/no go decision on the 18th, spin-off on the 19th, touch down on the 25th. The fact that there had to be a go/no go decision confirmed unambiguously they had enough fuel to take us into orbit in an emergency although they always maintained they didn't. Could this have been a 'porky'? If so, as usual they had let the cat out of the bag because they never thought the 'porkpies' through because they believed we wouldn't find out. Funnily enough they had found room on MEx for a camera aimed at the SUEM to make sure Beagle 2 had left. When I discovered this I persuaded them to point it in the other direction to show Beagle 2 heading towards Mars. It was on the grounds they'd be glad to see the back of Beagle 2.

Rudi was still at his pessimistic worst. MEx was out-gassing; a jet of gas would act like an additional motor. Con told Mark with the words "You know who'll get the blame?" "Does it begin with B?" Mark asked. The effect wasn't

309

that serious, it just had to be allowed for, but it didn't stop Rudi saying "It'll cause MEx to miss the planet."

Sponsorship meetings had become teleconferences arranged by EADS-Astrium. Miles mostly left them to Debbie. I would sit in, keeping quiet. He and David Leadbeater decided to be in on the next one after my complaints. Only the conference phone connections kept breaking. One minute a disem-bodied voice would say "Miles or David has joined," as soon as anybody spoke to them they had gone. The hosts tried to get them on another line only to be told by secretaries they had got fed up and gone to other meetings. They didn't miss much. The MasterCard meeting was still a week away and the Prince had become a Sheik. He was in London but SPA hadn't been able to get an audience. Fortunately Miles didn't hear SPA's wackiest idea yet. It reminded me of the day I'd been invited to go to the White City dog track. Tony and Matthew's new proposition was "Since there will be betting on whether Beagle 2 will find life, why don't we approach some bookmakers as sponsors?" When I indicated to Debbie to veto it, an EADS voice said "This is wasting days of my life." We weren't sure whether it was directed at the OU or Tony.

A week later Miles did join in, by this time even EADS-Astrium had got bored with MasterCard being jam tomorrow. "They've only had to put up with it for a few months," Miles said, "I've been hearing it for two and a half years." The stalking horse had fallen at the first fence; Judith had found just one article in a trade magazine. It announced "EADS-Astrium have become sponsors of Beagle 2," then went on "we thought they already were!" Miles challenged Matthew with it. Matthew responded "Oh, that bitchy little piece. We complained. It was written by a sub. They apologised." He should have stopped there but foolishly he continued, he was about to let another cat escape. "There was a very good report on the BBC," he said.

Judith and my secretaries didn't miss things like that. So back in the office they began to search for the BBC's coverage. They turned up something they didn't expect, an article written at the time Matthew was telling the Underwriters that he and Tony had become SPA. Matthew hadn't mentioned that WSS, the company they'd been involved with, had collapsed having lost ten million pounds and owing nearly two million. The coverage said "Chief Executive, Matthew Patten, has tried to save the company." A print-out was in Miles' hands inside an hour. He said "Very interesting, it might explain some of his wilder ideas."

A face-to-face Underwriters meeting was called at BNSC to which I went. The EADS-Astrium people were again very late. SPA still hadn't made any progress with MasterCard; the Sheik wanted to meet me in the Gulf; EADS wanted to discuss a new contender, Logica, who seemed to want the same kind of deal that EADS had suggested for themselves. They wanted to be seen as sponsors for the whole of Operations. The crunch was they wanted it for just £150k. I said "That isn't a good idea, SSSL have written all the Operations software. If Logica are seen to be taking the credit, I'll lose SSSL's cooperation. They are absolutely essential during Ops." I could still remember Mike Rickett's comments about the difficulty of getting these two companies to work together.

The suggestion that Logica could sponsor Operations was batted back and forth needlessly for a while until EADS-Astrium's top man got up and said "I have to go. My wife is going out. I have to look after the kids. I have to make sandwiches." I thought Miles was going to choke. Instead, he got up and said "I'm going too." The other EADS people protested. Miles repeated "I'm going." I said "Wait for me." EADS chorused "We want to discuss merchandising; somebody from the OU has to be here." Miles said "I'm going." Barrie Kirk, who was there, said "I'm going to minute that." Miles didn't answer. I left too, saying to Barrie "I think you have your answer. Slam is spelt S, L, A, M!"

I caught up with Miles on the underground. He said "I will see the VC first thing in the morning and draft a letter to David and EADS setting out the reasons why we are ceasing the search for sponsors. It will say SPA won't be continued at the end of their contract." We were interrupted by a young guy, who certainly wasn't a city slicker, he wanted to shake my hand and wish Beagle 2 good luck. With him satisfied, Miles went on "We've gone the extra mile! You can push on with the science and finding ways of saving money, rather than recovering it."

It was ninety-nine days until Christmas morning, 2003; has anybody ever produced a T-shirt for merchandising emblazoned 'My Dad went to Mars and I didn't even get a lousy T-shirt'? With emphasis on the lousy.

Chapter 21

THE VIGIL

So now we could get on with the real business. Because Beagle 2 was going to be nearly ten minutes away when we wanted to send or receive messages, and even then it would only be possible when an orbiter was in the right position to act as a relay, we had to pre-programme operation sequences into the computer. The Systems Team meetings became discussions of what we could do in the first fifty days on Mars.

Everybody had their own ideas, but top of the list had to be a series of pictures stitched together as a 360° panorama. From this we would try to identify a rock we could reach with the robot arm and another that we would burrow under using the mole. The planning meetings were held at the OU in the offices vacated by Beagle 2's AIV team. The official name was the Lander Operations Planning Centre (LOPC). Judith christened it the Bridge. Rehearsals of what we wanted to do were at the NSC in Leicester, the LOCC (Lander Operations and Communications Centre). Judith said "It should be the Engine room." Nowhere was called Mission Control.

We practised dropping samples into the GAP funnel, grinding the surface off rocks and showing pictures of known specimens, taken with Beagle 2 type cameras, to our resident photo-geologists, Dave Rothery and John Bridges, to see if they could identify them. They managed 7/10 from just looking at the images.

I was now able to meet some long-standing commitments. I had to give the opening plenary lecture at the International Mass Spectrometry meeting, a once-every-three years event. In 2003 it was held in Edinburgh. The auditorium where the talk was given seated three thousand delegates. It was created by three satellite theatres driven by hydraulics to create a clover leaf area. Before my presentation they surprised me with the Gold Medal named in memory of Aston, the man who had made the first mass spectrometer in 1919.

When I got back we went as a family, the whole family, to the Reading Festival, where Blur was headlining. The screens on the main stage showed the Beagle 2 animation. Although we could have been in the VIP enclosure, we stood out in the forty thousand strong crowd, pointing out the tiny red dot in the sky that was the planet Mars, still close and easily visible. I had been at numerous Blur gigs and always joined the fans. After having spoken at Edinburgh, I realised that now both Beagle 2 and I had now done stadium science. Probably the only other person from Kingswood to know the feeling would have been the preacher George Whitefield.

It went on and on. The following week, I had another plenary lecture to give at the International Astronautical Congress, a mainly industry event, in Bremen. Judith and I stayed at a hotel on the edge of the city and walked in to get a meal. Every lamp post had my picture on it advertising that I was speaking. Robbie Williams was also in Bremen but I got more exposure.

On the way home from Bremen we passed through ESTEC for the MEx Christmas dinner even though it was still only September! It was a chance to see Marcello, who was singing everybody's praises, including mine. "NASA invented smaller, faster, cheaper, but ESA has shown it can be done," he was telling anybody who would listen.

I'd been told to be there because Southwood wanted to give me something. When he stood up to make what I thought would be his usual long-winded after dinner speech, I scarpered to the loo. I arrived back just in time to hear him say "As ESA's Director of Science I get all kinds of people coming to me with all kinds of crazy missions…" I shouted "I've arrived right on cue." He didn't bother to finish his speech but gave me a bunch of signed special achievement certificates to have names added, be framed and distributed to the Beagle 2 team. I gave him a copy of 'Tales of two Beagles' in return.

Then everybody was giving everybody else presents, I got lots including a blow-up blue Martian. It went with an air-filled Mars globe, a Beagle 2 fan had sent me, which was hanging from the office ceiling. It had come in a package marked on the outside "with care, inflatable toy." The girls in the office had had hysterics whilst I was tearing off the brown paper. The presents distributed, everybody from MEx wanted to be photographed with me, including Rudi and his very nice wife, who I had sat next to. When I left I saw him sitting reading the book I had just given to Southwood.

It wasn't the only dinner I was guest of honour at; the *Eagle* Comic Society invited me to their annual event and made me an honorary member. I'm not sure which of all of these I appreciated most, maybe the latter. Until my next invite; it was to get a CBE for services to science from the Queen. As I stood before her, she said "And what branch of science do you do?" It was probably a stock phrase. So I answered "I'm leading a project to land a British Spacecraft on Mars." There was silence for a moment; I thought she hadn't heard until she answered "Mars has been in the news a lot lately, when it was so close." For a couple of minutes, we held a conversation about Mars until she wished me luck and I left, saying "I hope we can deliver Beagle 2 to Mars for you on Christmas morning." Patriotically I had thought of naming the landing site, as any British explorer would, Queen Elizabeth II Land.

I had had quite a bit longer than many of the others there, so I got to call her "Marm" which is the etiquette after first saying "Your Majesty". Next day the OU got a call saying Princess Anne wanted to visit. I imagined the Queen, at lunch, saying to her daughter "I met that nice man going to Mars this morning." To which the answer was "Yes, I've come across him already when he was looking for support, better go round and congratulate him."

I was back at the Palace four days later at the party for 'Pioneers' held to celebrate the Queen's sixty years on the throne. I was one of a small number of guests asked to wait by the door of the music room to be introduced to the Royal Party as they entered. The Queen clearly remembered me, so most of my conversation was with Prince Philip.

Afterwards, everybody mingled and I passed among the crowd receiving handshakes left, right and centre, lots of good wishes and opportunities to Beagle 2-brainwash people who recognised me. Amongst them were single-handed sailor, Sir Robin Knox-Johnson, astronaut Helen Sharman, dancer Wayne Sleep, Sir Cliff Richard, who said he was interested in Astronomy, mountaineer Chris Bonnington, Dot-com entrepreneurs Martha Lane-Fox and Brett Hoberman. Even cook Delia Smith wanted to know about Mars. Another person there was Sir Bernard Lovell. I bet there weren't many schools that had two representatives, other than Eton maybe; but we both came from a cow shed, at a less than salubrious end of town.

There was a big throng around Prince Andrew, I was about to move on but was grabbed by a man who ushered me into the Duke of York's presence. I stood talking to him for several minutes and then seized the opportunity to ask "Would you like to be Guest of Honour at the event when we spin Beagle 2 off Mars Express to send it towards the planet?" Now this is strictly taboo. There's a protocol for invitations to be followed; you have to go through the Lord Lieutenant of your County. Nevertheless it was pretty clear he wasn't going to be the Royal to be left out because he said "Arrange it with my private secretary," indicating the man who had pushed me into the circle. A few days later I explained that we would only get the all-clear, and the time it would happen, after the rehearsal on 18 December. "Don't worry," I was told, "the Prince wants to be there; we'll fit into the schedule, as long as he can get down to Sandringham for Christmas."

I didn't only go to celebrity events. I had just trekked all the way to Barrow-in-Furness to give a public lecture to which two hundred and fifty people turned up. The organisers told me how difficult it was to get speakers to come to their 'Culture' centre. Now the pace was hotting up, I travelled to a Workingmen's club in Yorkshire. It wasn't the sort of venue which is on the CV of most academic lecturers. From there it was to a group of five-year-olds who were getting a new classroom fitted out for IT teaching. Then a massive gathering of engineers for an annual special lecture. To impress me, repainted the lecture room. The paint was still wet when I arrived.

Between 1996 and 2004, we counted that I gave nearly two hundred and seventy talks, sometimes two on the same day at different venues. Just before Christmas, I returned to my old school. They wheeled out a Chemistry master, Mr Hyett, who had taught me. All that was left of what I remembered of the school was the woodwork room, the oak tree in the centre of the playing field and the 'temporary' asbestos classroom where I had started. The rest had burnt down. "If I find life on Mars they'll put a blue plaque on that classroom, then you'll never get rid of it," I joked to the Headmaster.

On the same day, I gave a lecture for five scientific societies, who joined together and hired an IMAX cinema to accommodate an enormous audience. As if I hadn't enough to do Judith fixed for me to film for a documentary being made by the local ITV as well. It was one of three I had on the go, including an episode of 'Meet the Ancestors' about the search for Darwin's Beagle. For the Bristol-based TV company I 'sailed' around Bristol docks on a replica of the 'Matthew', the ship in which John Cabot discovered the American mainland. This was followed by an interview in the Captain's cabin of Brunel's SS Great Britain after being photographed in a stovepipe hat.

Everybody was now trying to organise their own PR activity. BNSC held one at the NMM for Lord Sainsbury to launch the Beagle 2 Education Pack. Charles Clarke, as Education Minister, also turned up. I gave Lord Sainsbury a copy of my book. He asked me to sign it whilst we were photographed with a group of children around a Beagle 2 model. As we posed, Charles Clarke whispered in my ear "Can I have one too please? And if you could sign it…"

ESA held their press briefing at Darmstadt. All the PIs were supposed to be at it. During the SWT, a week before, ESA said they were going to announce

MEx and Beagle 2 was their most important mission ever, which caused grief with seven other instrument groups. As a result the press briefing became seven excruciating experiment descriptions to justify that each instrument was more important than the last. After almost two hours of it, "The media were bored out of their minds," Rachael with the BBC crew told me. I wasn't there when it came to Beagle 2's turn, Lutz Richter had agreed to do it for me I would just introduce him by video conference. ESOC's PR lady began to apologise on my behalf just as I appeared, on a giant screen, to a chorus of "behind you, behind you" from the Brits present.

The NSC also had its own event. Judith and I travelled separately to the meeting to plan it; Miles sent Debbie. The OU's Rights Department was paranoid that Leicester might try to upstage us by referring to the LOCC as Mission Control. OU Rights had even refused the Leicester VC permission to put a picture of Beagle 2 on his Christmas card which got me a few angry phone calls. Judith didn't materialise at the meeting, so we started without her. About half way through, as it always did, my phone went off; she'd just been involved in a high speed police car chase.

"I was coming up to the traffic lights by the station," she said, "when I heard the sirens and saw the blue lights flashing behind me. The man in front of me, for some reason, pulled to the right, I pulled to the left. The guy being chased tried to go between us, only his car was about a foot wider than the gap." That left her with a car less a side. I already had my software engineer in hospital as a result of being hit head-on by a driver who, being dazzled by low early morning sun, was on the wrong side of the road. Judith was unharmed; the software guy, Andrew Morse, had a broken arm, and a revised software package to deliver before it could be radioed up to Beagle 2 in time for the descent to Mars. We'd now had four car crashes and a near miss when another engineer had fallen asleep on the way home from the AAF one night.

Leicester's briefing went ahead with Alan Wells opening the proceedings by referring to England winning the Rugby World Cup the previous weekend. "Just as the forwards fought to get the ball to Jonny Wilkinson, so he could drop a goal," Alan said, "every time Beagle 2 had a crisis, the cry went up 'Give it to Colin'!" Outside, a group of reporters jostled for their turn to talk to me. Finally a young lady got to the front. She went through her list of questions then "And who are you?" The Russians who came to Leicester in Beagle 2's early days would have seen the funny side; it was a well known Russian joke "If you see a queue join it, because there must be something worth having at the front." I was needed elsewhere, so I exited left, only to be followed out to the car park by journalists who still hadn't got to talk to me.

Beagle 2 was now at the paparazzi level of interest.

I didn't tell Alan that we'd already thought of the drop goal routine for a PR stunt. We were going to use it to explain why Beagle 2 had to be spinning, like a scrum half's pass, when it left MEx. We'd contacted Lawrence McGinty at ITN because the Rugby World Cup had been shown on ITV. He arranged for Matt Dawson to film a sequence with me where he threw the spin pass and I kicked the ball over a cross bar. We went through it eleven times; I caught the ball every time but only scored on three occasions, all when the camera wasn't running. Matt gave up in disgust; he probably decided that even injured, Jonny was more use than me. But remember, I gave up rugby to play football.

PPARC organised a meeting to brief British journalists about what would be happening just before Christmas to send Beagle 2 spinning towards the Red Planet. Judith and I had christened the event the 'Wish me luck as you wave me goodbye' party. We also had to tell the journalists the arrangements over Christmas when the landing was due to take place. PPARC's press briefing at the Royal Society turned into a squabble over whose display board should have pride of place and whether EADS-Astrium could have two banners.

The journalists wandered off in search of more interesting angles. David Derbyshire of the *Telegraph* had found out that before the war the Royal Society's premises had been the Embassy of the Third Reich. He and some of the other science writers ignored EADS and explored the building, lifting up the edges of the carpets, looking for swastikas. They had been told they would find some decorating the marble floors. They didn't, but located a good doggy connection for their photographers: the tombstone of 'Giro', the Ambassador's German shepherd dog, hidden in what had once been the garden of No.9 Carlton House Terrace.

Southwood was the only person from ESA at PPARC's event. He blotted his copy book with me by recording an interview saying "Beagle 2 only made it by luck." Furious, I went round to News 24 to refute it. Live on air, I responded "There was no such thing as luck, we out-thought ESA at every turn. Anyway, nobody can stop us now!" It angered an astronomer called Michael Merrifield who afterwards kept making phone calls and sending emails accusing me of deceiving everybody. Goodness only knows what he'd have done if he'd found out about SPA's stalking horse.

I had just filmed for an appearance 'to lay down some rubber' on 'Top Gear'. I was taught how to drive a four hundred and fifty horsepower car, on the spot on the programme's race track. In other words to get the back wheels of the car spinning to perform a manoeuvre called a 'dough-nut', turning a car round in circles, in its own length. When it was shown on Sunday evening, a couple of weeks before Christmas, it was as part of a competition called 'Boffin burn'. I beat the *Evening Standard*'s Arts correspondent, Brian Sewell, for a plastic trophy presented by Jeremy Clarkson. Brian was very disgruntled. The following week he wrote a piece knocking Beagle 2 in his column. During an interview with Richard Hammond I was asked "What's the secret?" to which I answered "Not taking your foot off the accelerator." And indeed that was how we out manoeuvred ESA; we never touched the brakes.

Somebody else who never touched the brakes were the Japanese. Reluctantly, on 12 December, because fuel was low, they decided not to try to enter Mars orbit with their Mars spacecraft Nozomi, or 'Hope' in English. Instead they flew straight on past the Red Planet to remind us of the fragility of Mars missions. Nobody said Nozomi was a failure.

Our other big PR hit was 'Blur in the bowl'. To publicise the fact that we would be using Jodrell Bank to check if Beagle 2 was broadcasting its signal, the Blur call sign, on Christmas Day, Judith arranged for BBC News to film Alex and Dave in the radio telescope dish. This was a treat Jodrell reserved for VIPs. They turn the telescope receiver horizontal and the guests climb out of a trap door in the centre to walk around. We did the interview in the dish with newly appointed science correspondent, David Shukman, explaining how the signal to be picked up was only about the same power as a mobile phone but Jodrell's giant aerial would hear it even if it was 50 million miles away.

After, in the warmth of the café, David asked why such an iconic telescope was always having trouble getting funds from PPARC. The story which emerged was as follows: the PPARC CEO Ian Halliday's daughter was an Astronomy PhD student at Manchester – "She ran away with one of Jodrell's gardeners," our informant explained, "so Jodrell always gets what she did…" "Shafted," everybody at the table chorussed.

Peter Barratt and I were still searching for venues for the Beagle 2 spin up and eject event party. We settled on the Royal Geographical Society's seven hundred seat lecture theatre for 19 December. I owed them for allowing Everett and I to give our joint Mars meteorite talk there in 1996.

Everett kept us informed about all the press coverage he was giving us in the USA; he had a Beagle 2 model for the purpose. One of the stories he told me was about an event he attended. Ed Weiler, the NASA headquarters man who had handled the ALH84001 affair, showed up. Everett said "He walked straight across the room to me, standing by my model, shook hands and started a conversation." Everett went on, "He told me a story about a December night in Washington; I couldn't think where it was leading. Weiler said 'It was snowing hard and I had to collect my kid from the gym. Dan Goldin [the NASA Administrator] rang me and told me 'you've got two minutes to come up with something to save our faces over Polar Lander'. That's when I suggested sending two rovers'." Everett then came to the most interesting bit. He said "Weiler then added 'if I knew then what I know now I'd have told Dan to pepper the planet with Beagle 2s.'"

Trying to find a location for the press conferences we would need to hold from Christmas morning onwards, was proving more difficult. Judith and I tried Paul Leonard. "BT can host the Media Centre as long as you meet all the costs, including printing a few thousand copies of the guide book, so every school can have one," I said. It was more or less what Angus had wanted and BT would be having the honour at a pretty knock-down price. It wasn't what we wanted but it would be at no cost and at least they hadn't tried to exploit us at the launch party. So I also threw in "It would be nice to have the BT Tower for Christmas morning." Paul didn't come back to us so presumably the budget holders turned him down again.

Next we tried the Royal Society. They were doing maintenance, so no go there. After that Peter Barratt and I went round to the Science Museum. They wanted paying! At last we settled for the OU's offices in Camden. That pleased the VC no end; she anticipated endless OU name checks.

Getting the guidebook finished was a nightmare. Persuading the American Government to allow me to include details about the gas-bags were designed, and worked, was a real headache because of ITAR. Finally, in despair, I rang the US State Department using a number I'd been given by one of our American colleagues. After being shunted from one telephone to another, I was put on to some General. I explained "How to land on Mars is hardly a vital military secret but it's very important for encouraging people to take an interest in science." I then decided to push him a bit, "If you don't grant me permission, I'll do it anyway," I said. "You'll be arrested next time you come to America," he replied. In answer to that I retorted "I don't like flying so I won't be coming." He left me in no doubt they would attach the same importance to me as finding Saddam Hussein and Osama bin Laden, and invade Britain. Shortly after Carl Knoll, our man at ILC Dover, rang saying "You can include diagrams of the bags in the book and show videos of the tests in TV documentaries."

That didn't solve all the problems with the book. It was delivered to the printers a week before the day it was required for the 'Wish me luck' send off. We were promised we'd get the printed copies in time to distribute. When they arrived all the captions had slipped and were printed twice in two different colours. Back they went to the printer with similar threats to those made by my new best friend the General.

All the newspapers were now putting together special stories for the run up to Christmas, and even for the Boxing Day editions. I gave the interview I'd promised for Hard Talk. The *Daily Telegraph* was working on a pull-out supplement; The *Independent* and the Today programme both wanted me to do 'a week in the life' contributions; The *Daily Mirror* had me down for a full front page photograph drinking a toast. I did it with a bottle of beer brewed on the farm at the Wold Cottage where the first British meteorite fell. The label on the working man's tipple was "Mars Magic: grown on the Wolds, brewed on the Wolds, drunk everywhere, including Mars."

BNSC arranged for a special edition of the *Sunday Times* colour supplement. EADS-Astrium and some of the other companies paid for a poster to go with it and to have advertisements published. A photographer turned up at the OU saying he had been commissioned to provide a picture for the front cover. We ran the Beagle 2 animation for him and stopped it at the point where the flaming probe entered the atmosphere of Mars. As he posed me in front of the screen, with my arms outstretched as though I was catching Beagle 2, he casually dropped in "I was runner-up in the competition for Photographer of the Year 2002, perhaps I'll get one place higher this time." Impressed, Becky chipped in "Oh, have you photographed anybody famous?" "I only photograph people who are famous," he replied.

Brian Appleyard wrote the article which went with the picture. He turned up for a breakfast-time meeting. His first words were "I was told I was not to interview you!" It must have only encouraged him to come as soon as he could to find out why. In his article he wrote "This Colin Pillinger is quite a guy; he inspires adoration and anger in about equal proportions."

The news from the troops at ESOC was that MEx was on course. The spacecraft had survived the most violent solar flares measured since space travel began. It had known the storm was coming and turned its back. It had been in what was called 'safe mode' on a number of occasions. This meant they only had a limited amount of data to plot its position; nevertheless they had performed what they called a 'touch-up' manoeuvre. Mark said "ESA are saying Beagle 2 is pointed straight down the barrel." He gave me more technical details: "Entry into the martian atmosphere will be at an angle of 16.5 degrees. Beagle 2's battery is fully charged and its clock started."

He relayed the timetable of events given to him by ESA. "At 10.31am on 19 December we'll have acquisition of signal," meaning ESOC would start receiving data from MEx. It would take thirty minutes to read it and work out whether Beagle 2 had gone. Mark went on "It will take until 3.00pm to process the pictures of the probe disappearing into the distance at two metres/sec." I told him "Get them to speed up the processing; Boots could do it faster. I'll have a Prince wanting to go home to his 'Marm'."

The 19th began at 4.30am. When we arrived at the RGS Michele was waiting with a list of interview requests as long as your arm, Steve Wilkinson was coordinating the things we were going to show on the screen in the lecture theatre. He started running the animation exactly at 8.31am, timing it to coincide with what was supposed to be happening millions of miles away.

Lord Sainsbury arrived at 9.40am to head the welcoming party for the Duke, who was due at 9.55am. We, the great and the good, positioned ourselves at the front door; everybody else had been told "You have to come in via the tradesmen's entrance in Exhibition Road." Obviously nobody mentioned it to Charles Chilton who came in through the front door a few paces ahead of the Duke of York. Nobody cared as soon as they realised who he was.

Lord Sainsbury introduced me to Prince Andrew who replied "Yes, we've met before." Then I took over, leading him to various things we had put on display. As I gave their names, I asked the members of the project team to say their appropriate piece. I took him to a McLaren Formula 1 car to have our spacecraft's structure explained. At the Beagle 2 model lander, he said, as many before him, "Is that the actual size?" Lord Sainsbury gave him chapter and verse about the innovative nature of our spacecraft. Throughout the tour the news photographers were kept at arm's length, only my son, Joe, got anywhere near with a camera. Finally, we made it, via the gas-bags and the parachutes, to the probe, the star of today's performance. As I made introductions, I heard John Credland's phone ring behind me. Before I knew it Michele was whispering, loudly, the Duke must have heard, "They've got the signal. I heard Credland tell Colin Hicks." I had informed the Duke's secretary "Everything is going to happen real time; everybody will be living through the drama together." The silly *********s at ESA just had to have their thirty minutes to rehearse the excuses, or run for cover, if anything went wrong. And they wonder why people say "NASA does PR better".

For me, from then on, everything was anticlimax. I had to play out the charade of pretending I didn't know sitting on the front row next to a Royal guest who must have been thinking I'd misled him. I tried to ignore the photographers crawling in front of us on their bellies to get pictures for the next day's papers. At least the audience were kept in the dark until around 11 o'clock, when a series of ESA spokesmen (thank God they'd found some better actors) appeared on the screen to receive off-shot messages containing news of success. Eventually, Southwood was paraded to admit that he had been nervous but was pleased to announce that "Mother and baby are doing well."

We killed the feed from ESOC, and I gave the floor to Lord Sainsbury so he could thank the Duke and congratulate those involved in the manufacture of the SUEM. Steve Burnage from Hunting Engineering was probably the most relieved man in the hall. We headed outside; the Duke was whisked away leaving Lord Sainsbury happily besieged by reporters.

The celebrating crowd waited noisily, but patiently, for two hours before I called them, well lubricated and fed, back into the lecture theatre. I'd suggested to ESA that they trained a camera on the computer monitor, whilst the pictures from the MEx on-board camera were being processed, so that the world would see images appear at the same time as the mission controllers. They wouldn't hear of it. Instead they phoned Peter Barratt, not me, to say the picture was OK and they'd show it. I'd have blown my top if I had been called and told the image was fizzy and wouldn't be released.

All we received was a single view, presumably the best they had of the back cover of the Beagle 2 probe in the bottom left hand corner. In all, there were six pictures taken at different distances. They weren't all released but allowed the velocity of the disappearing probe to be calculated and shown to be correct. My biggest regret about those pictures was that we hadn't written "Made in Britain" around the periphery of the back cover, so that we could show the probe was rotating correctly, not to annoy anybody, of course.

I wound up the proceedings with one of my famous football analogies "We've just completed the home leg of a two legged semi-final. We've got a 1–0 lead," I said. I invited everybody to join us for the away leg at Camden on Christmas morning. Because the Cratchett family, of Dickens' *Christmas Carol* fame, lived in Camden, I closed with Tiny Tim's words from the end of the book "God Bless us, every one."

A deliriously happy audience spilled out into the street clutching their souvenir copies of the *Beagle 2 Bulletin*, containing a graphic and timeline for the next steps. They also had what we called the brown book: *The complete guide to Beagle 2*. We'd turned the screw on the printer to reprint in time for the event. Everybody also had a complimentary bottle of 'Mars Magic' beer. John Credland gave me champagne.

The coverage in the press that weekend was unbelievable, especially considering the other stories competing for the headlines: Colonel Gaddafi had a vision on the road to Damascus and renounced nuclear weapons; Saddam Hussein was captured, he wasn't on Mars after all, as most of the cartoonists believed; and Rio Ferdinand was banned for eight months for missing a drugs test. Saturday morning's BBC Breakfast TV had the picture of the disappearing Beagle 2 on the desk in front of the presenters for the whole time the programme was on air. Shusy phoned to say "The website's had 5.8 million hits."

And coming to the end of 'Frost on Sunday' there were a few minutes in hand, so Sir David threw a time-filler question to his guests, "Do you have any New Year resolutions?" With the politician's usual talent for answering the question they wanted to hear not the one asked, John Prescott launched into a eulogy of me, Beagle 2, and the importance of science and technology, finishing with "I'll be staying up to watch." If Lord Sainsbury hadn't already told Colin Hicks "I'm working out how to tell my wife I might be going out at 5.30am on Christmas morning," I knew who I would have been inviting to join us for the landing.

At 10.30pm on Christmas Eve Judith and I drove to Camden. In the back of the Discovery was a case of champagne. In my pocket were good luck messages from Arthur C. Clarke and Klaus Biemann, the last man to run a mass spectrometer on Mars during the Viking mission. In Judith's bag was a Union Jack we had bought in an Army surplus store. At 11.50pm, immediately inside the door, Judith gave her only live interview of the entire project. When Pallab Ghosh stuck a microphone under her nose, and said "Colin seems incredibly calm," she answered "Yes." Pallab's kept the recording as a collector's item.

At 12.20am I announced "Beagle 2 is at the top of the martian atmosphere." Two and a half hours later, I signalled Dave Revell to start a DVD we had made, stringing together sections of the animation with film of Beagle 2 being built and tested. The timing hopefully was synchronised to the various steps of the seven minute descent and landing process followed by the opening of the lid sequence. The video ran for a total of forty-five minutes, all the time sound tracked with various mixes of the the boy band East 17's hit record 'It's alright'. It wasn't everybody's cup of tea, but the sentiments were appropriate. The lyrics were intended to calm their nerves: 'Everything's alright, we will succeed, we are the new breed; our time has come'.

Then the long wait until 5.28am began. Some people tried to sleep; others arrived to join the vigil. Dave Dunford, head of the OU's Purchasing department, and his wife did a jigsaw; Mitch Harris, of the heavy metal band Napalm Death, used the time to propose to his girl friend.

With the sort of video recordings we had collected during Beagle 2, I could hardly be blamed for not handing over the copyright to anybody.

Chapter 22

GOD PROTECT ME FROM MY FRIENDS

On 20 January, 2004 I met David Southwood at Birmingham International Airport, where he was due to catch a flight. As we walked into the Hilton Metropole to buy a drink I was stopped by a series of well-wishers wanting to shake my hand. Most of them were furniture salesmen, attending a convention, not your average space trekky. As we stood by the bar with pints in hand I jokingly said to Southwood "I didn't have to bribe any of them to impress you." "You don't need to convince me of the effect Beagle 2 had," he replied and proceeded to relate a story about the ESA DG (Director General) who had just returned from a skiing holiday. "He put on a Mars Express sweatshirt," said Southwood, "and was immediately accosted by a fellow skier who opened the conversation with 'you must know Colin Pillinger'."

We got down to business. He began with an apology: "I deliberately looked depressed at the 7 January press conference," he said, and without any prompting from me, "We ought to be able to repeat Mars Express with multiple landers in 2007." This suited me fine. To talk about where we might go from here Judith and I had bought Mark Sims a New Year's Eve lunch at 'The George', an ancient Coaching Inn on the A1. We had gone there believing we wouldn't be recognised in the sleepy market town of Stamford. We were wrong. We asked for, and got, a table in a dark corner where we discussed the possibility of re-running Beagle 2 if necessary. Mark confirmed he'd want to be involved.

With a crew of at least one, I called a group of the relevant people together at the OU and we went through all the things we could have done better if we had been masters of our own destiny. Not things we had done wrong, but things that could have been included if landing had been the priority for

MEx and we had been given the mass we needed. Jim Clemmet, now working for Surrey Satellite Technology, was there. He said "SSTL will want to have a bigger role next time." Given the difficulties I'd been having with the new EADS-Astrium Management this was good news.

Top of the list if we were going again with Beagle 2, was to have two landers, not just a beacon to monitor the lander's descent to the surface but a feedback loop so that information gathered during the first attempt to land could be used to make sure any second attempt succeeded. Steve Squyres, PI for the Mars Exploration Rovers, would later say "In my opinion, if you are going to land on Mars, unless you have two landers you are nuts, in fact, two rockets, two launches, two of everything."

So we were all singing from the same hymn sheet, I thought. Southwood's only proviso was "It will have to be an ESA mission. The French will cause trouble because they want their own mission with Netlanders." He added "I suggested a 2007 mission to them a while back, expecting them to jump at it; they got quite shirty." As the conversation developed it was clear that the only thing Southwood wanted ESA to be in charge of was the entry, descent and landing system so the technology would be available to the Agency for the future, not an Astrium monopoly. He would be quite happy for us to build the landers. I said "We could take on board the seismometers to keep the French happy; there would be no need for meteorology packs, Beagle 2 already has environmental sensors." Throughout this exchange there was a guy sitting on a bar stool with his back to me eaves-dropping. If he reads this, please get in touch to confirm what was said.

Two days later I met with Lord Sainsbury at the DTI. I joined him alone in his office before Colin Hicks, two men from OST, whose names I didn't write down, and a note taker, arrived. During a meeting which took more than an hour I debriefed the Minister about the media coverage attracted by Beagle 2. I told him about my talk with Southwood and what could be done regarding a recovery mission in 2007. We discussed who would be in favour and who against in ESA; I told him "There are people who would rather Beagle 2 never happened than try to find it." I also said "I'm not pinning my hopes on Aurora; it will take too long," adding, "Southwood is no great lover of it; he thinks it's only technology. He wants it to be science." I went on "NASA has a mission in 2009; it will claim it's looking for life on Mars. Until at least 2007, we have competitive science with Beagle 2." He asked "How much will it cost?". My answer was "We haven't worked it out, but we've already done so much testing that we ought to be able to build three landers for about £10 million each if ESA pick up the bill for EDLS."

We considered alternative partners: the US, the Russians, Japan even the French. I left asking that he send thank you letters to a number of organisations. I said "If we stop here, there are a number of people whose contribution I want acknowledged." I didn't give names but I had a list. I thought it was clear what I meant and it wasn't a plastic replica; Judith said "You're too subtle; you should have spelled it out."

Although Southwood thought the Aurora programme was wishful thinking, he suggested I try to gain the support of the Human Spaceflight Division for a re-flight of Beagle 2. When I tried it they were willing to offer encouragement but didn't want us jeopardising their own Mars programme, which was to kick off with a rover mission called ExoMars. They'd had a 'Call for Ideas' about what might be included on the rover; knowing how busy I was, Franco Ongaro, who issued it, told me not to bother to send anything in. "We know what you would do," he said. In drawing up plans for ExoMars they had assumed Beagle 2 would be a success. I told them now "Before you embark on a big expensive rover project you need to show you have the technology to land on Mars. You need a Beagle 2-type lander as a demonstrator."

Still, the Brits wanted to support Aurora. It would mean new money for the space programme. The space mission community held a meeting to discuss involvement. PPARC had commissioned an independent 'think tank' to carry out a review. A lady presented their draft report to a packed audience. She suggested that new mission opportunities would be available thanks to the 'Beagle effect'. An astronomer present asked "What's the Beagle effect?" He was shouted down with cries of "Where have you been for the last few years?" She also put it to the audience "The report says Colin Pillinger should be made the 'Star Czar'." I'm told PPARC edited the Star Czar bit out of the final write-up and I naively thought reports weren't independent if the people who commissioned them edited them!

It was 5 February when Mark Sims and I were called to Paris to hear about arrangements for the 'Inquiry'. We met Rene Bonnefoy, ESA's Inspector General. He said "The Inquiry's remit is not to find guilty people," and gave us a list of the Commission's members. With the exception of a Russian, said to be an expert in re-entry systems, they were men who had worked for, or closely with, ESA. My instant reaction was "Where are all the NASA people ESA confronted us with when cancelling Beagle 2 was the name of the game?" There was no sign of the most obvious candidate for membership – John Casani. Indeed, he ought to have been chairman if it was going to be independent.

At one stage we were joined by the ESA DG, Mr Dordain, who gave us a similar message: "We want Beagle 3 or 4 one day. To do that we need to know what went right. MEx has been a fantastic experience for ESA; ESA's reputation is much better than before MEx." He made it clear that the Inquiry wasn't going to be allowed to change that. In fact he said "ESA aren't going to be found responsible for the loss of Beagle 2."

ESA sent a new man, Jacques Louet, to a Beagle 2 Board meeting next day. He clearly thought he knew what had gone wrong. "Beagle 2 went out of control as it entered the martian atmosphere and tumbled over and over," he said. Then added "ESA shouldn't have attempted to land on Mars unless there was a less than 0.5% chance it wouldn't succeed; there were too many single point failures [situations when if something goes wrong it's terminal]." He admitted spinning Beagle 2 off MEx six days before reaching Mars was an error. But he needed a reality check. There's no such thing as a 99.5% safe space mission: two thirds of more than forty spacecraft sent to Mars never got anywhere near the Red Planet. An even bigger number never got off the drawing board. I worked out NASA's MER landing sequence had more single point failure modes than Beagle 2. They got rid of some by using contingency mass to duplicate vital systems. More important, they had two attempts at landing with time for feedback in between. They changed their landing parameters for Spirit based on what happened to Beagle 2, and again for Opportunity after Spirit.

It had taken ESA more than three weeks to release the first images of Mars taken by the camera on the orbiter. I asked Louet "When are the Germans going to take some pictures of the landing site, as promised, so we can look for Beagle 2?" "There's no point," he replied "it's burnt up." He then looked round at the Board and told them "It's not a German decision; it's up to ESA whether we release any pictures." The Germans had obviously signed the PR document. Mark Sims said "We'll get Mike Malin, at NASA, to take some then." Over a year later we found out the German camera didn't work at high resolution in the northern hemisphere of Mars. To my knowledge nobody, certainly not ESA, has ever publically admitted this problem.

At least we had pictures to show Beagle 2 was headed in the right direction when it left MEx. It must have been spinning because the SUEM worked. Mark asked ESA's Operations Centre for MEx data to show Beagle 2's 'attitude'. We wanted to know whether it was it horizontal or was the heat shield tipped slightly up or down? We've never had any information about this critical condition.

Louet's biggest gripe was "The Beagle 2 PR was out of control; the public's expectations were built up too much. French and German journalists are reporting ESA has wasted 300Meuros." If Louet had anything to do with it, the Inquiry's outcome was going to be a foregone conclusion. I probably antagonised him by saying "I will have to explain the risks of landing on Mars to the public." He went back to Paris and an ESA press release appeared immediately containing the following statement: "The Beagle 2 Board have declared Beagle 2 is dead." I was present for the whole meeting; no individual said that; the Board certainly didn't collectively.

Even Southwood told me he was angry about the press release. Dave Hall went further. "At ESA's Science Programme Committee, Southwood called the French small-minded when they complained all the press coverage had been about Beagle 2," Dave said he told them. "The British got closer to Mars than the French ever have." The subject of a recovery mission was raised at SPC; ESA always had one when a mission was lost. Dave said "But somebody pointed out Beagle 2 wasn't a mission, it was an instrument!" Pity John Thatcher hadn't been there to correct that statement.

I had a meeting at the OU with three members of the Commission of Inquiry on 17 February; a fourth member came in late. I was there for an hour, answering questions about the project for forty minutes. They only wanted to know about certain things. They asked "Who approached MBA?" and "What was the relationship with them?" They had questions about the financial arrangements between the Underwriters, such as "How were Saatchis recruited?" and "Why was money channelled through the OU?" I thought "This is just being nosey; it has nothing to do with why we didn't get a signal from Beagle 2." I had just got to their questions about proposals submitted for Government funding and was explaining PPARC hadn't recognised the quality of the Beagle 2 science at first, when the people I was talking to decided they had to go. I had not been asked anything that resembled a technical question or about the organisation and management of the project. I assumed I had just given a bit of background information so far and the rubber hoses would come out later.

But they didn't; that was it! Mark spent even less time with the Commission. When I asked Barrie Kirk how long he had with them, he said "Twenty minutes." And if they were so interested in the Underwriters' agreement and how payments were made, if indeed it was relevant, why didn't they go to see Miles? It wouldn't have got them very far; he would have said "**** off, mind your own business!" if anybody labelled ESA had asked him about private money matters. Luckily for them, they didn't go near him.

Jim, as Beagle 2's Chief Engineer, was expecting the third degree: at least a full day's grilling, probing the technical issues. They didn't talk to Jim at all! Not quite true. He happened to be at Astrium the day they visited. Somebody casually asked about the system used to put gas in the gas-bags. Immediately one of the Commission members said "I can't hear this because of ITAR." He then looked at Jim and said "You can't either; you don't work for Astrium any more." Hold on, it was Jim who was telling them the answer to the question. Did they think his brain should have been 'washed'? The farce continued to unfold when the person who carried out the gas-bag tests said "What about me? I don't work for MBA now either." Talk about the Monty Python Parrot sketch. I think I can safely say the time the Commission devoted to investigating Beagle 2's landing system was negligible.

On another occasion when I spoke to Rene Bonnefoy he said, and I carefully wrote it down to quote: "If you can't figure out what happened to Beagle 2, we can't be expected to, you're the experts!" By this time we had been through the Beagle 2 design over and over again. Every time we thought we found something that could have caused a failure, those who knew most about the subject dissected it minutely, only to eliminate most of the suggestions out of hand. But I wasn't telling Bonnefoy that. I wanted to hear the Commission's independent conclusions.

The only thing we've never been able to cross off the list completely is the weather; a typically British excuse you might think. Beagle 2 was scheduled to land after the end of the martian dust storm season. On 22 December an astronomer rang me to say "There are still dust storms, in fact the dust storm season is the longest it's been since telescopic observations began [around 1610]." When Steve Squyres gave me data from his rovers they showed large amounts of dust in the atmosphere a hundred days after NASA's landings in January and February. Dust in the atmosphere equates with atmospheric warming which leads to a thinner more turbulent atmosphere. And that becomes a vicious circle: even more dust, more warming... The conclusion: don't try to land anytime near the dust storm season! And especially not in the middle of the martian afternoon like Beagle 2 did. You don't need to be a weather lady to know it's always calmest just before dawn, when it's coolest. For Beagle 2 we didn't bargain for bad weather, nor were we consulted over the landing date or time.

On 9 March we held what was to have been the 'peers' science meeting at the Royal Society. I used the opportunity to give a talk, not about what went wrong, but how we could do it better if we were allowed to try again in 2007. I had a slide with Beagle 2 on it, when I pressed return on the computer keyboard, 007 came across the screen to make Beagle 2007. Borrowing a phrase from James Bond, I said "Nobody does it better." I believed it; the Beagle 2 team had done a remarkable job. It was a think positive idea designed to boost morale. It angered the Commission of Inquiry. Next day I was instructed not to make public announcements until the Inquiry was over. I replied "Up yours! I'm talking about our ideas, not revealing anything you've found out."

I also reported the public's response to the loss of Beagle 2. Out of the hundreds of emails we received only three were spiteful. Two from American rednecks can be paraphrased as "That's what you get when you mess with Uncle Sam." There was also a postcard from a man in Newmarket who had probably had a bet on us. There were numerous versions of "Didn't you know a Beagle is the worst dog you could have named a space craft after? If you let them off the lead they run away, don't come back, no matter how much you call; they only come home when they're hungry and show no sign of remorse." One went on "Why didn't you call it Labrador?" There were several ransom notes. Beagle 2 was also advertised on Ebay as 'radio not working – buyer collects'. On the plus side, an unemployed man sent us his dole cheque towards another mission.

There were other critics. The National Audit Office held their own Inquiry and criticised BNSC for not telling the Office of Science and Technology there were risks attached to landing on Mars! Presumably they used actuaries.

Everett was at the annual Houston Conference when he phoned me to say "Rudi Rieder [the German who didn't make it onto MEx] is going around saying you put an explosive charge on Beagle 2 because none of the instruments worked." A researcher from BBC's Horizon then contacted me with "We think we might do a new treatment of Beagle 2 about what went wrong." I asked "Why the sudden interest, after all the time I spent trying to come to an agreement with you regarding showing the positive side of Beagle 2?" followed by "Don't expect me to participate." The programme probably would have been 45 minutes describing the US success prefaced by a five minute resumé of a British failure.

The Inquiry came back to the OU once. I waited patiently outside the room we gave them for their deliberations; they didn't invite me in. We now had a picture of the Beagle 2 landing site, provided by NASA, on the wall nearby. I asked the Commission "Can we film you looking at the picture in case we make a TV programme about what happened to Beagle 2?" They said "We have planes to catch."

At least there was now a picture courtesy of Mike Malin to study and we had a new ally to help us: Guy Rennie. He rang up to say "I hear you're studying photographs to see if you can locate Beagle 2 on Mars, I think I may be able to help." He was asked "What makes you think that?" He answered "I was in the RAF; I've spent five years studying photographs looking for Scud missile sites in Iraq."

The person who worries most about finding evidence of Beagle 2 on the surface of Mars is Stuart Hurst. Maybe the reason is Stuart's 'out-of-body experience'; he once told me "On Christmas morning I was coming down the hill to be at the LOCC in Leicester for their landing party when I had a premonition 'We've lost it'. I looked at my watch, it was 2.59am."

Jim Clemmet, also on the way to Leicester to be there at 5.28am, was passed by a speeding car on the A14; it hit something but didn't stop. Jim found a dead dog on the road. Lutz Richter went to ESOC at Darmstadt. Half way there he remembered he hadn't brought his copy of the Blur music. In two minds, he decided to go on rather than go back for it. Somebody else said "On Christmas Day, I woke up with a vision of gas-bags rolling on the martian surface then everything went black."

In September 2005 Stuart phoned me to say "I've found some features on two photographs provided by Mike Malin that look like the Beagle 2 gas-bags." I looked at the power-point he sent me and sure enough there was what looked like a four-leaved clover at the side of a twenty metre sized crater Stuart had labelled H20. The two pictures were taken nearly three months apart; whatever it was appeared in both and seemed to be real. We showed the pictures with Stuart's discovery in them to other members of the team, without drawing their attention to anything. Everybody pointed to the same feature. After an agonising debate lasting three months, our new expert, Guy, said "If we'd seen anything in Iraq that looked as good a candidate for WMD, it would have been vapour by now."

Two years to the day after the last time we saw Beagle 2, we 'leaked' Stuart's ideas to the press. The interest was immense. To do one live radio interview I turned my mobile off, when I switched it back on there were nineteen missed calls from the media wanting news. Only one journalist, Tim Luckhurst, writing as 'The Thunderer' the editorial in *The Times*, didn't seem pleased. His article asked "Is anybody still interested?" He found out very quickly, plenty were. I received an e-mail forwarded by Shusy from a friend working on the paper, it read: "I've just accidentally spilt coffee over somebody's keyboard and lap. It took me ages to find his desk, regards to your Dad." Unfortunately, when in 2006 we got better pictures of crater H20, from a new camera called 'HiRes' on another NASA spacecraft, Mars Reconnaissance Orbiter, what ever it was we had seen before no longer looked like the missing lander.

Stuart has continued to trawl through millions of pixels supplied by Alfred McEwen from the 'HiRes' camera. He has come up with a series of features around another small crater near H20 which could be evidence of a Beagle 2 landing event. They could be the heat shield, the parachute, and the partially open lander. Alfred, in emails, says he has seen similar things elsewhere; Stuart complains he doesn't ever give any examples. Stuart has a carefully thought-out hypothesis which would explain why Beagle 2 was unable to get a signal to us, because it lies on a slope with the radio transmission partially blocked by the lip of a crater. Stuart designed Beagle 2's electronics and believes there's a chance it would still be alive if the onboard computer was controlling the battery charging cycle. He's asked ESA to have another attempt to communicate with Beagle 2 at a time when MEx is in the right position. The request fell on deaf ears.

On 6 April 2004, I was phoned by David Leadbeater, "The Inquiry is ready to give its verdict," he said. It had been going on for seven weeks and nobody yet had asked "Can we see your video record of the build and the tests you carried out?" I would have thought watching it essential. I was tempted to reply "It hasn't done anything yet."

David went on "The Chairman will report to the ESA DG and Lord Sainsbury on the morning of 21 April, most likely between 11 and 12 o'clock." Now I said "I'd like to be there." He ignored me, and continued "Bonnefoy has offered to give you a personal briefing later." He added "The press conference will be on the 23rd. It will be Bonnefoy, me, David Southwood and you; copies of the report will come out before the press conference. The Minister has nothing in his diary but won't decide to come until he knows what's in the report." It was like listening to a written script. To the last bit I responded "I think he should be there whatever it says." Afterwards Judith spoke to the BNSC press officer, who was planning to make an announcement to the media on the Friday before the 21st. She told him "Leave it until the Monday or 'the Sundays' will jump the gun."

I went off to a Conference about another space mission. On the way back I had a strange phone call from Everett. He told me "I've had a letter from NASA HQ ordering me to cease all Beagle 2 activities; it says using any NASA money would be considered misuse of Government funds." He had no idea what they were talking about. Neither did I.

About 9.30am the following Sunday morning I found out when my mobile rang. I was outside in the yard. It was Southwood. He began "I've read the report." I knew from David Leadbeater there were supposed to be eight pre-publication copies, two each for BNSC and ESA, one each for me and EADS-Astrium; that left two unaccounted for. The b******s must have given one to NASA; it would explain Everett's mystery letter.

Southwood must have assumed I had a copy. I didn't. He jumped in with both feet, "The Commission have not done a good job. There are omissions. It has to be corrected," he was off on one of his verbal diarrhoea one-sided conversations. I was in total agreement so far; I got in "Our report will deal with technicalities," because I thought he meant the Commission hadn't talked to Jim or looked at our videos etc. He obviously didn't know we were putting our own investigation down on paper. But that wasn't what he was trying to say. On he went, "I'm seeing the DG on Monday. If it appears the way it is I'll have no choice but to resign; it's highly critical of the way I handled Beagle 2; too optimistic about the chances of success; says I misled SPC into putting up the money for a project that had no chance of succeeding. I can't represent ESA and remain in place if these criticisms are accepted. I have documents to prove these things are not true, letters from BNSC saying I was unhelpful to Beagle 2." I said sarcastically "I have plenty of evidence that shows you weren't too optimistic." A lot of times when he wasn't too optimistic have been described in earlier chapters of this book.

My comment didn't stop him. There was more. He claimed he didn't see the Commission. I corrected him because I'd been there one time when he and they crossed paths but I agreed it wasn't in private and it wasn't to give evidence. Then he took another tack "It's foolish to arrange a press conference before the Minister and the DG have seen the report and OK it." I almost said "What do you mean 'OK it'?" I'll say it again, in my world you don't get the chance to 'OK' independent reports. This was ****ing ridiculous; if the Inquiry was being 'OK'd, it wasn't finding out what happened.

Suddenly he remembered I'd said we were producing our own report and said "I'm going to get everything postponed on the grounds your report isn't ready." He began asking "What's in your report?" I refused to tell him. I had told Mark, who was doing the writing, not to disclose our findings to anybody on the Commission because I wanted to see if they came to the same conclusions. I said "We're under no obligation to provide our report, it's not part of the official Inquiry." If they weren't doing a proper job they weren't having our report to pretend they had.

There were more tirades before he rang off. I realised I hadn't had much chance to get more than a couple of words in. I rang him back to say "I didn't realise the Inquiry might criticise you, I was anticipating it having a go at me." He hadn't said anything about it mentioning yours truly, and didn't now. After ending the call, I went into the house and wrote down everything I could remember. I couldn't understand why he had phoned other than to change sides again. Throughout Beagle 2 Southwood had been a chameleon that changed colour according to the shade of the wallpaper. And he was off again now. For a few weeks it had been 'we'll fly Beagle again soon', now he was distancing himself as fast as he could.

Next morning David Leadbeater told me "Southwood has managed to get Friday's press conference cancelled on the grounds that <u>you</u> might react badly to some of the things said in the report." Words failed me. I said "I bet if I read the report, which I haven't, and said I might react badly, I couldn't get the press conference stopped." He didn't answer that, but said "The other reason they are giving for not going ahead is that the Beagle 2 team's internal report isn't ready." I said "I'm not handing over our report only for them to quote it back at us. I want to hear their independent view."

They were still going to go ahead with the briefing of the ESA DG and the Minister by Bonnefoy. I said "If they are going to use the occasion to doctor a report Southwood doesn't like, I want to be there." He said "No." I reminded him of the stalking horse affair and the Underwriters agreement which decreed I had to be at <u>all</u> meetings concerning Beagle 2 and said "I'm not being compromised by other people telling lies; my reputation with the media is too good." For good measure I added "It does the Minister no credit either." Again he refused when I said "I want to be at the meeting with Bonnefoy." This time before refusing he said "There's nothing bad about you in it."

Now Judith phoned the PPARC and BNSC Press offices again and got responses like "Yes it's true, Friday's press conference is off." Asked if they had alerted anybody to the fact that it was on in the first place, Peter Barratt said "I probably gave Helen Briggs at BBC Online a big hint." When I spoke to him later he said "I've been told there's more work to be done on the report." I answered what I took to be a question with "I couldn't say since I haven't seen a copy." 'More work' sounded ominously like changing some of the things it said.

By 5.00pm I'd had enough of the so-called 'independent' Inquiry that was no longer 'independent' or an inquiry and the attempt to conceal what the report said. I rang Sainsbury's office; they'd gone for the day. Overnight I'd decided I would say "I'm happy to defend Southwood against criticisms that he was too soft on Beagle 2. Nothing he's done could be described as helpful as far as I'm concerned. But I'll have to have a copy of the report and agree it's unfair to him." On Tuesday morning I tried Sandra, the Minister's PA, again and repeated my request to be at the meeting. I asked her to put it to the Minister. Whilst waiting for a response, I sat thinking about writing a letter to Leadbeater until Southwood's office rang and Michele put him through. All smarmy, he thanked me for my 'advice' on Sunday, adding "I suppose you know we've cancelled the press conference whilst things are removed from the report." I certainly hadn't given him any advice, only offered to defend him if it said he was too soft on Beagle 2. Now he'd admitted things were being removed from the report. I hoped he wasn't saying to people I'd advised him to have things taken out.

Southwood's problem is once he's opened his mouth he can't stop speaking. In the next quarter of an hour I learned that two members of the Commission had interviewed him. "But," he said "they didn't speak to the correct chairman of SPC." Technically he was correct; the chairman had changed since the decisions were made about giving some money to Beagle 2. He then told me "The report claims Beagle 2 wasn't peer reviewed." I said "That is definitely wrong." "It doesn't matter anyway," he said, "peer review is only advice; you don't have to take it." I was already aware ESA had consulted lawyers regarding SPC's procedures when considering issues involving Beagle 2 so "say it wasn't peer reviewed if you need to" was presumably some legal cop out advice they'd been given.

Then came the really interesting bit, Southwood said "They [the Commission] commented extensively on the communications [I understood this to mean PR] programme when they were expressly told not to. There is going to be another Inquiry." I couldn't tell where the full stop came so I asked "What, an Inquiry into the Inquiry or into the PR?" It was the latter; I said "Fine, they can interview me any time they like."

He changed the subject and started having a go at Bonnefoy who he clearly didn't get along with. "I like the French," he said "but don't like the French way of doing things." He began demanding our report again. I said "We're under no obligation to supply it," to which he answered "The Inquiry will remain open until you do." I now replied "We're doing it in our own time; we don't have the resources to go any faster." He retorted "You should ask the Minister for some." Again he demonstrated he didn't know when to stop by adding "What am I going to say to the Minister tomorrow?" Now I knew he had been added to those who would be present at the briefing whereas I was excluded from it.

I told him once more "The press conference should go ahead and you should defend yourself in public." His reply was "You can do that, I can't; I can't criticise my own Agency; I'd have to resign." Clearly his job and skin were more important to him than the truth or finding out what might have happened to Beagle 2. Just to wind him up a bit more I reminded him "You don't have to worry, I'll say you weren't soft on Beagle 2, I have plenty of evidence, even some on film." He was quick to say "I'd like copies." I thought "You wish, pal!" We finished with him saying "If the press conference goes ahead on Friday there won't be anybody from ESA at it." This was from a man who a few months before said he was proud of launching Beagle 2.

After he rang off I called David Leadbeater to relay the conversation of the last half an hour. He said "I agree with you 100%, your report is not to be issued as part of this." Then he shook me by adding "You remember when we last spoke, we talked about the parachute." I stopped him with "No we didn't; I'd remember." Undeterred, he carried on "Southwood is worried you damaged the parachute when you over-pressurised Beagle 2." Now this was complete nonsense: parachutes sometimes have to be packed using hydraulic rams giving two or three tons/square inch pressure to get them into the space available. As it happened Beagle 2's wasn't compressed, we had enough room. Yes, we calendered it, but that was a standard process to make materials impervious. Southwood was clutching at straws. He's an out-and-out pen-pusher, not a hands-on practical person, and probably completely unaware of anything to do with parachutes. He'd even ducked our meetings about the parachute.

This new development reminded me of something Southwood had said during our long Sunday phone conversation. I told Leadbeater now, "If you had mentioned the parachute before, I'd have told you Southwood said it was believed we had flown Beagle 2 with a dent in the heat shield. I told him that was crap and, if anybody said it, they were nuts. I guess that response could be interpreted as reacting badly." I was thinking if the Inquiry suggests we knowingly flew a damaged spacecraft at a press conference somebody is going to get punched, not just by me, there'll be a queue with Barrie and Jim at the front. We double-checked the heat shield including by laser profiling, its shape was perfect. The same went for possible consequences of the over-pressurisation; only the science pressure sensors could have been damaged.

Yet again I demanded to be at the meeting between the Minister, the DG and Bonnefoy, "especially now I know Southwood is going and he could be making outrageous accusations," I said. "Don't open all that again," he replied. I retaliated "Sooner or later I'm going to ask whether they are holding an Inquiry or an Enquiry." He knew exactly what I meant. The former is a full investigation; the latter means to ask questions. I passed English 'O' level. This Commission was holding an 'Enquiry' and even then they hadn't asked enough or the right questions. I pressed him with "Will I get a copy of the report tomorrow?" adding "I fear ESA will withdraw the drafts and shred them." He replied "You can have mine if necessary, complete with my hand-written notes."

I wasn't allowed to go to the Minister's meeting and Sandra hadn't told me whether it was Lord Sainsbury's decision. I went to an afternoon briefing afterwards. I was told "The report will not be published; two copies will remain with the Minister and will only be released when they have to be, under the thirty-year rule." Even though I'll have to live to be over ninety, I'm looking forward to reading Leadbeater's original copy with his notes, because I've seen neither. Instead, somebody, I forget who, said "David Southwood is going to draft a three-page summary." "This was going to be as good an example of 'lying by omission' as I've ever come across," I thought. They went on "The summary will be accompanied by a list of nineteen recommendations for the future. The list will be distributed." It was given to me verbally; nothing was on paper.

As far as I was concerned the first half dozen recommendations were entirely predictable: ESA had to have a customer; the mission had to be managed (not by us, by ESA); all the money had to be on the table right from the start (so that it could be managed); Agreements had to be signed at the beginning not in the middle of the project and a firm fixed-price contract agreed at the same time. They implied Beagle 2 had been designed as we went along without an internal review process (rubbish, we'd reviewed it every two weeks with ESA present) and recommended when something special came up there had to be an external review (we had plenty of those); ESA should make decisions as to whether risks were justified (no risk is justified according to Jacques Louet). Our greatest sin: we were too optimistic (no comment).

In the middle of this dressing down, I was told "Never again will _we_ discuss commercial sponsorship." I wondered who 'we' in this instance were. By seeking money, I had apparently been "unkind" (that was the exact word used) "to David" and "put him under pressure not to make negative statements." I sat there thinking I can just see Alistair Campbell telling Tony Blair "You shouldn't be saying Labour are going to win the next election." And "Am I supposed to believe this crap is the reason why Southwood thinks he will have to resign?" Ha! Ha! The whole thing was cooked up.

They really must have struggled to find something remotely technical to say. They patronised me with "Beagle 2 had an innovative design but there weren't adequate margins," (whose fault was that? What happened to the mass Casani told Rudi he had to give us?). "Beagle 2 should have had a radio beacon during the descent to Mars because NASA said this was essential after they lost Polar Lander." (Read the chapter and comment about Rudi Schmidt when he said "MEx won't listen for a Beagle 2 signal.") After they told me this, Southwood, who was there, had the gall to say "I suppose we should have made provision for that." Talk about guilty conscience, I assume he made this remark in case I reacted very badly to recommendations about beacons!

MY LIFE ON MARS

Then it became nearly technical: Beagle 2 shouldn't have relied only on software to command the entry, descent and landing (why not? ESA were doing it with their Titan lander and NASA managed to land on Mars successfully three times using only software). Next we should have conducted a high altitude test of the parachute (I've already detailed all the parachute tests. To have a high altitude drop would have cost, and time we didn't have; anyway we had access to ESA's data from a 10Meuros test they carried out with the Titan lander's parachute at high altitude). The best one in this section was "Beagle 2 should have used some mass for plugs to connect things, not solder wires together!" Come on, this was an engineering project with skilled technicians, not a TV bought at Dixons.

Finally it got really high tech: shock tests should be carried out after everything had been assembled (individual items making up Beagle 2 were over-qualified for shock because many of the tests were done before we changed the parachute to ensure a softer landing). They thought the heat shield might not have separated from the back cover although they didn't say why. Or how it should have been done (I had shown the animation over and over again at reviews without anybody saying "That won't work"). They recommended Europe should develop its own gas-filled bags (We contemplated this but dropped the idea because we thought ESA would say "Too risky, use the proven American design"). Next, the Commission were worried the gas-filled bags might have bounced up into the parachute (they might have, but they didn't bounce that high in the test; despite ITAR I have the video which shows how high they bounced and would have shown it to the Inquiry ITAR or no ITAR). There was nothing about pressure damage to parachutes or a dented heat shield. Presumably Southwood thought better of it. Neither was there any mention of the science, or recovering lost science.

It was a stitch-up. Most of it was motherhood statements. Some of the technical stuff was plausible, but they hadn't given a shred of evidence in support of any of their suggestions. But the recommendations would make them sound clever. I stayed behind afterwards to talk to David Leadbeater. I said "If they publish just the recommendations it will make us look as if we were incompetent and made trivial errors; we weren't and we didn't!" I told him "If the whole report isn't going to be made public, I won't read it" and left to watch Joe play football in a Cup Final.

Next morning the BBC rang me enquiring "What's happened to the report?" "Ask BNSC," I replied. A spokesman for EADS-Astrium, who had also been briefed, rang to ask "What are you going to say to journalists?". I answered "Not my report! If it was, I'd let you see what is in it, you know I would." This

338

same caller also informed me "Barrie Kirk went non-linear when he was told the list." I replied "I might have had my differences with you and Barrie, but I won't let them make us look complete idiots." Mark told me "I was called by the same guy. He was on his mobile on the A1. He was so angry I felt obliged to hang up in case he had an accident."

Five days passed with no sign of the three page summary, only another call from the BBC now asking "Is the report being held up because of David Southwood?" My next call was from Taff, at a conference in Nice. He blurted out "Agustin Chicarro has just stood up and said 'ESA will stand by its fallen comrades!'" He sounded incredulous. Then there was yet another call from Southwood. He was mouthing off about how he had replaced Bonnefoy in a previous job causing bad feeling. "I'm on Eurostar coming back to England for a job interview," he said. I didn't need to know that, I'd have preferred him to forewarn me he'd given an interview about the Inquiry to the *Sunday Times*. It came out the following weekend under the headline: "Official Inquiry damns Beagle 2." David Southwood was quoted as saying "I told them it would never work. We'll never do it again." He seemed to have forgotten our conversation at Birmingham Airport and about 2007, and that you don't give interviews about your own embargoed press releases.

Soon the rest of the media were asking me to comment. Truthfully, I said "I haven't seen the report." Some didn't bother to ask, the next week I read in *News of the World* that I would have to pay the money back. When I complained about the *Sunday Times* article to Colin Hicks, he responded with "I had an angry Minister on the phone to me at home on Sunday morning." I was summoned by the OU's VC to explain; when she heard about Southwood and his phone calls, she said "That's dishonest." I gave her a look which said "Tell me something I don't know."

Southwood's comments generated a lot of correspondence for Lord Sainsbury's red box. He must have been expecting it. Soon the Minister had letters from me and, I'm told, EADS-Astrium's Mr Dudok. Then there were probably a couple from angry Vice-Chancellors, the OU's and Leicester's, to read. Astrium's demanded ESA reconvene the Inquiry to discuss technical points with the Beagle 2 team. BNSC put it to Mr Dordain, who answered "It will be too difficult!" He wanted a press release issued at the end of the Berlin Air Show. I said "By Thursday nobody will be there. ESA will make sure Southwood is unavailable to journalists." BNSC didn't want a press release then either; it could embarrass Lord Sainsbury, who was due to meet the Parliamentary Science Committee that week. "They realise there will have to be a press conference and are worried what you'll say," I heard from Astrium.

It took BNSC almost two weeks to come up with the three pages. They were unacceptable. Atrium's opinion of them was "The language is inflammatory." The document was an undisguised attempt to rubbish Beagle 2. It implied we were stupid and ESA could have done it much better. I said this to people at Astrium and was told "They wouldn't have done it any differently, except it would have cost a lot more and taken infinitely longer whilst we sorted out the Greek mole, the Irish gas-bags, the…"

David Leadbeater said "I'll redraft it." It came back no better, almost the same text but a different cover and a page inserted which was supposed to be our response. I said to David "How can I respond to something I haven't read?" to which he replied "Come down to BNSC, we'll find an empty office and I'll leave you with the report to satisfy yourself about what's in it." I declined his offer saying "It's too late for that; it's already gone out in the *Sunday Times* that we're being blamed. What Southwood said to Jonathan Leake [the reporter who wrote the article], was scandalous." He agreed and told me "The Minister is going to get a question from the Parliamentary Science Committee." I thought "Only one?" I said "David, we could have sorted this out but I've been ignored. I don't want to see the Minister in trouble after the support he's given me but he should never have agreed to collude with ESA to suppress the report."

The next day, Wednesday 12 May, I was called by Lord Sainsbury. The phone call lasted for fifty minutes and could be described as a full and frank exchange of views; mostly my views. He began hesitantly, acknowledging he'd read my letter expressing concern about the Inquiry. "In the first place," I said, "it was foolish to let somebody who wanted to say 'I told you so' run an Inquiry bearing your name. The Commission wasn't independent, it was mainly ESA people. The Inquiry may have been used to settle old scores." He misunderstood, not realising I meant between Bonnefoy and Southwood. He tried to reassure me "There's nothing in the report specifically about you." I told him "It doesn't matter, they can say what they like about me, I can look after myself."

He moved on "Whether we publish the report or not I want you sitting beside me, not standing in the audience at that press conference." I had threatened Leadbeater, if they went ahead with the press release without a press conference I'd hold my own. I now told Lord Sainsbury "We shouldn't be in this situation. If I had been at the meeting [when he was briefed by Bonnefoy] I'd have advised you to publically disown the Inquiry and pull back to Beagle 2's own investigation which is an objective attempt at cataloguing lessons learned." He then wanted to know "Can you go along with the recommendations?" I conceded "We agree with some, but any recommendation which is written in such a way as to imply we did something wrong when we didn't is unacceptable."

I gave him my advice about the folly of not holding a press conference and how to handle it if he did hold one. "I know I'll bear the brunt of the media's questions. I've always been open with the media and can't be expected to defend any decision not to publish the report or any suggestion that only ESA could have done the project better." I went on "You can say: 'nobody to blame, everybody did their best, blah, blah'. Say some nice things about MEx and about how difficult it is to know what went wrong without finding Beagle 2 on the surface of Mars. Repeat what you said two days after Christmas [2003, when he said the search for life on Mars should continue]."

He was left in no doubt I was bitterly disappointed. I told him so, saying "We, and I include you in we, captured the hearts and minds of the public of all ages. That was good for science, good for the country. I won't stand by and let that be sacrificed." There may have been a whole load of expletives about placating European bureaucrats along with the advice.

Next thing I knew, Lord Sainsbury wanted a press conference as soon as possible. Astrium were amazed he'd backed down. David Leadbeater said "ESA will never wear it." There were negotiations over what to say in the announcement. 'Organisational difficulties' was suggested as a phrase to use when they wanted to criticise Beagle 2's Management. 'Difficulties' being a euphemism for the fights I'd had with ESA. After a week of this, Leadbeater reported "The Minister has personally intervened. I sat down with him and David Southwood to draft the announcement." He said "I'll send it to you, Astrium and Leicester in a couple of minutes." At 6.00pm several hours later we were still waiting, he was presumably still arguing. Mark Sims and I 'took off' to be guests of the Red Arrows at a display. Our phones were off all next day.

When I put my phone back on it was to find that arrangements had been made for Monday's press conference. "Lord Sainsbury and Southwood will speak, David Leadbeater and you will be on the platform; David will phone you Sunday evening with the details," Michele said. I hadn't heard anything by Monday morning so, when I arrived at the DTI, I was not in a good mood. On Sunday a journalist who had queued up a few weeks previous with his son for my autograph had written a piece, in the *Sunday Telegraph*, criticising the Beagle 2 Management. He hadn't spoken to me, only read the press conference announcement. It was lazy journalism. Going in, I was stopped by Pallab Ghosh who told me "I've known for three weeks the report isn't being published." Then he asked "Who's suppressed it?" "Not me," I answered.

"Southwood?" he mouthed; he had a running tape recorder in his hand. I nodded.

I went in search of David Leadbeater, he was going to get a 'We told you the Sundays would jump the gun,' from me. He was nowhere to be found. Instead I came across Colin Hicks; I asked "What are the arrangements?" It was only then I learned "You'll be on the stage only to answer questions, not to speak." I was in no mood for this. "In that case I'll speak from the floor," I said. He reacted like I'd head-butted him. "Let's go and see the Minister," he said, "I'll round up Southwood." So Southwood's at the back of this, I thought.

They might have wanted to go and see Lord Sainsbury, only we couldn't. Southwood and I only had badges for the public areas. Security weren't going to let us in the lift let alone the Minister's office. The Mountain had to be summoned to see Mohammed. A huddle was formed whilst the situation was explained. After some wrangling, which must have been obvious to all and sundry, Lord Sainsbury asked me to step to one side and talk privately to him. He said "If you make a row, I'll publish the full report." I told him "Fine, I've had enough of recommendations made on the basis of mistakes we're supposed to have made but didn't, continuous criticisms of Beagle 2 Management and Southwood briefing against us." He answered "Southwood has denied it." I could have said "And so did every mass murderer claim he was innocent."

The beginning of this conversation was being filmed by Dave Revell, until Colin Hicks noticed him with his camera and told him to stop. And I was 'miked' for sound. Lord Sainsbury said to me "Sit on the stage with everybody on the same side." I said "I have to speak, and what I say will depend on what is said earlier." He didn't say yes or no but "Let's go back and join the others." I replied "No, I'm going back to my team."

The press conference was a typical Southwood performance; he bumbled forever going through the minutiae of every recommendation. At the end he said "The institutional system let Colin down." No, it just got in the way. As Ronald Reagan once said "The most frightening words in the English language are when a government official says 'I'm here to help you'."

Lord Sainsbury asked me to say a few words. I decided to totally ignore what had gone before except to say "I could go through every one of the recommendations and add our qualifications." The sigh of relief that I wasn't going to was almost audible. "Instead," I said, "I'm more interested in the future. If the science Beagle 2 was going to do was competitive in 1997 then it's even more so now." I assumed the journalists knew all about the successes of NASA rovers. "We can still be the first to discover if there is or was life on Mars. We've all recognised the longer you delay the decisions about spacecraft, the less time you give the engineers to reduce the risks. A few weeks ago the MEx project scientist said ESA always stands by its fallen comrades; that's a proud boast. You don't re-fly missions for the sake of the mission but for the sake of the science. So I call on ESA to commit to a re-flight of Beagle 2. I don't say ESA could do it better but with more resources they could reduce the risks. If you want to land on Mars you have to make it the priority."

I wasn't letting the Minister off scot free, I said "And for Lord Sainsbury, I'm not complaining about BNSC, they've been fantastic, nobody more than David Leadbeater, but it's time to move on. If Britain wants to run a project like Beagle 2 again we need a Space Agency, a professional body representing the community. Give us a Space Agency Lord Sainsbury, a lasting legacy of your commitment to us which I sincerely thank you for." I could have made the point more emphatically by saying "There's a standard joke in the community: when the British role in Space is discussed, up rolls an empty taxi and out gets the Director of BNSC."

"Finally, I don't want to hear of criticism of the project, not the Management, not the people working for it, not our bosses who backed us when it made no economic sense. When Beagle 2 flew to Mars it was with the best effort we could give it within the constraints put on us." The last sentence was as close as I came to retaliating for the lack of help with mass and telecomms Rudi had given us. Perhaps I should have said more.

The questions focused on "Why isn't the report being published?" Southwood answered one "Openness in Europe isn't the same as openness in the UK." The journalist, provided with this pearl of wisdom, said "I don't understand." Neither did anybody else. Afterwards I used a radio studio to do interviews for people who hadn't attended. Left on the table were some notes made by Pallab Ghosh for a BBC lunchtime broadcast. He had written down a quote from an unidentified ESA person who had said "[I] never wanted the mission to go ahead anyway". I can't think who would say such a thing. There were no notes about attempts to take over Beagle 2.

One reason I was in the studio was to join a discussion which had already started. When I arrived out of the ether, Southwood was saying "Colin Pillinger shouldn't have been managing the project and looking for money at the same time." I rejected his implied criticism that I had neglected building the spacecraft with "You must have a strange idea of how space missions are run, the PI doesn't manage the engineering." He just couldn't stop blaming somebody, anybody but ESA; he wasn't brave enough to do the project himself but quick to criticise those who were.

Since I had a live microphone I challenged him about ESA 'standing by its fallen comrades'. He answered "You have to enter a competition to fly again." I replied "That's not standing by your fallen comrades." Heinz Wolff, who was also part of the programme, chipped in "I think Beagle 2 has been very badly treated," adding much to my surprise, and Southwood's too, "and ESA stole half his mass!"

We did learn one thing from their Inquiry. During an unguarded moment, one of the members of the Commission let slip that MEx had reached the launch pad with 80kg of its mass contingency unused. It was enough to have built a second lander, let alone to make sure the one we did build had a fair chance of succeeding. We could easily have had the radio beacon Rudi didn't let us have, then we'd know how close we got. Instead he put more fuel on MEx to extend the orbiter's mission.

I ended the day on Newsnight with Jeremy Paxman. The Minister's advisers told me "You're stupid to accept the invitation," they weren't letting Paxman anywhere near Lord Sainsbury. It was one of the most benign interviews I've ever had to give. There was no doubt whose side the interviewer was on. Pity David Southwood wasn't there; I'd have enjoyed Paxman making him squirm.

There were two more Inquiries to be gone through. The first one must have really bothered Southwood because he would have no control over it. I arrived home one evening to be told by Judith "Southwood's secretary has been frantically trying to contact you all day; he must speak to you tonight." When he called at 9.00pm it was because he'd been told MPs wanted to ask questions. "It's been started by some small science biologist named Gibson," he said, "Do you know him?" Of course I did, he was a Beagle 2 supporter but I thought I might as well let Southwood stew a bit.

When the Parliamentary Science Committee Inquiry took place in one of those Westminster committee rooms in the corridor, Southwood gave me the benefit of his advice on PR. He told me "Early in my career, I decided I needed to lose my Devon accent if I wanted to be credible as a scientist." If my sister had been there she would have said "You pompous prat" and probably slapped him. He also said "I've just come from speaking to a school; there were some boys there who had been excluded for attacking teachers and so on. They wanted to send their good wishes to you." It was a cheap shot and made it pretty clear he wasn't enamoured by me taking the Beagle 2 message to an audience never before included in public awareness campaigns. If he was expected me to apologise he was unlucky, I answered "Now you know where I recruit my staff!"

Inside the Inquiry he told them "Colin Pillinger's a good scientist but not a manager." He answered a variety of questions with damning remarks like

"I thought it would fail; the Management was flawed; Beagle 2 was a shambles; I thought the project would be abandoned when Astrium realised they weren't going to get any money; Beagle 2 [Colin Pillinger] wasn't giving the true picture to the public; we had to change the design of MEx to take them." When he was asked how ESA could have done it better, he responded "ESA could have been in charge of the EDLS" and explained this was the landing system. It was clear he was saying he thought we had a deficient landing system so Beagle 2 crashed. Rudi, who was seated alongside him, was clearly suffering from amnesia at this point, not remembering he had been offered and accepted Management of the EDLS only to have the idea turned down by Science Director Bonnet. Southwood went on to claim "MEx looked [with the high resolution camera] for Beagle 2"; it was a bare-faced lie.

One member of the Committee had obviously had enough of this character assassination. He said "You appear to have a very negative attitude to Beagle 2." He then asked his question: it was short and to the point. "Where is your criticism directed?" The answer he got was not an answer. Southwood said "I was not in charge." The MP persisted "Who are you firing bullets at?" Now the answer was "Not anybody." The MP retorted "You could have fooled me!" I could have said "No, he wouldn't go anywhere near bullets; he stayed hidden in the hills during the battle and has now come down to bayonet the wounded." Ian Gibson had the last question "Why don't you publish the report?" It was answered "The decision isn't for me; it's for the British Government." I don't think that was true either.

Then Southwood scarpered. To me, Ian Gibson said "I'm looking forward to writing this up." Everything Southwood said was protected by Parliamentary privilege. All I can say is "It was just as well for him he wasn't under oath." At the end a nameless MP told me "I'm pro-Europe, but if you ever get the chance, put the boot into those people!" When Gibson's report appeared it had a line in it about ESA needing a lander to liven up an uninspiring orbiter mission. Southwood rang me to say "We have been friends for a long time; I want you to know I took no pleasure in the failure of Beagle 2!" There's no answer to that.

It wasn't Southwood's last throw of the dice. When we finished our report, Mark Sims sent him a courtesy copy. Back it came with Southwood's suggested changes, particularly regarding our comments about the mass budget. I told Mark to ignore them. He said "ESA have found a letter from their DG to Lord Sainsbury upping the mass to 71kg." I retaliated "Since when was Lord Sainsbury the Engineering Manager, nobody answered the waiver request from Jim." Alan Wells had retired so it was Mark's new boss who told me "Mark is being put under incredible pressure by Southwood." I said "If Mark makes those changes I won't be an author of the report." To see whether I was – look on the cover of the document.

The OU was also invited to meet the Public Accounts Committee; Miles allowed me the honour of representing the University. I was told "Lord Sainsbury wants you briefed to toe the party line." You can imagine my reaction, I told the Minister to his face "I'll tell the truth as always." Lord Sainsbury looked puzzled. If you ever get an invite from PAC find another engagement. Their idea of a good day out is a resignation in the first ten minutes, a flogging by coffee time and an execution on Tower Green to give them a good appetite for dinner only they'd probably call it lunch. Colin Hicks told me he had his letter of resignation already written in his pocket.

I told the PAC chairman a few home truths about inspiration and motivation when he said "You should have been 95% certain it was going to work if you were spending Government money." I replied "Don't you think somebody wouldn't have done it already if that was the case?" He thanked me "for enthusing the Nation, even if it cost £42 million." I answered "It worked out about twenty minutes' pay from somebody on the minimum wage, spread over five years. I haven't met anybody who begrudged me their share." To which he replied "You've been dying to say that all afternoon." We adjourned for drinks, courtesy of the senior civil servant at the DTI, who was pleased we had got off so lightly.

On the way home after my Newsnight interview with Jeremy Paxman, Judith said "Now you can write the book, ESA don't want another Beagle at any price." I thought "Yes, and I know what I'll call this chapter: God protect me from my friends"; the title comes from the biography of a Robin Hood-like Mafia Don, who spent his life evading the law, only to be gunned down by those he benefited most.

Epilogue

BEAGLE 2 – A WASTE OF SPACE

I suppose I should have heeded Judith's advice. Beagle 2 could have begun and ended on Newsnight. But my philosophy is you haven't lost until you've given up. You don't get rid of the Pillingers that easily. Mr Dordain suggested there might be a Beagle 3 or 4; Agustin Chicarro's words were "ESA will stand by its fallen comrades." Southwood had said "We could have two landers in 2007." Maybe his performance in the aftermath of Beagle 2 was all part of a strategy for gaining control; he'd tried just about every other tactic. Anyway if we couldn't have another Beagle 2 mission with ESA's Science Directorate maybe we could have one without them. So I carried on.

I had had lots of support from people who thought we'd been badly treated. Many of the messages, not unexpectedly, were from the public but not all. Another journalist in the guise of 'The Thunderer' for the *Times* obviously didn't want hot coffee in his lap, so was less than complimentary about ESA's Inquiry. Matt in the *Telegraph* couldn't resist a barb about the 'missing' report. Both the retiring and the new Speaker at the House of Commons, Betty Boothroyd and Michael Mates respectively, congratulated me. I found out from the latter you aren't allowed to approach the Speaker; I didn't, he approached me. Jeremy Clarkson was definitely on my side in the *Sun*.

There were enormous numbers of requests, too many to list, from people: Societies, Companies and from some quite surprising quarters, wanting me to come and tell them about the project and what happened. Steve Wilkinson, Dave Revell and I put together a video (it was screened at a film festival) to show at the beginning of lectures. I introduce it by saying, "It comes with a health warning; it's a bit of a weepy at the end so hankies at the ready." At one talk a lady with distinctly red eyes, came up at the end to say "I've never cried at an Astronomy lecture before."

But my most unusual venue yet was when I lectured to Category A prisoners in Whitemoor maximum security prison at the invitation of a double murderer; he'd requested a 'life means life' sentence because he couldn't control his temper. Some people on the outside should be grateful his wish was granted; he was fairly cross about the treatment Beagle 2 received. Having three inch thick steel doors slam shut, and locked behind you, is not good preparation for talking about a space mission that cost millions but didn't get any results. Going through the entry process they took away my belt so it couldn't be used as a weapon against me. It's the only time I've ever given a talk to a truly captive audience and whilst holding up my trousers up with one hand.

In less enlightened times my audience might have been looking forward to becoming the first colonists on Mars, but this was the education programme and it wasn't just the prisoners but most of the warders who also wanted to hear me. As result we broke a few more rules; we were all locked in with just one prison officer outside. I had to give the talk twice because the different category prisoners have to be kept apart to stop them killing each other. The only time there looked like being any trouble during my lecture was when the second shift thought they were being short-changed because they had to finish on time even though I'd started late because of fog. At the other end of the scale I was invited to judge the science prize at Eton. The prisoners paid my expenses in full; the school said it could only give me 22p/mile!

I also gave out the annual awards at a dinner for cartoonists. During the evening we played a game which involved everybody wearing a Tony Blair mask. I still had mine in my overnight bag the next morning when I was searched going into the DTI to see Lord Sainsbury. I never did get to meet the Prime Minister. When he decided to come to the OU on a pre-Election walkabout in 2005, his office sent instructions that I wasn't to be there; their words were "The Prime Minister can't be seen in a picture with Colin Pillinger because he was a failure." Who, me or Tony Blair?

We went on studying possible successors to Beagle 2. Beagle 2007 morphed into Beagle 2e, the 'e' stood for evolution because the lander was evolving into something that might have a better chance of surviving. It was designed to land with the 'vented' gas-bags we had wanted to use in the first place but were worried about suggesting to ESA because they would have been frightened off by new technology. Vented gas-bags released more mass to play with but we had to have a way to get across them to do science so we re-introduced Lutz Richter's original self-righting rover concept.

The British signed up to the Aurora programme. It was announced at a press conference at the Royal Society. Somehow the message got garbled. Aurora was going to be a programme of Mars exploration: the first mission was to be a 2007 test, in Earth orbit, for a much later Mars sample return. The journalists went home believing we were going back to Mars very, very soon. PPARC, who ran the event, did nothing to dispel the false impression.

In spring 2005, there was a meeting at ESTEC to announce more results from MEx. The audience were given a briefing on the status of Aurora. It transpired there wasn't going to be as much money as was first thought. A programme of missions was going to become only two. We were sent away to think about what they might be before having another meeting. By now the Beagle 2 team had come up with an ingenious idea for placing a seismometer on the martian surface. The 'Marsquake' detector was built into a sphere carried in the middle of the rover chassis. Dave Barnes made an animation showing the little vehicle jacking itself up and 'laying' the sphere like an egg. I contacted Philippe Lognonné and suggested we join forces for a two lander mission as part of Aurora to be called BeagleNET.

At the next Aurora meeting we learned that the amount of money was now only enough for one mission. There was a thinly veiled ultimatum to the audience: you can either have the ExoMars rover mission you've already been 'selected' for or something else (which you haven't been selected for called BeagleNET). The word 'selected' was the key; all of a sudden all the people in the audience who had submitted ideas for ExoMars thought they were on the mission. Beagle 2 hadn't submitted any ideas. I'd been told "You don't need to." It was a no-brainer, like asking turkeys to vote for Christmas. Philippe and his Netlander friends jumped ship and gave ExoMars not BeagleNET their support. In the corridors, they'd been promised that there would be a geophysics package on the big ESA rover.

PPARC appointed an Aurora Advisory Committee, AURAC, to discuss the British participation in the programme that wasn't a programme, only a mission. I became a member. Britain was going to be asked to be the second biggest contributor of money, 17% of six hundred million euros, almost £75m, more than three times what the Government had put into Beagle 2. But since the goalposts had been moved, first AURAC had to re-confirm participation.

AURAC was told there had to be an outstanding science return to justify the investment. After a few Committee meetings it became apparent to me there wasn't. In order to have US support, ESA had agreed that the main life detection experiment would be built in America. It had one British Co-investigator. Our other roles were with the environmental sensors as part of the geophysics package, providing the support structure and filter wheels for the cameras, plus minor contributions to a couple of other instruments. Mark Sims was making an electronic device called the 'life marker chip' to detect specific organic compounds, but this was by no means certain to be ready to fly or to fly if it was ready. I argued these few involvements weren't enough. PPARC's immediate response to my objection was that, as the second biggest funder of Aurora, they could negotiate a role for the GAP on ExoMars.

I wasn't keen, I said "I want a better Mars programme for Britain as a whole, not just for the OU's mass spectrometer." Nevertheless I went to talk to the ExoMars Project Management and to an ExoMars Science Team meeting to keep the peace. I knew exactly what to expect: an ESA compromise. ExoMars was as perfect an example of 'Europeanisation' as you'll see. Everybody had to have a role. There were people with ideas who'd never built an instrument for the lab, let alone space; others who'd never analysed samples on Earth to look for life. In fact most of them had never analysed samples at all. They'd all heard looking for life was a good business so every idea, even those involving seismic measurements, had become the key to life detection. What really made me laugh was that the suite of instruments centred on a two metre long Italian drill on the rover (named Brigitte after Brigitte Bardot) was called the 'Pasteur payload'. I decided ExoMars was going nowhere fast, especially not downwards.

I was told "The GAP can be combined with two other mass spectrometers and one, possibly two, other life detection experiments." My answer was rude; the expurgated version was "Thanks but no thanks, you know nothing about mass spectrometers. It's bad enough getting one to work; three instruments coupled together is a non-starter."

I suggested an alternative way forward to AURAC. At the meeting we'd held at the Royal Society in March 2004 I had been approached by some Russians. They were building a mission to be sent to the larger of the two martian moons to carry out in situ analysis but also collect and bring back samples. It was going on a giant rocket that could take eight tons to Mars. The mission was called Phobos Grunt, not because of the size of the rocket but, because 'grunt' is Russian for soil.

At first it seemed as though they were after a mass spectrometer for their lander, but then I found out they had more than 250kg of spare capacity for additional payload. As usual the Russians were strapped for cash so when two members of their team came to visit me at the OU it was to offer a ride on Phobos Grunt at $10k/kg. We could have the 250kg for £12m; the dollar to pound exchange rate was nearly two at the time. Phobos Grunt, like Viking, would have to go into a very precise orbit around Mars and could drop off two BeagleNET or Beagle 2e type landers. I asked PPARC for some funds to continue talks saying "If we collaborate we could, as a bonus, get some Phobos samples for lab studies." They wouldn't hear of it. The Russians turned to the Chinese with their spare capacity.

I still thought I could win over AURAC and persuade them to adopt another strategy with PPARC. Mark Sims, who had been made Chairman of the Committee, said at one meeting "They joked about Beagle 2 being designed on the back of a beer mat, what ESA have done on ExoMars so far wouldn't fill the back of a stamp."

The Government was reputed to have around £200m of new money, over ten years, up for grabs for Aurora so I suggested "Why not join ExoMars for the long term, but ask for some of the money for a re-run of a Beagle 2-type mission?" But then PPARC introduced John Zarnecki, as a new member to AURAC. At his first meeting he argued that lobbying for a repeat of a Beagle 2 was too risky; it might jeopardise the whole budget. "Better to stick with just ExoMars" he said. "Any Mars mission is better than no Mars mission." The way ExoMars was going it certainly wouldn't arrive until after NASA's next mission; it might therefore be the second project to 'discover' life on Mars. My answer was "I don't do 'me too' missions. I'd rather not do a Mars mission than be involved in one I don't think is worthy of us."

The lure of going to Mars at any price was too strong for the rest of the people at the next AURAC meeting. ExoMars was going to bring industrial contracts. And there were some on the Committee who didn't care how long ExoMars took. They weren't in any hurry to answer the question "Is there life on Mars?". It wasn't them who would do it and work was work.

There was a new Chief Executive of PPARC, Keith Mason. I decided to go and see him to warn that if Britain got locked into ExoMars we might regret it. The mission wasn't going to give us the returns to justify the amounts of money we would have to contribute. The space programme would get a boost in the short term but in the long haul we could find ourselves back in the days of Margaret Thatcher being asked this time "Is this all we get for £200 million?"

He must have been forewarned I was coming and what I wanted to see him about. As I stood waiting in the area outside his office, I was engaged in conversation by another senior administrator who offered me the chance to become a member of PPARC's ruling Council. Politely I turned him down saying "At the moment I prefer to be outside the circle of wagons shooting in." Only I didn't say shooting. Then I went in to see Keith; we were alone, no witnesses. I explained why I'd come and my concerns about ExoMars. His reply blew me away. "Don't rock the boat, let's get the money first and sort it out later." He went on "When this is over I'll fund a study of a Mars mission for you." I'd been made offers like this before and now I'd been propositioned twice in ten minutes. I told him "I don't want another paper study, I want a mission." He repeated his instruction that I shouldn't rock the boat.

As far as I was concerned PPARC were going to try to get £200m for Aurora on the back of an inferior mission. It wasn't necessary; we had a perfectly good project in BeagleNET or Beagle 2e to use to ask for an increase in the British space budget. By not admitting that Aurora wasn't now what it had been when they first decided to support the programme, they were going to get deeper and deeper into trouble with it. It was going to be a text-book example of what happens when you lie by omission. I didn't part the best of friends with Keith Mason. On the way out, I said "If you continue to deceive people about Aurora, don't be surprised by what I might do!" He asked me to keep him informed. I answered "Why should I give you the chance to counter my moves?"

I had to go abroad but I decided to write to Lord Sainsbury; I thought I owed it to him. He was being misled over the worth of the ExoMars mission. I don't think I would have done it if PPARC, and particularly its CEO, hadn't tried to include me in their plan. I copied the letter to the new Director of the Research Councils since his predecessor, John Taylor, had also stuck his neck out for Beagle 2.

That letter caused a furore. The CEO of PPARC and the Chairman of the PPARC Council rang up the OU's VC. They wanted to know if my letter was a University view. A new Pro-Vice-Chancellor threatened me with disciplinary action. "Your activities will have to be curtailed," she said and forbade me to talk to the media without her permission – another person who didn't understand what being accessible to the media means. Fat chance she had of me ringing her up every time I was approached by a journalist. And if I told the media I had to get approval to talk to them they'd smell a bigger story immediately. I wrote again to Lord Sainsbury on a blank sheet of paper saying "The views expressed in my previous letter were entirely mine; I'm sorry they were on OU stationery." I was summoned to see his Lordship and predicted he wouldn't see anything for any money put into Aurora until at least 2016.

I was cycled off AURAC soon after. Three years later Keith Mason was severely censured by the Parliamentary Committee dealing with science for his running of PPARC, now called STFC. Their report accused him of 'secretive management'. The senior man who offered me a place on the Council took early retirement. The subject of Aurora/ExoMars, for which the STFC had reconfirmed its participation, wasn't mentioned.

There were other opportunities for flying a Beagle-type package to Mars. First of all I offered NASA a complete lander (no EDLS was needed) to be carried, and dropped off as an autonomous station, by the Mars Science Laboratory's car-sized rover. The idea of Beagle 2 as a passenger on what is referred to by its initials as MSL was rejected. ESA were aware it had been turned down before I was!

Then I found out from Mike Malin, whose camera had provided the first pictures of what should have been Beagle 2's landing site, that he was interested in having a GAP on a NASA mission he was championing called MARGE. This would have been a fabulous mission. It involved sending two landers, each carrying two rovers to work in tandem at two landing sites. The first site he had identified was likely to have had water activity recently (within the last five years!) and the other looked like a sedimentary delta. Imagine the PR and inspirational opportunities afforded by moving pictures from one rover watching another being put through its paces and carrying out experiments to look for life on Mars. Malin was prepared to give me 80% of the payload on one rover at each site. NASA turned their nose up at that idea as well. It must have been too adventurous even for them but more likely politics got in the way. I expect Harold Urey was turning in his grave.

What Beagle 2 had going for it was eventually acknowledged in the USA. It was selected for a concept study, <u>after peer review</u>, as a possible part of NASA's future human return to the Moon. Everett Gibson and I suggested a Beagle 2 derived package to be landed on the Moon by 2015 or earlier. It was designed to prospect for volatiles at the lunar South Pole, a place where it would be advantageous to establish a permanent base.

The existence of water on the Moon will allow missions to 'live off the land' and produce fuel for journeys to other places in the solar system. It could be the key to humans going to Mars. In recent times the Moon has become more attractive than Mars as the countries of the Far East, China, India, and Japan have pursued lunar programmes to encourage their young people to take up careers in science and engineering. The very latest news however is that President Obama doesn't want any more astronauts on the Moon.

The advances in mass spectrometry PSSRI made for Rosetta and Beagle 2 have found another use. I had promised the Wellcome Trust when they gave the money for an instrument on Beagle 2 that when the mission was over I would use the team's skills to investigate medical applications. The one that Wellcome liked most was rapid diagnosis of TB in Africa. At present it takes six to eight weeks to obtain a confirmatory test result. Often the patient providing a sample of sputum doesn't come back to hear the outcome; all too frequently because they are dead. Taff Morgan and I are carrying out a pathfinder study.

I wasn't proved wrong about ExoMars; I was just over optimistic. It wasn't long before ESA decided they wouldn't be able to make a launch in 2009 (2007 was forgotten altogether). Notice I said launch, not land on Mars. A 2009 launch wouldn't get to the Red Planet until more than half way through 2010. Not very long after there was another slip: it became launch in 2011, land 2012. Then it moved again to a 2013 launch, but if you launch in 2013 you arrive when dust storms might be raging so you have to fly on a long ellipse trajectory to land in 2015.

In order to get the Netlander investigators to back ExoMars, ESA had promised a geophysical station, N.B. station not stations. Now the single British Co-I on the American life detection experiment was designated the 'European' PI. The group supplying the structure and filter wheels for the cameras were proclaimed Principal Investigators for this key instrument. This sounds a little cosmetic to me to make the British role look bigger (to justify them asking us for the 17% contribution to the cost). It allowed ESA to make a big song and dance about how ExoMars was now an enhanced mission with more payload. But a 'larger' mission means a larger rocket was needed for a 2015 launch to land in 2016. The cost had also risen from 600Meuros to 1.2 billion. The subject of the bigger rocket caused friction between the Italians and the French. The Italians, who are meeting half the costs of ExoMars in order to fly their big drill to obtain sub-surface samples, didn't see why they should pay the French for an Ariane rocket. ESA started discussing a Russian launch.

In November 2008 ESA asked the European Science Ministers to sanction the increased amounts of money. They were told reduce the size of the mission and find a partner, either the Russians or NASA. Then I heard the geophysics package with Zarnecki's environmental sensors had bit the dust. The rover was being made smaller, the science package reduced and the Americans couldn't fund the life detection experiment because of cost overruns on their MSL mission, already delayed until 2011. Mark Sims' life marker chip 'might' get a flight in 2018. All these changes were heralded as a huge ESA success.

The Directorates in ESA have since been restructured and the robotic exploration of Mars passed from the Human Spaceflight Directorate to Science. At last it's under the control of David Southwood, so my friend Marcello is using a power point presentation (I have a copy) which describes the ESA Mars programme as a pathfinder orbiter mission in 2016, 'possibly' with a demonstration lander which will have a life time of only a few hours and a very small science payload. Could this be the camera Rudi wanted to show that ESA is on Mars? The much trumpeted rover and its drill (now only about twenty centimetres long) are shown as a joint mission with NASA in 2018. The rover has had a name (and a sex) change from Brigitte to Bruno. If they ever find out it was me who suggested honouring Pasteur you can bet the name chosen for the instrument package will be for the chop. Most recently David Southwood signed what is called the 'Plymouth Accord' with NASA. I liken it to a load of b***s. Plymouth is famous for bowls.

ExoMars is receding farther into the distance as the mission proceeds; astronomers would describe it as having 'redshift'. The way things are going the Universe will end before ESA arrives on Mars. And this is the organisation that criticised my Management. Never mind, with David in the Management seat all their troubles will soon be over! When I'm asked how long it will be before humans go to Mars, I answer "an eternity," and paraphrase Woody Allen, "The trouble with eternity is it drags towards the end."

Beagle 2 happened at a time when the circumstances were unique, and there is no way we could duplicate the list of people who made it possible: Sir John Daniel, Paul Murdin, John Hobbs, Mike Rickett, Ian Taylor, Miles Hedges, Everett Gibson, Robert Hutchison, Tony McWalter, Lord Sainsbury, Davids Leadbeater and Hall, Colin Hicks, Matthew Patten, Steve Wilkinson, Sir John Horlock and the Wellcome Trust, NASA who provided the competition, Marcello Coradini, Giacomo Cavallo, Blur, Damien Hirst, Mark Sims, Alan Wells, John Thatcher, Jim Clemett, Barrie Kirk, Andy Spry, Lutz Richter, Ian Wright, Shusy, Joe and most of all Judith. We had the additional spur of those we loved to hate: David Southwood, Rudi Schmidt, John Credland and the Editor of *Nature*; their efforts to obstruct, criticise and frustrate us only served to make us more determined. I was just the Pied Piper who played the magic tune.

Beagle 2 was never a failure although what followed was a tragic wasted opportunity. All we had achieved for the British space programme was thrown away because we weren't allowed to do what NASA would have done – get back on the horse before we lost our nerve. Maybe Judith was right when she asked for another horse. She usually is.

Dramatis Personae

Sir John Daniel – Vice-Chancellor, Open University

Sir John Horlock – former Vice-Chancellor, Open University

Miles Hedges – Finance Director, Open University

Alan Wells – Director, Space Centre, University of Leicester

Mark Sims – Beagle 2 Mission Manager

Andy Spry – Beagle 2 Planetary Protection Officer

Paul Murdin – British Representative to ESA

Lord David Sainsbury – Minister of Science

Colin Hicks – Director General, British National Space Centre

David Leadbeater – Deputy Director, British National Space Centre

Dave Hall – British National Space Centre

Mike Rickett – Head of Earth Observation and Science, Astrium UK

John Thatcher – Beagle 2 Programme Manager

Jim Clemmet – Beagle 2 Engineering Manager

Barrie Kirk – Beagle 2 Programme Manager

Stuart Hurst – EADS-Astrium

Evert Dudok – Head of Earth Observation and Science, Astrium Bremen

David Southwood – Director of Science, ESA

Giacomo Cavallo – Secretary, Science Programme Committee, ESA

Marcello Coradini – Solar Systems Mission Coordinator, ESA

John Credland – Head of Space Projects, ESA ESTEC

Rudi Schmidt – Mars Express Project Manager, ESA

Ton Linssen – Space Management Department, ESA

Agustin Chicarro – Mars Express Project Scientist, ESA

Rene Bonnefoy – Inspector General, ESA

Jean-Jacques Dordain – Director General, ESA

Matthew Patten – Sponsorship Director, M&C Saatchi

Tony Simpson – SPActive

Everett Gibson – Johnson Space Center, NASA

John Casani – Jet Propulsion Laboratory, NASA

Alex James, Dave Rowntree – Blur

Damien Hirst – representing himself

Jargon Buster

OU – Open University

ESA – European Space Agency

NASA – National Aeronautics and Space Administration

BNSC – British National Space Agency

NSC – National Space Centre

JSC – Johnson Space Center

ESTEC – European Space Agency Technical Centre

JPL – Jet Propulsion Laboratory

MMS – Matra Marconi Space

MBA – Martin Baker Aircraft

NHM – Natural History Museum

SSSL – Space Science Systems Limited

SSTL – Surrey Satellites Technology Limited

SEA – Systems Engineering Assessment

PDR – Preliminary Design Review

CDR – Critical Design Review

AO – Announcement of Opportunity

ITT – Invitation to tender

FFP – Firm Fixed Price

SERC – Science and Engineering Research Council

PPARC – Particle Physics and Astronomy Research Council

STFC – Science and Technical Facilities Council

PP – Planetary Protection

AAF – Aseptic Assembly Facility

EDLS – Entry, Descent and Landing System

SUEM – Spin Up and Eject Mechanism